Anatographica

Anatographica

General Editor: Thomas McCracken

Contributing Editor: Richard Walker

Senior Writer: Jim Glenn

BCL Press

All digital anatomy images copyright © 1999-2011 by Visible Productions, LLC
Visible Human Project™ is a trademark of the National Library of Medicine
Additional illustration credits appear in the acknowledgements on page 272

This edition published by BCL Press, an imprint of Book Creation, LLC
by arrangement with Anatographica, LLC
Publishing Directors: John Kelly and Hal Robinson

ISBN: 1-932302-16-6
ISBN 13: 978-1-932302-16-5

General Editor: Thomas O. McCracken, MS
Contributing Editor: Richard Walker, BSc, PhD
Senior Writer: Jim Glenn

Editor: Martin Griffiths, BSc, PhD
Editor: Sheila Buff
Designer: Tony Meisel

Designed, edited and typeset by Anatographica, LLC

Printed and bound in China

141516TT87654

TNTN

Contents

Foreword

A S MANKIND'S DRIVING NEED TO KNOW PUSHED US OUTWARD—FIRST TO THE ENDS OF THE EARTH, AND THEN TOWARD THE BOUNDARIES OF THE UNIVERSE—IT ALSO PROMPTED US TO DELVE INWARD IN AN ATTEMPT TO EXPLORE AND UNDERSTAND THE WORKINGS OF OUR BODIES. ATTEMPTS TO DISCOVER AND MAP THE "INNER-SPACE" OF THE BODY AND ITS SYSTEMS WERE BEING MADE LONG BEFORE WE EVEN KNEW OR UNDERSTOOD THE TRUE FUNCTIONS OF MOST OF ITS PARTS.

While the ancients knew little of what we now know, we probably have even more questions today about the many mysteries of this incredible collaboration of cells, tissues, organs, and systems. More often than not we find that every new discovery merely presents a new set of queries.

Take the apparently simple cell—as our knowledge increases it just serves to put us in further in awe of these specialized microscopic factories that swiftly and efficiently import, process, and export nutrients, energy and waste. How exactly do they get their instructions? New chemical triggers and their receptors are constantly being discovered, and we learn that the process is even more complex then we originally thought.

The purpose of this volume is to help us understand how the incredible machine that is the human body is built and how it works. How do the eleven different systems that are required to keep us alive and keep the race going function – first on their own and then together?

While there are many books with this goal, *Anatographica* is unique in that the amazing imagery presented here is of the first anatomically exact and complete, three-dimensional reconstruction of an actual human body.

Starting with the thousands of cross-sections of a human body created by the National Library of Medicine's Visible Human Project™, the hundreds of elements revealed in each micro-section were painstakingly traced and identified, and a 3D matrix was created (see the following few pages for the fascinating details of the process). The result was a recreation of the exact forms of the body and all its parts.

Since the images represented here exist in three dimensions, they can be turned, opened, even passed through. It has never before been possible to "see" inside real tissue—just look at the eerie beauty of the "tree" of vessels within the liver. Subjects can be made as lifelike as possible, or be manipulated to emphasize specific systems or organs. For example, the skin and muscles can be removed to show underlying tissue, or the cardiovascular system can be highlighted on its own. All the images are anatomically correct, meaning they are completely accurate in terms of their spatial relationships and how they appear in an actual individual.

The illustrations presented in this book are so breathtaking that they may be seen by many to reside more in the realm of art than science. Not only are they fantastic to look at, but they are at the same time real. It is the way we are.

The human respiratory system. From the sinuses in the forehead and cheeks, to the trachea, lungs, and diaphragm, new developments in digital imaging techniques allow the organs and systems of the human to be visualized as they actually are.

The Study of Anatomy

The Western tradition of anatomical study goes back almost as far as recorded history. The Greek physician Hippocrates practiced in the 5th century BC. Formal medical study, including dissection and the science of anatomy, were part of the schools of Alexandria, Egypt in the 3rd century BC. Archaeological evidence shows that a profound knowledge of anatomy had clearly been acquired long before this time—not only in the Mediterranean, where the Egyptians had been preparing their dead for mummification for hundreds of years, but also in Asia, where the Chinese medical tradition entailing detailed study of the body and its parts had long been established. Ancient teaching traditions tend to rely on transmitting knowledge from person to person, master to student, expert to novice, and such communication leaves little in the way of permanent records. The codification of medical knowledge in the Roman world was undertaken several hundred years later, by a Greek physician called Galen. He lived from about AD 130 to AD 200, and his two most famous works on the human body can be translated as *The Usefulness of Parts* and *On Anatomical Procedures*.

By the Middle Ages medical schools in Italy (Bologna and Salerno) and France (Paris and Montpellier) had been established. The most influential anatomical work of this time was an Italian dissection manual, *Anatomia Corporis Humani*, by Mondino de' Luzzi.

The humanist views of Renaissance philosophers and scientists presented them with potentially conflicting aims—on the one hand they were eager to re-establish the classical authority of the Greeks; yet on the other hand, they valued the scientific process of empirical observation. The generalized descriptions of Galen and others, and what could actually be seen as tissues were lifted or pared away, were often quite at odds. The anatomical drawings of Leonardo da Vinci can be seen to reflect these contradictions—some idealize the body and its parts, following traditional views, while others represent meticulously what his eyes observed.

The most significant change in the history of anatomical study is often attributed to the work of Andreas Vesalius, who was born in Belgium in 1514, four years before Leonardo died. After studying medicine in Paris and other great European centers of learning, Vesalius settled in Padua, in Northern Italy, and established his reputation there as an anatomist. His major work, *De Humani Corporis Fabrica,* translated as *On the Structure of the Human Body,* was published

A Vesalius woodcut. The art typically shows the dissected subject in a living pose.

in 1543, and established definitively the science of anatomy based on observation. *De Humani Corporis Fabrica* marks the beginning of modern medical and biological science.

Succeeding centuries witnessed increasing refinement in the search for realism in explaining and representing human anatomy—both in terms of the techniques used and the ability to display them. By the 1830s the development of cost-effective print and coloring techniques, enabled reproduction of large color plates of great detail and remarkable beauty to be made widely available. Another landmark was the 1858 first edition of Henry Gray's *Anatomy Descriptive and Surgical*. While Gray's first book was considered unremarkable at the time (the illustrations were smaller and not as artistically executed as some others) it initiated a new tradition: anatomy primarily for the instruction of medical students and practising doctors.

In the 20th century anatomical illustration continued to focus on medical teaching. Different types of publications serve different educational needs: systemic texts focus on the systems of the body, their location, composition, and how they work, separately

Gray's illustrations may have lacked the aesthetic appeal of some of his competitors', but succeeded tremendously in their educational objective

or together; regional texts, intended for advanced students and practising surgeons, have a high level of detail; the anatomical atlas is essentially a visual guide for students to the organs and components of the body. Abstracted from the specific models on which it is based as systemic anatomy would be, they try to appear as "real" as it possibly can. A new type of visual guide emerged in the late 20th century— cross-sectional anatomy, made possible by new imaging technologies such as computerized axial tomography (CAT) scanning and magnetic resonance imaging (MRI). Because such publications use actual images, their foundation in reality is sure. But the cross-sectional slice bears little visual resemblance to a real person, living or dead.

The dawn of the 21st century was also the dawn of a new anatomy—digital anatomy.

A typical example of popular 19th century anatomy: attractive, idealized, and easy to understand.

The Visible Human Project™ and Virtual Anatomy

The creation of the "virtual human" that illustrates this book derives from cross-sectional images of real bodies. The Visible Human Project™ came about in 1988 after the National Library of Medicine (NLM), in Bethesda, Maryland—one of the largest collections of medical knowledge in the world—decided to further medical knowledge by creating a digital database of data that would represent a complete adult body as a computer model. The search started for a suitable cadaver; the body of a man between 21 and 60 years of age, less than six feet tall, less than 22 inches wide, less than 14 inches from front to back, and with a normal height for his body weight. These criteria were set mostly on the basis of the limitations of the equipment necessary to image the body.

In 1993, a suitable body was donated to medical science. The body was first documented and imaged using different common radiological procedures: X-rays, CAT, MRI, ultrasound, and positron emission tomography (PET). The cadaver was encased in a foaming agent that hardened to form a cradle in which it could be kept in a stable position throughout the imaging procedures. It was then frozen to -94°C, quartered, and embedded in a gelatin-ice mix. Starting at the feet, a cromacrotome (a highly accurate cutting device) planed 1-mm coronal (horizontal) sections from each section, revealing slice-by-slice the intricate detail within. Each slice was then photographed using a high-resolution digital camera. The result was 1,878 color photographs that were stored as high-detail digital images.

While the Visible Human Project™ was an achievement in itself, in terms of virtual anatomy it was just the beginning. The next stage was to process the information in such a way that 3D structures could be constructed. The digital photographs were outlined using a contour tracer, translating real human anatomy, tissue type by tissue type, into points that describe a structure. Once the contours that defined the outside of a structure had been produced,

they were stacked together to form a wireframe image. A surface was generated to connect the shapes by linking lines between the contours, forming a lattice-like effect. This is known as triangulation as the lines between the contours create triangles.

Horizontal (transverse) sections through the head of the Visible Human. In the top photograph the frontal sinuses can be clearly seen as the space in front of the brain. The lower photograph shows the eyes and the optic nerves as well as the nose.

Once the basis of the wireframe structures was complete, surfaces and shading were added to make the images more realistic. By photographing identical tissue specimens to the ones of interest and then texture mapping—wrapping the surface around each structure—a real, live image could be generated. Since individual systems, organs or structures are created from separate files they can therefore be colored and shaded, deleted, or made transparent. Because the original versions of the images we see here are three-dimensional in their digital form, are also truly "virtual." The body they represent can be turned, opened, even passed through by the viewer. Systems can be viewed in isolation, like the pieces of a jigsaw, and (unlike a cadaver in the dissecting room) put back together again when the examination is complete. Regions can be "dissected" progressively, by peeling away layers or even seeing "through" some tissues to reveal others underneath. And from an academic point of view, this virtual human has one enormous advantage over any other digitally constructed body or body part: this one is real, based on an actual body, without generalization.

Virtual anatomy allows us to look at a structure any number of ways. Top, the lobe of the liver is made semi-transparent to show the network of bile ducts. Middle, the files with the images of the veins and arteries are brought up to show how blood circulates. Bottom, the vascular and billary networks are shown on their own.

Virtual Anatomy, Step by Step

The process is a progression from massive raw data, to algorithm-produced matrices, created between parallel planes. Once the individual components' shapes are defined, the 3D structure is "wrapped" in the correct tissue surface. Each part is discrete, but its coordinates are exact in terms of its relationship with the rest of the body—now also expressed as digital files.

From the simple building blocks shown in the sequence to the right it has been possible to recreate an entire human body in exact detail. The resulting images of the brain and how they can be manipulated are examples of the tremendous value of virtual anatomy. The virtual human can be viewed from any angle, by system or region, or for the first time, by both.

For every structure, an incredibly detailed "wireframe" image is generated (top right, detail center) To this a surface is added by contour mapping—wrapping a surface around each structure to produce the final image (bottom).

These two digital images of a real human brain show the incredible detail and capabilities of virtual anatomy. In the top picture, the gray matter of the brain has been removed revealing the white matter underneath. The lower brain has had the right cerebrum removed revealing the underlying structures. The ability to produce images with such detail and accuracy and with such flexibility in presentation is groundbreaking.

How to Use This Book

There are two traditional ways of looking at the body: systemic and regional. Since the purpose of *Anatographica* is to show both how the body is made and to understand how it works, the largest part of the book is systemic anatomy, examining the body system by system. The regional overview at the end of the book is designed to be a useful guide for seeing how all the different systems fit together by region or area (for example, the head and neck).

Terminology

It is necessary to have universally acceptable names for the different structures of the body, and for their different spatial relationships. Partly for the standardization, and partly because of historical precedent, anatomical names are Latin or are derived from the Greek.

Some anatomical names are explained in the text, and a glossary is included at the end of the book. Terms in the glossary appear in **bold** the first time they are used in the text.

Planes of section

To standardize the way anatomists view the human body, the standard anatomical body is assumed to be in an upright position, with the arms down by the side, and the eyes and palms of the hands facing forward. In this position, the body can be imagined in three dimensions. There are specific terms for the way these three dimensions can be divided; the lines of division are called planes of "section".

• The median (or sagittal) plane divides the body vertically into right and left halves;

• Vertical planes at right angles to the median plane are known as coronal planes;

• Horizontal planes cut the body at right angles to both coronal and median planes. Different terms are used to describe the way parts are arranged in relation to others.

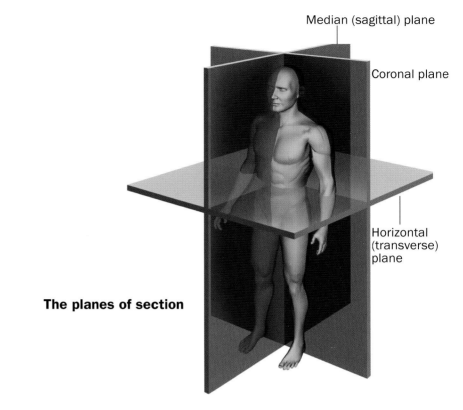

The planes of section

• The terms anterior (ventral) and posterior (dorsal) are used to refer to the front and back surfaces, respectively, of the head, trunk and limbs. So the spinal cord is dorsal to the wall of the abdomen and ventral to the skin of the back.

• The terms superior (cranial) and inferior (caudal) refer to the relative positions in the vertical plane, where a superior (upper) surface is above (or dorsal to) an inferior (lower) one.

• In the limbs, proximal is used to refer to something that is nearer the root of the limb (i.e. nearer the shoulder or hip), whereas something farther away (toward the hand or foot) is referred to as distal.

• Palmar and plantar refer to the bending (flexor) or front (anterior) surface of the hand and foot—i.e., to the hand's palm and the foot's sole.

• In the forearm, radial and ulnar, following the bones, may be used instead of lateral and medial, and in the lower limb fibular and tibial are often used, for the same reason.

• Finally, superficial and deep refer to the relative distance of organs between the surface and the center of the body.

15

THE CELL IS TO LIFE AS ATOMS ARE TO MATTER. ALL LIVING THINGS ARE COMPOSED OF CELLS, WHETHER IT BE A SINGLE-CELL BACTERIA OR A HUMAN BEING—OUR BODIES ARE BUILT FROM ABOUT 60 TRILLION CELLS. CELLS COME IN A WIDE RANGE OF FORMS, SHAPES AND SIZES; THEY CAN BE MICROSCOPIC—SMALLER THAN 1/10,000 OF AN IN (2 MICRONS)—OR AS LARGE AS SOME NERVE CELLS THAT EXTEND FROM THE WAIST TO THE FOOT. WHATEVER THEIR SIZE, THE TINY STRUCTURES PERFORM AN AMAZINGLY COMPLEX AND EFFICIENT AMOUNT OF WORK.

THE CELL

The four main tissue types of the human body are epithelial (skin); muscular; connective (cartilage and bone) and nervous tissue—these in turn subdivide into over 200 individual types of cell depending on their final use. No matter what their function, all cells share basic characteristics.

Cellular Anatomy

The cell barrier is a porous, oily membrane composed of fats and proteins that controls what enters and leaves the cell. Certain molecules (like oxygen or alcohol) can pass directly through while others (like amino acids or glucose) require processing. Within the membrane is the cytoplasm, the viscous material that contains the organelles, the internal structures that carry out the cell's different functions.

The cytoskeleton helps move parts of the cell, provides physical support to organelles and helps in cell division; ribosomes assemble proteins while the endoplasmic reticulum and the Golgi apparatus work together processing and assembling amino acids and other chemicals into proteins and lipids to be used within the cell or in other parts of the body. Peroxisomes create enzymes that detoxify harmful substances. Mitochondria are the cell's power stations—they convert nutrients into the chemical ATP, the cell's fuel.

Most cells have a nucleus, which contain the DNA that provides the instructions for building the cell's parts and how they will function. This DNA coding is passed along as the cell reproduces. Certain cells that do not reproduce, like red blood cells, do not have a nucleus or carry DNA.

Cells have varied life and reproductive cycles. They may live for as little as a day—or as long as we do. The nerve cells that make up our brains and the cells of our heart muscle do not replace themselves and are meant to last a lifetime.

Cancer is the name for a wide range of diseases that share one trait - the loss of the genetic code that controls cells' regular cycle of life, growth, and death.

Cancer starts because abnormal cells divide and grow uncontrollably.

Without the body quickly recognizing and killing the rogue cells, they will rapidly reproduce.

Cytoplasm

Cytoskeleton

Cell membrane

Nucleus

Ribosomes

Mitochondrion

Peroxisome

Golgi apparatus

Endoplasmic reticulum

Nucleolus

Invasive cancers are the most dangerous; they spread through the body in a process called metastasis.

Tumors, or clumps of cancerous cells, can grow their own blood vessels to feed themselves in a process called angiogenisis.

Invasive cancers can spread to surrounding tissue and travel through the bloodstream or lymph system to other parts of the body.

W

E ARE SURROUNDED BY PATHOGENS—DISEASE-CAUSING AGENTS—WHEREVER WE ARE. THEY LIVE IN AIR, WATER, SOIL, FOOD—AND EVEN OUR OWN BODIES.

INFECTIOUS DISEASES

The E. coli bacteria is common in our intestines, but some strains produce potentially lethal toxins. The cell features a hair-like filament that can rotate, acting as a propeller.

Bacteria

An estimated 1,000 or so types of bacteria live in or around our bodies—mostly without causing us any harm. Certain strains of bacteria can produce toxins that can cause damage to cells or trigger dangerous immune responses. Common bacterial infections include tooth decay, strep throat, and Lyme disease.

When antibiotics were introduced over 65 years ago, there were tremendous and immediate advances in eradicating a great number of diseases caused by micro-organisms. However, strains of bacteria that were not killed by antibiotics due to mutations in their genetic makeup have reproduced over the decades, producing drug-resistant strains.

Now, some diseases that were once easy to treat are becoming harder to treat and more common. A particular concern are so-called superbugs, very common bacteria generally known as staph. One of the possible reasons for why drug resistance develops in bacterial DNA includes inappropriate overuse of antibiotics for viral infections like colds.

Viruses

While not considered living cells, viruses are potentially lethal miniature machines that take over cells' genetic capabilities and mutate them to reproduce more copies of themselves – spreading the virus while destroying the host cells.

HIV

AIDS is caused by a virus called the Human Immuno Deficiency Virus Type I, or HIV 1. Like all viruses, HIV 1 "hijacks" the infected cells' DNA and reprograms them to make more viruses—destroying those cells in the process.

The virus has an outer envelope or membrane covered in spikes made of proteins. Just below is a layer called the matrix or capsid. The capsid covers the components used for replication. These include three enzymes called reverse transcriptase, integrase and protease and two strands of Ribonucleic acid or RNA which carry genetic information.

HIV 1 infects cells of the immune system such as helper T-cells and macrophages. These cells are critical for fighting off viral invasion and infection. Spikes on the virus' surface attach to receptors on the target cell.

Once docked, the virus' inner capsid enters the target cell. The virus' outer membrane is left behind as part of the target's cellular membrane. Inside the cell, the viral capsid dissolves.

This releases the virus' reverse transcriptase and RNA. Reverse transcriptase creates a circular sequence of viral DNA from the viral RNA.

The viral DNA is taken through a pore in the target cell's nucleus where it is then spliced into the target cell DNA. Target cell mechanisms create messenger RNA which serves as a template for viral proteins. Ribosomes produce these proteins after messenger RNA leaves the nucleus.

New viral RNA strands float through the cellular space joining with vital enzymes and are encapsulated near the target cell's surface. They bud from the cell surface in an envelope formed from the host's cell membrane. As many as 10 billion HIV virus particles are produced a day in an infected person.

THE INTEGUMENTARY SYSTEM

THE SKIN IS THE LARGEST ORGAN OF THE HUMAN BODY. IT AVERAGES ABOUT 3,000 SQUARE INCHES IN AN ADULT, AND WEIGHS IN AT AROUND 6 POUNDS— NEARLY TWICE THE WEIGHT OF THE LIVER.

THE SKIN COVERS AND PROTECTS THE BODY AND, WITH ITS DERIVATIVES, HAIR AND NAILS, FORMS THE INTEGUMENTARY SYSTEM. AS A PHYSICAL BARRIER, SKIN PREVENTS WATER LEAKING OUT OF, OR INTO, THE BODY'S TISSUES, THEREBY HELPING TO MAINTAIN HOMEOSTASIS. IT ALSO PREVENTS THE ENTRY OF HARMFUL, DISEASE-CAUSING MICRO-ORGANISMS; REPAIRS ITSELF IF CUT OR OTHERWISE DAMAGED; FILTERS OUT HARMFUL ULTRAVIOLET (UV) RAYS IN SUNLIGHT; ACTS AS AN IMPORTANT SENSORY STRUCTURE FOR DETECTING TOUCH, PRESSURE, PAIN, HEAT, AND COLD; AND PLAYS AN IMPORTANT PART IN MAINTAINING THE BODY'S TEMPERATURE AT AROUND 37°C (98.6°F) REGARDLESS OF THE AMBIENT TEMPERATURE.

THE INTEGUMENTARY SYSTEM

All parts of the body are covered and protected by a living "overcoat" in the form of the skin. The skin also provides a sensory interface between the body and its surroundings that enables humans to experience a wide range of sensations.

Skin structure

Skin is made up of two layers, the epidermis and dermis. The superficial epidermis is primarily protective and consists of a number of layers, or **strata**. The outermost layer, the stratum corneum, consists of dead, flattened cells packed with **keratin**, a tough, waterproof protein also found in hairs and nails. As this protective "overcoat" is constantly worn away and lost as skin flakes, living cells in the deepest epidermal layer—the stratum basale—divide to provide replacement cells. As these are pushed upward through the other strata they flatten, fill with keratin and die. Other cells in the deeper epidermis produce granules of the brown pigment melanin that protects against the harmful effects of UV light.

The thicker dermis is a flexible, strong layer embedded with collagen and **elastin** fibers that give it resilience and elasticity. It also contains sensory nerve endings and receptors; blood vessels; sweat glands that produce cooling sweat and release it though ducts onto the skin's surface; hair follicles, deep pits from which hairs grow; and sebaceous glands that release an oily liquid called **sebum** that helps keep the skin and hairs soft, flexible, and waterproof.

Two types of skin are found in the human body. Thick skin, up to 4 mm (¼ in) thick, is hairless and has a thicker, protective epidermis. It is found in those areas, such as the palms, soles, and fingertips, that are involved in movement and manipulation and have a greater need to resist abrasion. Thin, hairy skin, which covers the rest of the body, has a much thinner epidermis and lacks one of the five layers—the stratum lucidum—found in thick skin.

Hair and nails

Apart from the lips, parts of the genitals, and the undersides of the hands and feet, the body is covered by millions of hairs. Cells in the bulb, or base, of hair follicles divide to produce cells that move up the follicle to form the shaft of the hair. The coarse terminal hairs of the head are protective, while the finer vellus hairs on the rest of the body aid sensation. Nails are scaly outgrowths of the epidermis that serve to protect the ends of fingers and toes and to help the fingers to grip objects.

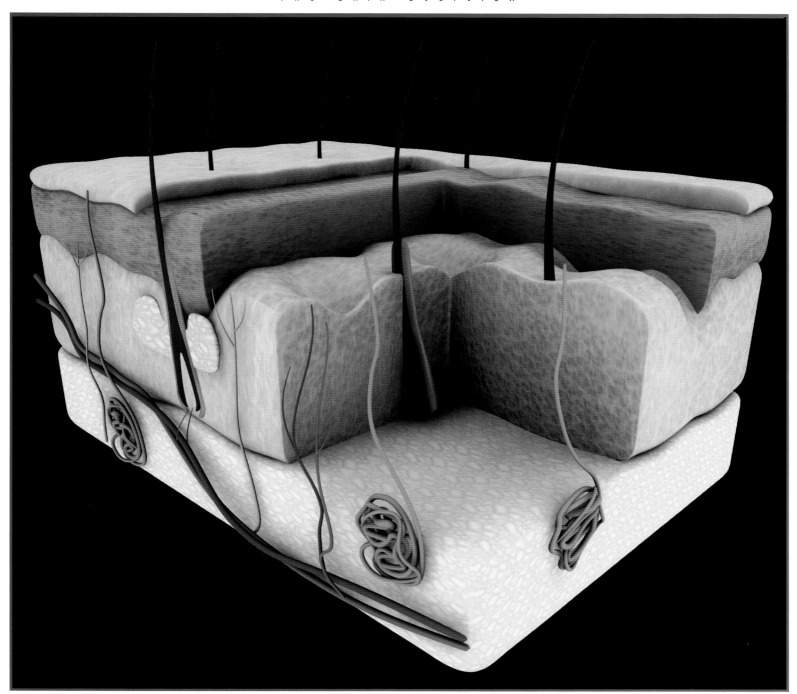

KEY

1. Epidermis
2. Basal epidermal layer
3. Dermis
4. Sweat gland
5. Nerve
6. Sebaceous gland
7. Blood vessels
8. Subcutaneous fat

TYPES OF SKIN CELLS

Skin types vary with location and use. Here are examples from three parts of the body.

Above: Cross section of the thin skin of the scalp. The epidermal layer is much thinner than that found in thick skin. Also present are hair follicles, pits in the dermis from which hairs grow, and prominent sebaceous glands which empty their secretions via the follicle.

Below: A section of the skin of a finger. The thick stratum corneum in the epidermis resists abrasion caused by repeatedly touching objects. The dermis is rich in sensory receptors, making the fingers very sensitive to touch.

Left: This section of thick skin, like that found on the sole of the foot, reveals a relatively thick epidermal layer. The prominent stratum corneum resists friction and protects the layers above it.

KEY

1. Shaft of hair
2. Stratum corneum (horny layer)
3. Stratum basale (basal layer)
4. Epidermis
5. Dermis
6. Hair follicle
7. Sebaceous gland
8. Hair bulb
9. Sweat gland
10. Duct from sweat gland
11. Stratum corneum (horny layer)
12. Stratum lucidum (clear layer)
13. Stratum granulosum (granular layer)
14. Stratum spinosum (spiny layer)
15. Dead cells flaking off from epidermis
16. Collagen fibers

Sebum produced by the sebaceous, glands normally lubricates hair follicles and escapes to the surface. When it becomes trapped beneath the skin, bacteria gather and the buildup of sebum and bacteria becomes a whitehead.

A blackhead is similar to a whitehead, except that the blockage allows air to enter the clogged pore and the melanin, or pigment, turns dark on contact with oxygen.

SKIN DAMAGE

The skin is a living organ, and the cells beneath the relatively thin epidermis are easily damaged. Skin cells are constantly renewing themselves, and skin damage compromises the ability to keep producing healthy replacement cells.

Sunburn: Redness, soreness and blistering can occur from too much exposure to the sun's ultraviolet or UV rays. It's important to use a high SPF factor sunscreen that blocks both UVA and UVB rays.

Melanoma: Excessive exposure to the sun can damage the DNA of skin cells called melanocytes, which produce the pigment melanin. This cancer, or uncontrolled growth, leads to the mutated cells breaking through the surface in the form of a dark mole.

First degree burns effect only the epidermis, which turns red. **Second degree burns** damage both the dermis and epidermis and usually blister. **Third degree burns** can penetrate all layers of the skin and can cause permanent damage.

As we age, the constant replacement of cells slows and more imperfect cells are produced. The skin reflects this process. The dermis, the layer of skin right below the outer layer, thins and loses elastin and collagen, proteins that keep the skin flexible. Muscle and fat cells become smaller. The skin sags and becomes dry and wrinkled. Blood vessels, tendons and bones are more visible. Age spots appear. The risk of skin cancer increases and the ability to maintain a constant temperature is diminished.

THE SKELETAL SYSTEM

THE 206 BONES THAT MAKE UP OUR BODY'S FRAMEWORK COMPRISE ABOUT 20 PERCENT OF ITS TOTAL MASS. WHILE HARD AND SOLID, BONE IS LIVING TISSUE THAT IS VITAL TO MOST OF THE BODY'S OTHER SYSTEMS.

Unlike the dry and dusty skeletal remains found in archeological museums, the living skeleton is a strong, lightweight framework that is both dynamic and flexible. As well as supporting and shaping the body, the skeleton also provides an anchorage for skeletal muscles, which contract to produce movement, and surrounds and protects internal organs that would otherwise be damaged in the course of everyday life.

THE FULL SKELETON

Strong yet lightweight and flexible, the skeleton provides the ideal framework for support, movement, and protection.

The human skeletal system is made up of on average 206 bones, many of which can be seen opposite; flexible cartilage (gristle), which plays a structural role in the ear flaps, nose, and part of the ribs, as well as covering the ends of bones in joints; and tough ligaments that stabilize the skeleton by holding bones together at joints, where two or more bones meet. Altogether, the skeletal system makes up about 20 percent of our body mass.

Types of bones

Bones can be divided into four main types—long, short, flat, and irregular—according to their shape. Shape also provides an indication of mechanical function.

• Long bones, which include all the limb bones, with the exception of the wrist and ankle bones and the patella (kneecap), are longer than they are wide. Each consists of a diaphysis (shaft) and, at each end, an epiphysis (extremity or bone end), which is usually more expanded than the shaft. They act as levers that make the body move when pulled by contracting muscles, and some, notably the bones of the legs, have an important weight-bearing role.

• Short bones—the carpals (wrist bones) and tarsals (ankle bones) are roughly cube-like in shape.

They form a connective "bridge" in the wrist and ankle where only limited movement is needed but stability is essential.

• Flat bones, which include the sternum (breastbone), ribs, scapulae (shoulder blades), and the cranial bones of the skull, are thin, flattened and slightly curved. Some, such as the ribs and cranial bones form protective cages, while each scapula provides a large surface for muscle attachment.

• Irregular bones, which include the facial bones of the skull, the vertebrae (the bones that make up the vertebral column), and the pelvic or hip bones, are those that do not fit into the other three categories.

Cartilage

Cartilage is a specialized **connective tissue** that covers the ends of joints and plays a small structural role in the ear, nose, and ribs, as well as forming the spongy cushion between vertebrae. This resilient and elastic jelly-like substance is rigid, has a high tensile strength, and is resistant to both compressive and shearing forces. At joints, cartilage is highly wear-resistant, smooth, and has a polished surface that is bathed with a lubricating **synovial fluid** that has an extremely low coefficient of friction.

Anterior view of the full skeleton with the arms in the correct anatomical position.

KEY

1 Skull
2 Clavicle
3 Humerus
4 Ulna
5 Pelvic (hip) girdle
6 Femur
7 Patella
8 Tibia
9 Scapula
10 Sternum
11 Rib
12 Vertebral column
13 Radius
14 Fibula

THE SKELETON EVOLVED INTO ITS PRESENT FORM SOME FIVE MILLION YEARS AGO WHEN HUMAN ANCESTORS FIRST WALKED ON TWO LEGS. THE S-SHAPED BACKBONE KEEPS THE BODY UPRIGHT AND SUPPORTS THE HEAD, WHILE STILL PERMITTING BENDING. THE NEAR VERTICAL PELVIS BALANCES THE UPPER BODY DIRECTLY OVER THE FEET, WHILE STRONG LEG BONES SUPPORT ITS WEIGHT.

Bone contains two types of **osseous** (bony) tissue that together give it its strength and lightness. Compact bone, found on the outside of bones where stresses are greatest, consists of parallel cylinders called **osteons** made up of concentric tubes of matrix. A central canal in each osteon carries blood vessels. Tiny spaces within osteons contain isolated osteocytes. Lighter spongy, or cancellous, bone has a honeycomb structure of spaces and bony struts called **trabeculae**. The spaces contain jelly-like marrow. Yellow marrow

THE FULL SKELETON

The curvature to the body conveys mechanical support and strength, from the S-shaped, spring-like vertebral column to the slight curvature of the long limb bones.

For descriptive purposes the skeleton can be divided into two broad categories. The axial skeleton—the backbone, skull, ribs and sternum—forms the main axis of the body. The appendicular skeleton consists of the limb bones and those of the pectoral (shoulder) and pelvic (hip) girdles, which connect the limbs to the axial skeleton.

forms a fat store, while red marrow, found mainly in flat bones in adults, manufactures blood cells. Covering and encasing most of the bone is a thin membrane called the **periosteum**.

KEY

1. Scapula
2. Vertebra
3. Radius
4. Ulna
5. Fibula
6. Cranium
7. Humerus
8. Ilium
9. Sacrum
10. Ischium
11. Pubis
12. Tibia
13. Calcaneous

Bone structure

Bones are made of living tissues that, in addition to their mechanical functions, store calcium and other minerals and make blood cells. Bone consists of cells surrounded by a matrix. This matrix consists of about 35 percent protein, particularly collagen, which provides hardness and flexibility; and about 65 percent mineral salts, particularly calcium and phosphate, which confer hardness. Weight for weight, this combination makes bone five times stronger than steel. Bone cells include **osteocytes**, the cells that maintain the matrix; **osteoblasts**, cells that manufacture bone; and **osteoclasts**, cells that erode bone matrix. Between them, osteoblasts and osteoclasts constantly remodel bones according to the forces exerted on them by muscles and either release or store calcium according to the body's requirements.

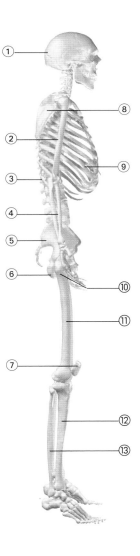

Posterior (left) and lateral (right) views of the full skeleton. In the lateral view the S-shaped curvature of the spine, which places the trunk over the feet to facilitate balance, can be appreciated.

KEY

1. Cranium
2. Humerus
3. Vertebra
4. Radius
5. Ilium
6. Ischium
7. Patella
8. Scapula
9. Rib
10. Greater trochanter
11. Femur
12. Tibia
13. Fibula

BONE IS LIVING TISSUE: WITHIN ITS HARD MINERALIZED MATRIX ARE LIVING CELLS THAT CREATE, DESTROY, SHAPE, AND RESHAPE THE BONE. THE MATRIX ITSELF SERVES AS STORAGE FOR MINERALS, PARTICULARLY CALCIUM, WHICH IS VITAL TO NERVE AND MUSCULAR FUNCTION AND FOR BLOOD CLOTTING. BLOOD CELLS ARE ALSO MADE WITHIN THE BONES.

BONE TYPE & DEVELOPMENT

Bone composition

The bone matrix is composed of protein (about 35 percent, especially **collagen**) and mineral salts (about 65 percent, mainly calcium and phosphate).

Protein gives bone its toughness and some elasticity; minerals provide hardness—it is reckoned that weight-for-weight bone is five times stronger than steel. These materials combine to form two chief types of osseous (bony) tissue: compact bone and cancellous, or spongy, bone. Compact bone is the stronger of the two, built from tubelike structural units called **osteons**, which have, on average, about six matrix layers from the outside surface to a blood-carrying canal that runs up its center.

Osteons run lengthwise with the bone and parallel with one another. They surround the bone's inner core and comprise spongy bone and marrow. Cancellous bone comprises a lighter honeycomb lattice of bony struts called **trabeculae**; marrow fills the spaces within this spongy tissue.

Cells called **osteoblasts** manufacture bone. As osteoblasts wall themselves up within the bone matrix, they may become less active **osteocytes**. These maintain the matrix but do not play a part in creating it. A third kind of cells, **osteoclasts**, break down the matrix.

Thus, osteoblasts and osteoclasts are constantly reshaping bones—a process called remodelling—to best meet the stresses applied by muscles or external forces and to store or release calcium, as needed by the body. Osteoblasts are present chiefly in the inside layer of the thin outer membrane, the periosteum, which encases a bone.

Connective tissue

Closely related to bone in terms of its development and function is cartilage, a type of connective tissue. In common with bone, it arises from specialized cells, young chondroblasts and mature chondrocytes, which form a matrix on a framework of collagen fibers. The resulting tissue, however, is a tough, amorphous, flexible material.

Cartilage develops into three main types, all of which are resilient, elastic, and resistant to compressive and shearing forces. Within the joints it is often present as a smooth, polished surface, which is lubricated by **synovial** fluid. This cartilage helps minimize wear and tear. Superficially, cartilage also gives shape to some of the body's features, such as the nose and ears.

During the development of the fetus, most bones start out as flexible cartilage, gradually to be replaced, ossified by osteoblasts in a process called endochondral ossification. This process starts before

A section of human bone showing a typical Haversian canal system. The lacunae and canaliculi, the clefts and tubes that suffuse even the densest bone, can clearly be seen.

birth and continues through to adolescence. The skull and a few other bones, including the clavicles, develop from fibrous connective membrane, a transformation termed intra-membranous ossification.

In newborn babies the skull is incompletely ossified, which aids the baby's passage down the birth canal and early brain growth; areas of unhardened membrane are called fontanelles. These have usually closed up completely by the age of eighteen months.

Bone marrow

Bone marrow is a soft, jellylike substance that fills the spaces within a bone—both within its central cavity and in the spongy bone. It comprises:
• Red marrow, which makes blood cells (producing about two million red cells per second). Red marrow is found mainly in flat bones and in the vertebrae, clavicles, pelvis, and the femur's upper end. :
• Yellow marrow, which mostly comprises stored fat and is found in long bones.

Young: Spongy bone provides lightweight strength to structures like the breastbone, hip, and vertebrae.

Old: As we age, calcium depletes and spongy bone becomes thinner, lighter and more fragile.

KEY

① Marrow
② Osteon
③ Periosteum
④ Blood vessels
⑤ Spongy bone with marrow
⑥ Vein
⑦ Artery

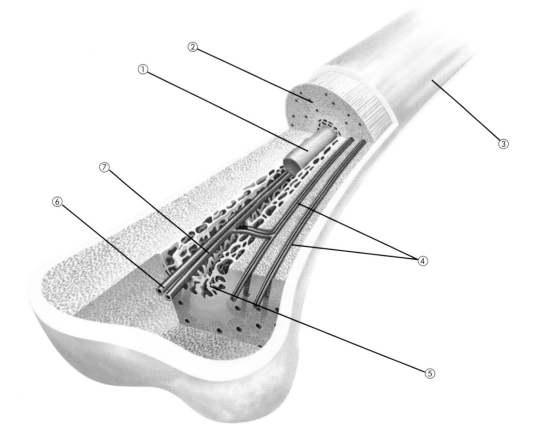

This cross section of a long bone shows how the bones not only provide structural support, but are integral to many of the body's functions.

Housing the body's control center—the brain—and most of its sense organs—eyes, ears, tongue, and nose—the skull is the most complicated part of the skeleton. It consists of a collection of 22 bones that are divided into two groups: eight cranial bones form the cranium, which surrounds the brain, while 14 facial bones form the framework of the face.

THE SKULL

The skull houses and protects not only the brain but also the sense organs that enable a person to hear, see, taste, and smell.

In addition to the large cavity formed by the cranial bones, there are other smaller cavities in the skull including the nasal cavity, the orbits (eye sockets) that hold the eyes, and the ear cavities within the temporal bones. Each ear cavity houses three additional tiny bones, called ossicles, which transmit sounds into the sensory part of the ear.

Small holes in skull bones called foramina (sing. foramen) and canals enable blood vessels, such as the carotid arteries, and nerves, to enter and leave the skull. The spinal cord passes through the largest hole, the foramen magnum in the base of the cranium, to join the brain. The occipital condyles on either side of this foramen articulate with the first vertebra of the backbone to permit nodding "yes" movements of the head.

How skull bones are made

Early in its development the skeleton of a human fetus consists of either fibrous connective tissue membranes or cartilage. Gradually, these structures are replaced by bone tissue, a process called ossification. The replacement of fibrous tissue is known as **intramembranous** ("inside membrane") ossification, while cartilage replacement is termed **endochondral** ("within cartilage") ossification.

Skull bones are formed by intramembranous ossification. Osteoblasts secrete bone matrix directly within the fibrous membrane at a "center of ossification" to form first spongy bone, and later an outer layer of compact bone. In the skull of the newborn, this process is still incomplete: skull bones are linked by areas of as yet unossified fibrous membrane called fontanels. These flexible patches allow the skull to be slightly compressed during birth, and accommodate the growth of the brain during early infancy. By the age of one and a half, intramembranous ossification is complete and the fontanels have disappeared.

View from below

KEY

1. Occipital bone
2. Temporal bone
3. Foramen magnum
4. Occipital condyle
5. Vomer
6. Palatine bone
7. Zygomatic bone
8. Maxilla
9. Parietal bone
10. Lambdoidal suture
11. External auditory meatus
12. Sphenoid bone

Small holes (foramina) within the surface of the skull enable blood vessels, arteries and nerves to enter the skull.

KEY

1. Frontal bone
2. Parietal bone
3. Temporal bone
4. Orbit
5. Lacrimal bone
6. Zygomatic bone
7. Maxilla
8. Mandible
9. Nasal bone
10. Sphenoid bone
11. Infraorbital foramen
12. Mental foramen

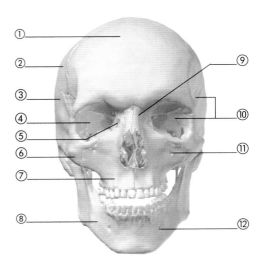

IN ADULTS, ALL BUT ONE OF THE 22 SKULL BONES—THE
EXCEPTION IS THE MANDIBLE, OR LOWER JAW—ARE HELD
TOGETHER BY IMMOVABLE JOINTS CALLED SUTURES. WITHIN
A SUTURE, THE EDGES OF BONES LOCK TOGETHER LIKE PIECES
IN A JIGSAW TO FORM A STRUCTURE THAT IS BOTH RIGID AND
STRONG. THE THINNESS OF THE CRANIAL BONES COMBINED WITH
THE PRESENCE OF HOLLOW, AIR-FILLED SPACES CALLED SINUSES
IN CERTAIN CRANIAL AND FACIAL BONES SERVE TO REDUCE THE
SKULL'S WEIGHT.

THE SKULL

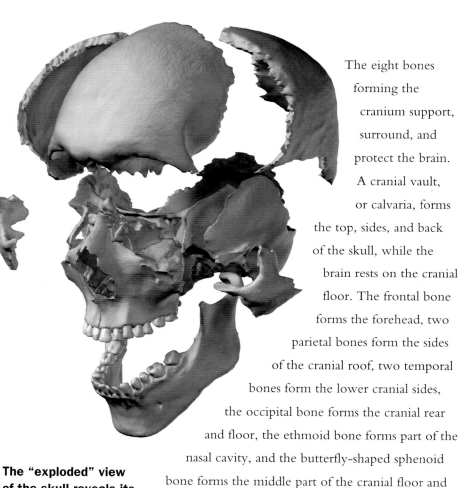

The "exploded" view of the skull reveals its component bones and the jagged edges that fit together in sutures.

The eight bones forming the cranium support, surround, and protect the brain. A cranial vault, or calvaria, forms the top, sides, and back of the skull, while the brain rests on the cranial floor. The frontal bone forms the forehead, two parietal bones form the sides of the cranial roof, two temporal bones form the lower cranial sides, the occipital bone forms the cranial rear and floor, the ethmoid bone forms part of the nasal cavity, and the butterfly-shaped sphenoid bone forms the middle part of the cranial floor and acts as a keystone that holds the other cranial bones together.

As well as forming the framework of the face, the fourteen facial bones also provide the openings through which food, water, and air enter the body. Muscles attached to the facial bones pull on the skin to produce the wide range of facial expressions.

The paired facial bones are the maxillae, which form the upper jaw and front of the hard palate, acting as a keystone with which all other facial bones, apart from the mandible, articulate; the zygomatic bones or cheek bones; the nasal bones, which form the bridge of the nose; the lacrimal bones, which form part of the orbit; the palatine bones, which form the rear of the hard palate; and the inferior nasal conchae, which form part of the nasal cavity. Occurring singly, the vomer makes up part of the nasal septum, which divides the nasal cavity; while the mandible forms the lower jaw. Teeth are secured in sockets in the maxillae and mandible.

Bones as chemical factories

In addition to their mechanical roles—support, protection, and movement—bones perform the vital physiological roles of storing calcium and making blood cells.

Calcium is one of about 20 minerals—others include iron and zinc—obtained from food and essential for the normal functioning of the body. Ninety-nine percent of the body's calcium is stored in bones. Calcium confers hardness on bones and teeth, and is needed for muscle contraction, the transmission of nerve impulses, and blood clotting. To maintain constant levels of calcium in the blood, two hormones with opposing effects either cause the release of calcium from bones into the bloodstream, or stimulate the sequestration of calcium from blood and its storage in bones.

Blood cells—red blood cells, white blood cells, and platelets—are manufactured by red bone marrow found, in adults, inside the cranial bones, vertebrae, clavicles, sternum, ribs, scapulae, pelvis, and the upper ends of the femur and humerus. In healthy adults, about 2 million red blood cells are produced per second.

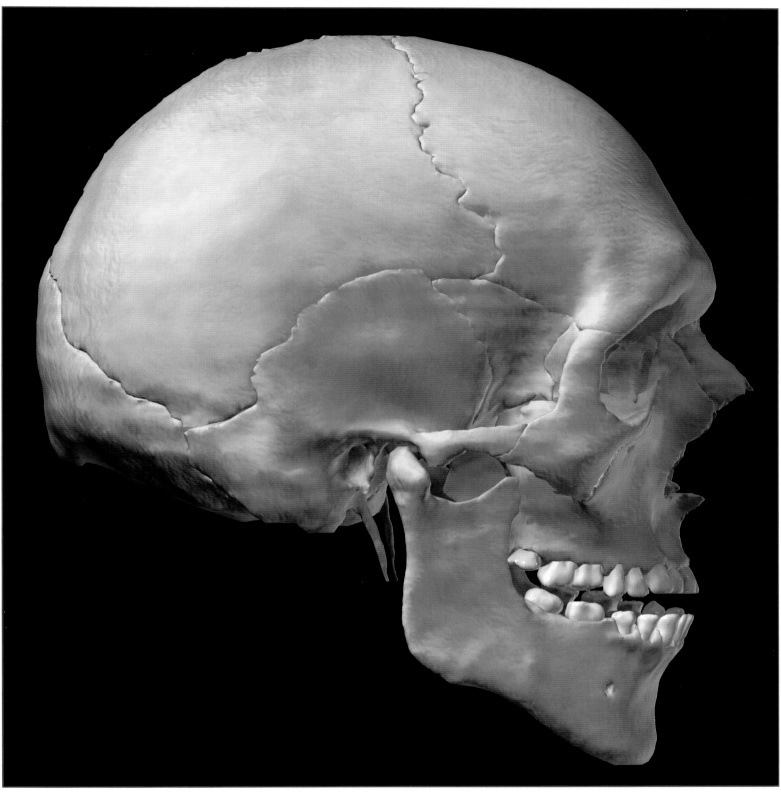

**Lateral view of
the skull. In this
position the sutures
connecting the
different skull bones
can be clearly seen.**

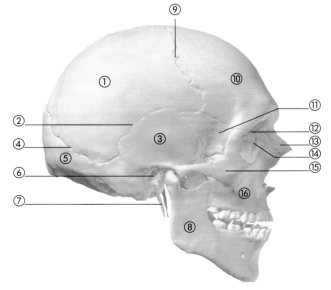

KEY

① Parietal bone
② Squamous suture
③ Temporal bone
④ Lambdoidal suture
⑤ Occipital bone
⑥ External auditory meatus
⑦ Styloid process
⑧ Mandible

⑨ Coronal suture
⑩ Frontal bone
⑪ Sphenoid bone
⑫ Ethmoid bone
⑬ Nasal bone
⑭ Lacrimal bone
⑮ Zygomatic bone
⑯ Maxilla

P ROVIDING SUPPORT FOR THE BODY'S HEAD AND TRUNK IS THE VERTEBRAL COLUMN—ALSO KNOWN AS THE SPINAL COLUMN, SPINE, OR BACKBONE—A STRONG BUT FLEXIBLE CHAIN OF BONES KNOWN AS VERTEBRAE. THE JOINTS BETWEEN NEIGHBORING VERTEBRAE (SING. VERTEBRA) PERMIT ONLY LIMITED MOVEMENT, BUT COLLECTIVELY THEY GIVE THE VERTEBRAL COLUMN CONSIDERABLE FLEXIBILITY.

THE VERTEBRAL COLUMN

The vertebral column extends from the skull to its anchoring point in the pelvis *(see page 48)*, through which it transmits the weight of the head and trunk to the legs. It surrounds and protects the delicate spinal cord *(see page 104)*, which runs downward from the base of the brain. The springlike, S-shape of the vertebral column, visible in side view, enhances its strength and flexibility, facilitates balance by positioning the trunk directly over the feet, and absorbs shocks during movement.

Adults have 26 vertebrae, although two of these— the sacrum and coccyx—are composites composed of fused vertebrae. All vertebrae have the same basic structure. A short, pillarlike, weight bearing bone, called the centrum or body, is attached posteriorly to a ring-shaped neural arch. Together, the centrum and arch surround an opening called the vertebral foramen through which the spinal cord passes. Bony projections on the neural arch—two transverse processes and a single spinous process—form attachment points for the ligaments and back muscles

that stabilize the vertebral column by preventing excessive bending, and hold it upright. Lying between the centra of adjacent vertebrae are intervertebral discs, cartilage pads with a jellylike filling, which allow limited movement and cushion the vertebrae against sudden jolts that occur during walking, running, or jumping.

Vertebrae are divided into five types according to their position, size, shape, and role. Seven small, light cervical vertebrae form the flexible neck. The uppermost, the atlas, articulates with the skull to produce nodding, "yes", movements, and forms a pivot joint with its neighbor, the axis, that allows the head to shake in a "no" movement. Twelve thoracic vertebrae form the central part of the backbone, each one articulating with a rib. Five large lumbar vertebrae, which form the small of theback, bear most of the weight of the trunk and head.The triangular sacrum, formed from five fused bones, forms strong joints with the bones of the pelvis. The coccyx, or tailbone, consists of four fused vertebrae.

An anterior view shows some of the processes to which the muscles and ligaments that support the vertebral column are attached.

KEY

1. Atlas
2. Axis
3. Centrum of thoracic
   vertebra
4. Spinous process
5. Transverse process
6. Intervertebral disc
7. Intervertebral foramen
8. Coccyx
9. Cervical vertebrae (7)
10. Thoracic vertebrae (12)
11. Lumbar vertebrae (5)
12. Sacrum

This lateral view (right) of the vertebral column reveals the four curvatures that give it an S-shape.

THE SPINE: Function and Repair

The column of vertebrae that make up the spine are named based on their location. The cervical vertebrae are in the neck. Thoracic vertebrae are in the upper back and the lumbar vertebrae are in the lower back. Fused bones at the bottom of the spinal column are called the sacrum and coccyx.

Vertebrae are not stacked directly on top of each other; the spaces between them are maintained by round, spongy pads of cartilage called intervertebral disks.

The disks act like shock absorbers throughout the spinal column to cushion the bones as the body moves: they contract with downward pressure.

...and expand when the back stretches.

Each disk is made up of two components: the anulus fibrosus, a tough outer portion which surrounds the nucleus pulposus, a soft inner gel material. These disks and the space between the bones that they fill give the lower back flexibility.

Damage to a disk can cause the soft rubbery center to bulge out of the outer layer. This is called a herniated disk.

If the expanding center presses on nearby nerves, the herniated disk can cause severe pain.

The spinal cord passes through the center of the vertebrae.

Spinal stenosis occurs when the spinal canal narrows, reducing space for the spinal cord. This increases pressure on nerves coming off the spinal cord and can cause back pain, numbness, weakness or pain in the leg.

When a disk or vertebra is damaged, a procedure called spinal fusion can prevent further damage or pressure on the spinal cord. A piece of bone, often from the patient's pelvis, is removed.

The disk is removed and the bone segment is placed between the vertebrae.

Rods and screws are often used to strengthen the join and prevent the three affected vertebrae from too much movement.

Posterior view of the spine

Cervical vertebrae

Thoracic vertebrae

Lumbar vertebrae

Sacrum

Coccyx

WHY THE SKELETON OF THE THORAX (CHEST) IS CALLED THE RIBCAGE IS PLAIN TO SEE. WITH RIBS FORMING ITS "BARS," THIS BONY CAGE ENCIRCLES AND PROTECTS THE HEART AND LUNGS, AS WELL AS MOST OF THE STOMACH AND LIVER IN THE UPPER ABDOMEN. THE RIBCAGE IS ALSO SUFFICIENTLY FLEXIBLE TO PERMIT THE UP AND DOWN MOVEMENTS THAT MOVE AIR INTO AND OUT OF THE LUNGS DURING BREATHING.

THE RIBCAGE

The ribcage consists of 12 pairs of curved ribs, that section of the vertebral column containing the 12 thoracic vertebrae and, anteriorly, the sternum or breastbone. The ribs are flat bones, each with a bowed, slightly-twisted, shaft, that curve forwards and downwards to the anterior bodysurface. At its posterior end, each rib articulates with its corresponding vertebra through plane joints, called vertebrocostal joints, that allow limited gliding movements. At their anterior ends, the upper 10 pairs of ribs are connected directly or indirectly to the sternum by flexible costal ("rib") cartilages. Together, vertebrocostal joints and costal cartilages give the ribcage its flexibility. The ribs gradually increase in size up to the seventh

Below: posterior (left) and lateral (right) views of the ribcage; opposite: an anterior view showing the sternum.

pair, after which they progressively decrease in size. Rib pairs 1 through 7—called true or vertebrosternal ribs—are attached to the sternum through their own costal cartilage. The remaining rib pairs are called false ribs: the costal cartilages of rib pairs 8 through 10, the vertebrochondral ribs, attach to each other and to the costal cartilages of rib pair 7; rib pairs 11 and 12, the floating or vertebral ribs, are attached solely to the vertebral column, terminating in the abdominal muscles at their anterior end.

The dagger-shaped sternum has three parts. The upper manubrium articulates with the clavicle, which is part of the shoulder girdle, at the clavicular notch, and with the first rib. The central sternal body is notched where it articulates with the costal cartilages of ribs 3 through 7. Where manubrium and sternal body meet, at the sternal angle, a hinge-like cartilaginous joint allows the sternal body to swing forward while breathing in. At the sternum's lower end, and not attached to any ribs, is the xiphoid process.

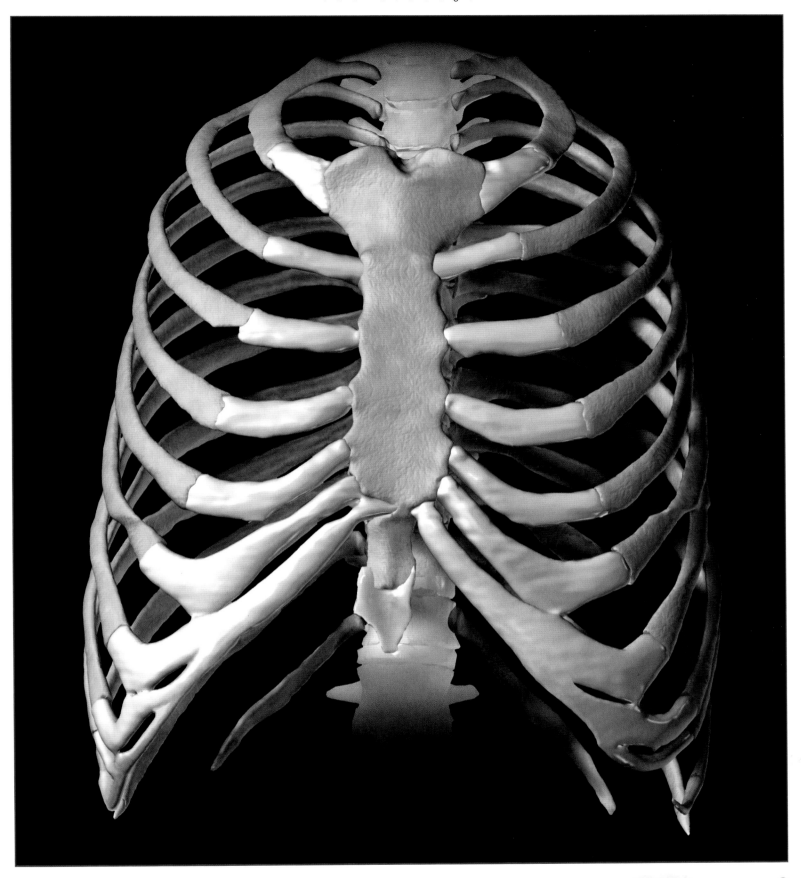

Anterior view of the ribcage. The flexible bony cage consists of a combination of bone and cartilage that houses and protects the delicate thoracic organs while still allowing sufficient movement for breathing.

KEY

① Clavicular notch

② Sternal angle

③ Body of sternum

④ Xiphoid process of sternum

⑤ Articulation of rib with vertebra

⑥ Vertebrochondral ribs

⑦ 1st thoracic vertebra

⑧ Manubrium of sternum

⑨ Vertebrosternal (true) ribs

⑩ Costal cartilage

⑪ 12th thoracic vertebra

⑫ Vertebral (floating) rib

U NLIKE THEIR CLOSE MAMMALIAN RELATIVES, HUMANS WALK ON THEIR HINDLEGS, LEAVING THEIR FORELIMBS FREE FOR THE MANIPULATION OF OBJECTS. HUMAN FORELIMBS, AND THEIR ASSOCIATED SHOULDER GIRDLE, ARE ACCORDINGLY ADAPTED FOR MANIPULATION RATHER THAN LOCOMOTION.

THE SHOULDER & ARM

Each shoulder is formed by two bones, the clavicle or collarbone, and the scapula or shoulder blade. Together they comprise half of the pectoral, or shoulder, girdle, which attaches the arms to the axial skeleton. The pectoral girdle is lightweight and flexible compared to the pelvic girdle, and is not attached to the vertebral column. This arrangement reflects its lack of weight-bearing role, but gives it a flexibility and mobility not found anywhere else in the body. The long, narrow clavicle articulates at one end with the sternum, and at the other with the scapula, and serves to support the shoulder and arm. The triangular scapula provides a large surface for muscle attachment, and has a hollow, called the glenoid fossa. The head of the humerus, the upper arm bone, fits into the glenoid fossa to form the

highly mobile shoulder joint, a ball and socket joint.

Three bones make up the skeleton of the arm— the humerus in the upper arm, and the ulna (inner) and radius (outer) in the lower arm. They are not as heavily built as the femur or tibia in the leg. At their proximal ends, the ulna and, to a lesser extent, the radius form a hinge joint with the humerus at the elbow. Here the radius also forms a pivot joint with the ulna; this allows the radius to cross over the ulna enabling the palm of the hand to move through 180°. At their distal ends, the radius and, to a lesser extent, the ulna, articulate with the carpal bones in the hand to form the wrist joint.

The single upper arm bone and the two forearm bones form a hinge joint at the elbow.

Joints

Wherever two or more bones meet in the skeleton, a joint is formed. Joints allow bones to move. They also maintain stability because the bones in a joint are held together and stabilized by strong strips of tough fibrous connective tissue called ligaments that while unyielding are, at the same time, pliant and flexible.

There are three types of joints. Fixed joints, such as the sutures between skull bones, do not permit

movement. Partially movable cartilaginous joints, such as the discs between vertebrae, allow limited movements. Synovial joints are freely movable.

Most joints are synovial. Inside a synovial joint, oily synovial fluid lubricates the glassy cartilage that covers the ends of the bones so that they slide over each other easily. Different types of synovial joints each have their own range of movement.

• Ball and socket joints, such as the shoulder and hip joints, permit movement in many directions.

• Hinge joints, such as the elbow, knee, and ankle, work like a door hinge to allow movement in just one plane.

• Pivot joints, such as the joint between the atlas and axis in the neck, allow one bone to swivel around another.

• Plane, or gliding joints, between

carpals (wrist bones) and tarsals (ankle bones), allow short, sliding movements between the flat surfaces of bones.

• Ellipsoidal, or condyloid, joints, such as those found between the radius and carpals in the wrist, allow movement from side to side and backward and forward.

• Saddle joints, found at the base of the thumb, allow movement in two planes.

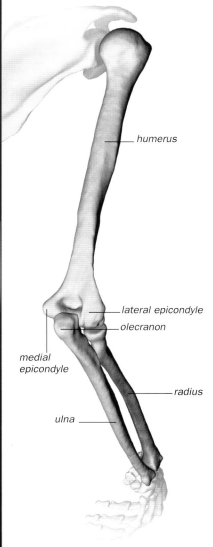

humerus

lateral epicondyle

olecranon

medial epicondyle

radius

ulna

Above: posterior view of the right arm. The hinge joint of the elbow allows a variety of movements of the forearm.

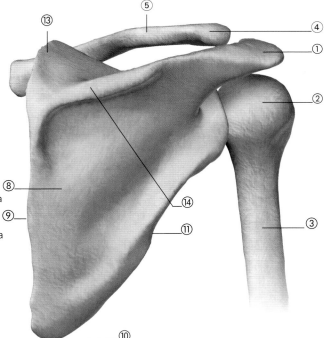

KEY

1. Acromion
2. Head of humerus
3. Shaft of humerus
4. Acromial end of clavicle
5. Clavicle
6. Sternal end of clavicle
7. Coracoid process
8. Scapula
9. Medial border of scapula
10. Inferior angle
11. Lateral border of scapula
12. Glenoid fossa
13. Superior angle
14. Spine of scapula

Above is an anterior view of the bones of the shoulder, while to the right is a posterior view.

THE HANDS ARE THE MOST FLEXIBLE AND VERSATILE PARTS OF THE HUMAN BODY: STRONG ENOUGH TO HOLD AND GRIP HEAVY WEIGHTS, PRECISE ENOUGH TO CHOP VEGETABLES WITH A KNIFE, YET SUFFICIENTLY DELICATE TO PAINT A WATERCOLOR. SUCH VERSATILITY RESULTS FROM THE NUMBERS, SHAPES AND ARRANGEMENT OF THE 27 BONES THAT FORM THE FRAMEWORK OF THE HAND. THESE BONES FALL INTO THREE GROUPS.

THE HAND & WRIST

The large number of small component bones found in the hand give it great flexibility and versatility.

Eight short carpal bones, arranged in two rows, make up the carpus or wrist. The bones are named for their shapes. In the proximal row are the pisiform (pea-shaped), triquetral (three-edged), lunate (crescent-shaped), and scaphoid (boat-shaped); while in the distal row are the hamate (hook-shaped), capitate (round-headed), and two four-sided bones, the trapezium and trapezoid. The pisiform can be felt and seen easily as the "bump" on the lower wrist. The carpals form a "bridge" between the forearm bones and the palm and fingers. They articulate through plane joints, but their gliding movements are restricted by stabilizing ligaments.

Five long bones called metacarpals make up the metacarpus or palm. The metacarpal of the thumb forms a saddle joint with the trapezium that gives it extra mobility, enabling it to swing across the palm and oppose, or touch, the fingers. This opposability allows the hand to perform its precise movements and power grips. The distal ends of the metacarpals can be seen as "knuckles" in a clenched fist.

The digits, or fingers, and the pollex, or thumb, are formed from 14 long bones called phalanges (sing. phalanx). Each finger has three phalanges—proximal, middle, and distal—while the thumb has two—proximal and distal. The large number of joints—condyloid joints between metacarpals and phalanges, and hinge joints between phalanges—in the fingers gives them great flexibility.

Endochondral ossification

Ossification is the process by which bones are made both before birth, and during infancy, childhood and adolescence. Most bones—apart from those in the skull and clavicles—are made by a process called endochondral ("inside cartilage") ossification. Initially, the skeleton is made up of flexible cartilage "templates." Gradually these cartilage models break down to be replaced by bony tissue—both compact and spongy bone—produced by osteoblasts. During childhood, bones also lengthen and broaden, allowing the body to grow in size. By late adolescence, when growth ceases, the process of ossification is largely complete.

KEY

1. Ulna
2. Lunate
3. Triquetral
4. Hamate
5. Metacarpal
6. Proximal phalanx
7. Middle phalanx
8. Distal phalanx
9. Radius
10. Scaphoid
11. Trapezoid
12. Trapezium
13. Capitate
14. Proximal phalanx of pollex
15. Distal phalanx of pollex
16. Pisiform

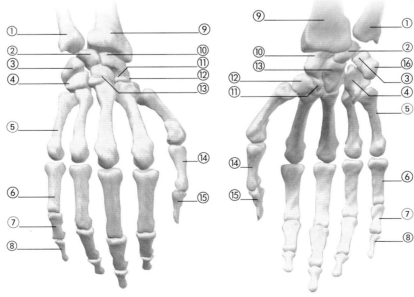

Palm downwards

Palm upwards

Two views of the bones of the right hand and wrist: on the left a dorsal (palm downward) view; on the right the right a palmar (palm upward) view.

THE PELVIS FORMS THE KEY LINK BETWEEN THE LIMBS AND THE TRUNK. ITS BASINLIKE STRUCTURE CONSISTS OF TWO **COXAL,** OR HIP, BONES—THESE FORM THE PELVIC GIRDLE—AND THE SACRUM AND COCCYX, THE LOWEST REGIONS OF THE VERTEBRAL COLUMN. AS WELL AS KEEPING THE BODY UPRIGHT, THE PELVIS TRANSMITS WEIGHT FROM THE TRUNK TO THE LEGS AND, IN RETURN, TRANSMITS THE FORCES GENERATED BY MOVEMENT IN THE OPPOSITE DIRECTION. IT SUPPORTS AND PROTECTS THE REPRODUCTIVE ORGANS AND THE URINARY BLADDER IN THE LOWER ABDOMEN. ITS LARGE SURFACE ALSO PROVIDES AN ANCHORAGE FOR POWERFUL MUSCLES, SUCH AS THE GLUTEUS MAXIMUS (BUTTOCK MUSCLE), WHICH EXTEND INTO THE LEGS AND TRUNK.

THE PELVIS

The female (left) and male (right) pelves, viewed from above. The female pelvis is wider and rounder compared to the male, which is heart-shaped. These differences reflect the female's role in childbearing.

Each coxal bone is formed from three bones—the ilium, ischium, and pubis—that fuse during adolescence. The ilium, which forms a major part of the coxal bone, articulates with the sacrum at a sacroiliac joint at the rear of the pelvis. The ischium, which is inferior and posterior, bears a person's weight when sitting. At the front of the pelvis the pubis, or pubic bone, is linked to its opposite number by a cartilaginous disc called the pubic symphysis. Strong ligaments reinforce both the sacroiliac joint and the pubic symphysis to maintain the structural stability of the pelvis. On the lateral surface of each coxal bone, where the ilium, ischium and pubis meet, is a deep socket, called the acetabulum, which articulates with the head of the femur. This ball and socket joint allows less freedom of movement than the one formed between the upper arm and shoulder bones because it is constrained by strong stabilizing ligaments.

Male and female pelves differ. The female pelvis is shallower than the male, and its central opening—the pelvic inlet—is rounder and wider compared to the narrow, heart-shaped opening found in males. The female sacrum is also wider and shorter, making the pubic arch correspondingly broader. These differences reflect the female's role in childbearing. The pelvic inlet must be—and is just—big enough to accommodate the head of a full-term fetus as it passes through the uterine cervix and the vagina during birth.

Female pelvis

Male pelvis

The female (top) and male (bottom) pelves, viewed from the front. The pelvis forms an important central point in the body. It is not only a link between the trunk and the lower limbs, but provides a large surface area for muscle attachment and also houses and protects the bladder and reproductive organs.

Female pelvis

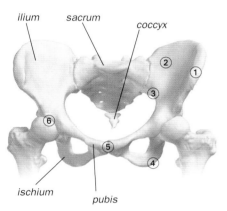

ilium   *sacrum*   *coccyx*
ischium   *pubis*

Male pelvis

KEY

1. Iliac crest
2. Iliac tuberosity
3. Greater sciatic notch
4. Ischial tuberosity
5. Pubic symphysis
6. Acetabulum
7. Sacral promontory
8. Greater trochanter of femur
9. Inferior pubic ramus
10. Superior pubic ramus
11. Iliopubic eminence
12. Anterior inferior iliac spine

THE LEG & ANKLE

WHILE THE LOWER AND UPPER LIMBS SHARE THE SAME NUMBER OF BONES (30) AND OVERALL STRUCTURE, THEIR FUNCTIONS DIFFER. THE LONGER, STRONGER BONES AND BROAD FEET OF THE LOWER LIMB PROVIDE STABILITY, BEAR THE BODY'S WEIGHT, AND ABSORB THE FORCES GENERATED BY RUNNING AND JUMPING. THE THREE PARTS OF THE LOWER LIMB ARE THE UPPER LEG, LOWER LEG, AND FOOT.

The femur, or thighbone, is the largest of the body's bones and bears its weight. At its proximal end, a rounded head fits into the acetabulum, the socket in the side of the pelvis, to form a ball and socket joint that is reinforced by strong ligaments. An angled neck leads to a long shaft, which is curved like that of other long bones to provide more resistance to stresses. Where neck meets shaft can be found the greater and lesser trochanters, which are sites of attachment for thigh and buttock muscles. At its distal end the femur broadens into medial and lateral condyles that form a hinge joint—the knee—with the lower leg bones. The patella, or kneecap, is a triangular bone that is enclosed in the tendon of the thigh muscle, the quadriceps femoris, and protects the knee joint anteriorly.

The larger of the lower leg bones is the tibia, or shinbone, which transmits the weight of the body to the feet. The lateral and medial condyles of its proximal end articulate with the femur at the knee, while at its distal end the tibia forms the ankle joint—a hinge joint—with the talus, one of the ankle bones of the foot. The slender fibula, the other lower leg bone, articulates at both ends with the tibia. Unlike the forearm bones, these joints do not permit movement, but provide stability. The medial malleolus of the tibia and the lateral malleolus of the fibula form the characteristic bony bulges on each side of the ankle.

Bone remodeling and repair

Bone shape and size do not remain unchanged throughout life. Bones are made of dynamic and active tissues that constantly renew themselves by a process called remodeling. This is the result of two complementary processes: bone deposition by osteoblasts and bone resorption by osteoclasts. Bone shape is altered in response to mechanical stress caused by the pull of muscles and by gravity. Bone deposit is also responsible for the process of self-repair that occurs when bones fracture or break.

KEY

① Greater trochanter
② Lateral epicondyle
③ Lateral condyle
④ Fibula
⑤ Lateral malleolus
⑥ Head of femur
⑦ Neck of femur
⑧ Femur
⑨ Patella
⑩ Medial epicondyle
⑪ Medial condyle
⑫ Tibia
⑬ Medial malleolus

The three major bones of the leg—one in the thigh and two in the lower leg—articulate at a hinge joint in the knee.

KEY

① Fibula

② Distal tibiofibular joint

③ Lateral malleolus of
   fibula

④ Tarsals

⑤ Metatarsals

⑥ Phalanges

⑦ Tibia

⑧ Medial malleolus of tibia

⑨ Articular surface of medial
   malleolus

⑩ Talus

⑪ Calcaneus (heel bone)

⑫ Hallux (great toe)

The ankle joint of this right leg and foot is a hinge joint formed by the tibia—the shinbone—and the talus, one of the tarsal bones in the foot.

THE FEET BEAR THE BODY'S WEIGHT, KEEP IT BALANCED AND STOP IT FALLING OVER WHETHER STATIONARY OR MOVING. THE FEET ALSO ACT AS LEVERS THAT PUSH THE BODY FORWARD DURING MOVEMENT. WHILE EACH FOOT HAS 26 BONES, JUST ONE LESS THAN EACH HAND, IT IS FAR LESS FLEXIBLE AND MOBILE THAN A HAND. THE BONES OF THE FOOT ARE BROADER AND FLATTER THAN THOSE IN THE HAND; THEIR ARRANGEMENT COUPLED WITH THE PRESENCE OF STRONG LIGAMENTS ALLOWS LITTLE FREE MOVEMENT OF BONES, BUT FACILITATES THE FOOT'S FUNCTION AS A WEIGHTBEARER AND MOVER. DESPITE THE LACK OF MOBILITY, BEING MADE OF MANY BONES MAKES FEET PLIABLE, SO THAT THEY CAN MOVE COMFORTABLY OVER BOTH SMOOTH AND UNEVEN SURFACES.

THE FOOT

KEY

① Calcaneus
② Cuboid
③ Metatarsal
④ Proximal phalanx
⑤ Middle phalanx
⑥ Distal phalanx
⑦ Talus
⑧ Navicular
⑨ 3rd cuneiform
⑩ 2nd cuneiform
⑪ 1st cuneiform
⑫ Distal phalanx of hallux

Like the hands, the feet contain three sets of bones. Seven tarsal bones form the tarsus or ankle. The talus articulates with the tibia and fibula to form the ankle joint. The calcaneus, the largest ankle bone, forms the heel, and is the attachment point of the large calcaneal (Achilles tendon) from the muscles of the calf. On standing, both calcaneus and talus bear the body's weight initially before transferring it forward. The other tarsals are the navicular (boat-shaped), cuboid, and first, second, and third cuneiform (wedge-shaped).

Five metatarsals form the tarsus, or sole, of the foot. At their distal ends, where they articulate with the toe bones, they form the "ball" of the foot. The first (medial) metatarsal is the strongest and bears more body weight. Together, the bones of the tarsus and metatarsus, by virtue of their arrangement and the reinforcement of ligaments and tendons, form an arch shape that keeps the sole off the ground. These springlike arches absorb impact experienced during walking and running—by first flattening and then springing back into shape—and spread the weight of the body. The tarsal and metatarsal bones also act as levers, raising the body and pushing it forward during walking and running.

The fourteen phalanges in the toes are much shorter and less mobile than those in the fingers. Each toe has three phalanges except for the hallux, or great toe, which has two. Functionally, the toes play a subordinate role to the tarsus and metatarsus, but they do contribute to stability.

Two views of the bones of the right foot: on the left, a dorsal view from above; on the right, a plantar view from below.

View from above   **View from below**

This lateral view of the bones of the right foot shows the springlike arches that flatten to absorb shocks and then recoil back to their arched shape.

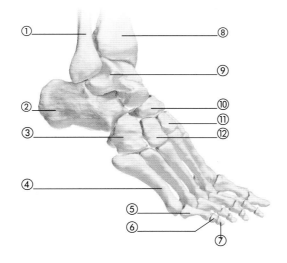

KEY

① Fibula

② Calcaneus

③ Cuboid

④ Metatarsal of little toe

⑤ Proximal phalanx

⑥ Middle phalanx

⑦ Distal phalanx

⑧ Tibia

⑨ Talus

⑩ Navicular

⑪ 2nd cuneiform

⑫ 3rd cuneiform

The foot carries us everywhere for our entire lifetime. It supports our bodies and acts as a lever to push us off the ground when running or walking. Its flexible and resilient base allows us to negotiate both flat and uneven surfaces. With all of its parts and all of the punishment it receives, it is no wonder that there are many common problems with our feet.

MECHANICS OF THE FOOT

When you take a normal step, the first part of your foot to touch the ground is your heel. Your weight is then transferred to the long bones of the foot, the metatarsals.

Some people are over-pronators. This means the foot rolls too far inward as weight is transferred from the heel to the metatarsals to the big toe and distributed unevenly with too much weight on the big toe. Sometimes the arches collapse or the ankle rolls inward.

A bunion is a lump of bone and tissue on the outside of the big toe caused by abnormal stress on the joint over an extended period. The stress causes enlargement of the first metatarsal, the bone that joins the big toe.

The foot rolls from the outside inward, or pronates, to distribute the weight across the bones. It starts at the back of the outside metatarsal, moves to the front of the inside metatarsal and ends with the push off from the big toe. Neutral pronation means that weight is distributed evenly as the foot rolls inward.

People can also be under-pronators. This means the foot does not roll in enough as weight moves from the heel to the long bones and too much weight is borne on the outside of the foot.

This is a complex joint where bones, tendons and ligaments work together to transmit and distribute our weight during movement. This outward movement of the joint can form a bunion. With continued stress, it becomes larger. The tissue around the bunion may become swollen and inflamed, causing pain and making it difficult to walk.

In severe cases, surgery may be performed to relieve pain, remove the enlargement, and realign the joint. The surgery may simply involve removing the extra bone and realigning the muscles, tendons and ligaments of the joint.

In more severe cases, the bone may need to be cut and moved into its proper position with insertion of screws, wires, or plates to hold it together while it heals. Tendons and ligaments may also need to be repositioned.

Hammer toe is a deformity of the foot caused by a permanent bend at the middle joint of the toe.

If the tendons that bend and straighten the toes are held in one position for too long they tighten and cannot stretch out.

When the condition is advanced to the point where the toe is rigid, surgery can correct the condition by cutting the tendon to relax the joint.

Sometimes a section of bone is removed and the joint is fixed in place with a steel pin.

Where bones meet they usually form a joint, which permits movement in certain directions and allows stability. Immobile joints, such as the **SUTURES** of the skull, are sometimes referred to as fibrous: that is, their seams are knitted together by cartilage—which often undergoes **OSSIFICATION** with age. Mobile joints fall into two general classes: synovial and cartilaginous. Strengthening and stabilizing the joints, attached to the bones, are the ligaments, which are composed of fibrous connective tissue. Joints that allow relatively free motion (the elbow, shoulder, and knee) are surrounded by protective cartilaginous capsules, within which the bearing surfaces are glassily smooth and bathed in **SYNOVIAL FLUID.** Less mobile joints, for example, between the vertebrae, lack synovial lubricant and are simply cartilaginous, with pads or disks between the bone surfaces.

THE JOINTS & LIGAMENTS

The rounded condyles (from word roots meaning "knuckle") at the lower end of the femur rest on cartilaginous wedges, called the medial and lateral meniscus— they are part of the capsule surrounding this synovial joint.

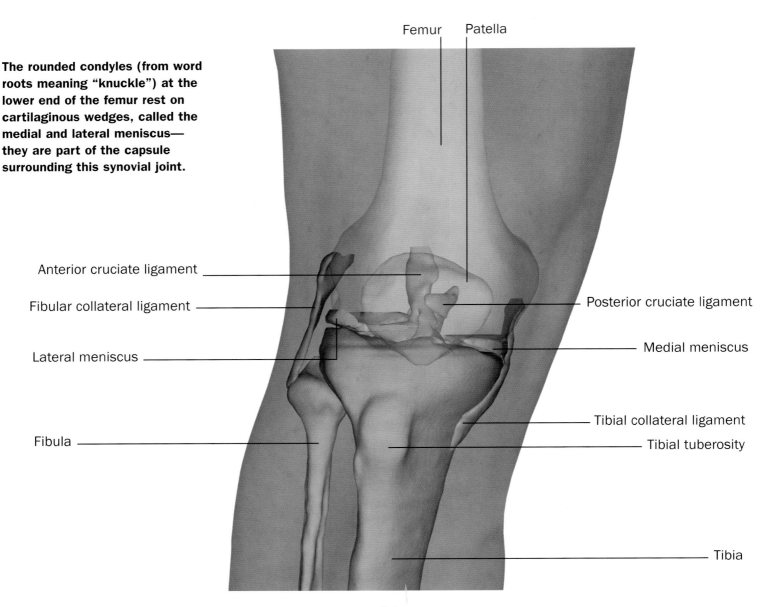

Femur Patella

Anterior cruciate ligament

Fibular collateral ligament

Lateral meniscus

Fibula

Posterior cruciate ligament

Medial meniscus

Tibial collateral ligament

Tibial tuberosity

Tibia

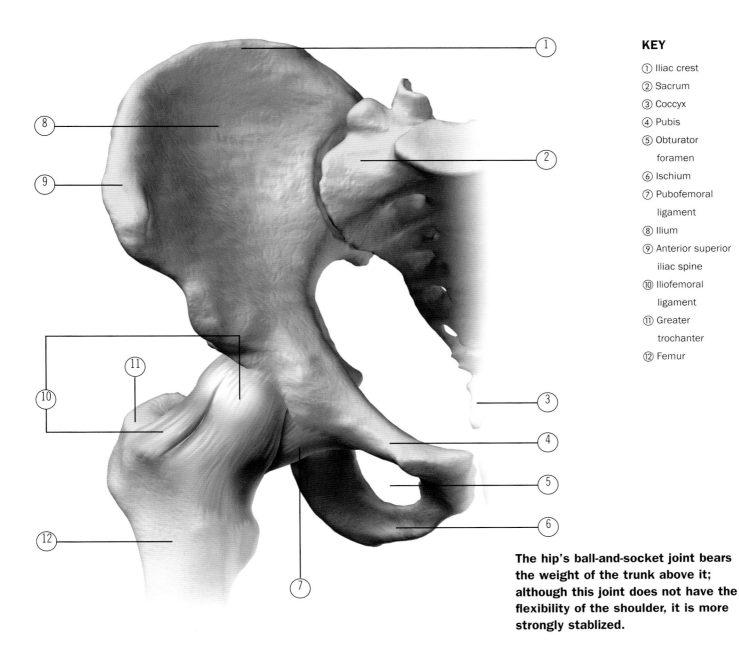

The hip's ball-and-socket joint bears the weight of the trunk above it; although this joint does not have the flexibility of the shoulder, it is more strongly stablized.

SYNOVIAL JOINTS

The freely moveable synovial joints are broadly classified as:

• BALL-and-socket: allows motion in many directions; the rounded end of one bone fits into a rounded cuplike depression in another, e.g., the shoulder or hip.

• HINGE: swings in one direction, often with especially strong ligaments to limit the range of motion, e.g., the elbow or knee.

• PIVOT: works as a swivel, e.g., between the atlas and axis bones of the neck, to permit a wide range of head movements. The body's pivot joints all consist of a central, roughly cylindrical bone surrounded by a ring of ligament and bone. Either of these elements may move: in the case of the atlas and axis, the surrounding ring (of the atlas) moves; in the upper joint between the radius and ulna, the central bone (the radius) rotates within a ring of ligament and bone.

• PLANE, or gliding, joint: permits short, sliding actions between bones, e.g., within the wrist or ankle (between the carpals or tarsals). Such joints are found between flat or only slightly curved surfaces.

• ELLIPSOIDAL, or condyloid, joint: with rocking side-to-side and forward-backward movement, but more limited in one plane than the other, e.g., at the junction of wrist or ankle with the longer limb bones. The fit in a condyloid joint is between an oval cavity in one bone and a matching oval protuberance in the other.

• SADDLE: also allows movement in two planes, e.g., the thumb joint, at its base. Here, the junction is between a mating cup and knob on each bone.

THE
MUSCULAR
SYSTEM

Over half the body's tissue is muscle; the majority of
which is comprised of over 600 skeletal muscles that
allow us to make our way through the world.

THE MUSCULAR SYSTEM MOVES THE BODY. IT CONSISTS OF OVER 640 SKELETAL MUSCLES THAT ARE ATTACHED TO THE BONES OF THE SKELETON ACROSS THEIR JOINTS. SKELETAL MUSCLES MAKE UP ABOUT 40 PERCENT OF THE BODY'S WEIGHT AND, WITH THE BONES AND SKIN, GIVE THE BODY ITS SHAPE.

Anterior view of the body's muscular system. Together the skeletal muscles make up about 40 percent of the body's weight and help define its shape.

THE FULL BODY

Muscle tissue uses energy to contract, or get shorter. This shortening movement provides the power to pull bones and produce a wide range of body movements from running to smiling. Muscles also maintain the body's posture, and stabilize joints. Heat released as a byproduct of muscle contraction helps to keep the body warm.

Origins and insertions

Typically, each skeletal muscle is attached to bones at two or more points by cords of connective tissue called tendons. When a muscle contracts, one bone remains stationary and forms a fixed point, while the other bone moves. The end of the muscle attached to the immovable bone is called its origin; the other end, attached to the moving bone, is called its insertion. The body moves when muscles contract across joints and insertions move toward origins.

Range of movements

The movement, or movements, produced by a muscle depend on its position, the other muscles it may work with, and the type of synovial joint it crosses. The main movements produced by muscles are listed below. The principal action of a particular muscle—such as flexor or extensor—may be included in its name.

- **Flexion**—a decrease in the angle of a joint bringing bones together, such as flexing (bending) the arm.

- **Extension**—the opposite of flexion; an increase in the angle of a joint, such as straightening the arm.

- **Abduction**—moving a bone away from the midline of the body, such as moving the arm laterally and upward (sideways).

- **Adduction**—the opposite of abduction, moving a bone toward the midline, such as moving the arm medially and downward (inward).

- **Elevation**—lifting upward, such as the jaw, or the shoulder blades when shrugging the shoulders.

- **Depression**—the opposite of elevation, a downward movement.

- **Supination**—movement of the radius around the ulna in the forearm to turn the palm upward.

- **Pronation**—the opposite of supination, turning the palm downward.

- **Rotation**—moves a bone around its long axis.

Procerus

Zygomaticus minor

Zygomaticus major

Orbicularis oris
Platysma

Deltoid

Pectoralis major

Triceps brachii

Biceps brachii

Latissimus dorsi

Serratus anterior
Rectus sheath
Pronator teres
Brachioradialis

Palmarus longus
Flexor digitorum superficialis

Flexor carpi ulnaris

Tensor fasciae latae

Levator ani

Rectus femoris

Iliotibial tract

Sartorius

Vastus lateralis

Vastus medialis

Patella

Peroneus longus

Tibialis anterior

Extensor digitorum longus

Extensor retinaculum

Abductor digiti minimi

Abductor hallucis

Frontalis

Temporalis
Orbicularis oculi
Levator labii

Sternocleidomastoid
Infrahyoid
Trapezius

Pectoralis minor

Coracobrachialis

Intercostals (anterior)

Brachialis

External abdominal oblique

Supinator

Rectus abdominus

Flexor pollicis longus
Flexor digitorum profundus

Internal abdominal oblique

Flexor retinaculum
Flexor pollicis brevis

Abductor digiti minimi

Gluteus medius
Iliopsoas
Pectineus
Vastus intermedius
Adductor longus
Gracilis

Gastrocnemius

Extensor digitorum longus

Extensor hallucis longus

Soleus

Tibia bone

Dorsal interosseous

THE FULL BODY

At first sight, the names of skeletal muscles may appear incomprehensible. The majority are in Latin or derived from Latin or Greek roots. However, most muscle names are based on one or more of the structural or functional characteristics listed below.

- Shape—the relative shape of a muscle such as the deltoid (triangular), the trapezius (trapezoid), or rhomboideus (rhomboid).

- Location—the body region or bone with which the muscle is associated. For example, the intercostal muscles (costal means "ribs") run between ribs; the frontalis muscle overlies the frontal bone of the skull.

- Number of origins—some muscles have more than one origin or head ("-ceps" indicates "head"). The biceps brachii and triceps brachii in the arm have, respectively, two and three origins; the quadriceps femoris in the thigh has four origins.

- Direction of muscle fibers in relation to the midline of the body—rectus (straight) fibers run parallel to the midline, as in the rectus femoris (the straight muscle of the thigh); transversus fibers run at right angles to the midline, as in the transversus abdominis (the transverse muscle of the abdomen); and oblique fibers run diagonally to the midline, as in the external oblique (the diagonal muscle of the abdomen).

- Relative size—"maximus" means largest and "minimus" smallest, as in the large and small buttock muscles (gluteus maximus and gluteus minimus);

"longus" means long and "brevis" means short, as in the lower leg muscles—the peroneus longus and peroneus brevis—that move the foot.

- The origin and insertion of a muscle—the sternocleidomastoid in the neck, for example, has two origins on the sternum ("sterno-") and the clavicle ("-cleido-"), and inserts on the mastoid process of the temporal bone of the skull.

- Muscle action *(see page 60)*—for example, "flexor" means the muscle bends a joint. Other terms that relate to muscle action include extensor, abductor, adductor, levator, depressor, supinator, pronator.

- Combination names—for example, the extensor carpi radialis longus is an extensor muscle that straightens the wrist ("carpi"), lies along the radius bone of the forearm ("radialis"), and is longer than other wrist extensors.

Posterior view including both superficial muscles on the right hand side and deep muscles on the left. The muscles' size is often indicated in its name – for example, in the gluteus maximus of the buttocks the name "maximus" indicates that it is one of the large muscles. *Minor, longus* and *brevis* refer respectively to small, long and short muscles.

Semispinalis capitis

Sternocleidomastoid

Splenius capitis

Supraspinatus

Rhomboideus minor
Infraspinatus
Teres minor
Rhomboideus major
Teres major

Triceps brachii

Posterior intercostals

Flexor carpi ulnaris

Supinator

Abductor pollicis longus

Extensor pollicis brevis

Dorsal interosseus

Gluteus medius

Piriformis
Adductor minimus
Quadratus femoris

Vastus lateralis

Plantaris

Flexor digitorum longus

Flexor hallucis longus

Gracilis

Galea aponeurotica

Epicranius

Trapezius

Deltoid

Triceps brachii

Latissimus dorsi
External abdominal oblique

Anconeus
Extensor carpi radialis longus

Brachioradialis

Extensor carpi radialis brevis
Extensor digitorum
Extensor carpi ulnaris

Extensor digiti minimi

Gluteus maximus

Levator ani

Iliotibial tract

Adductor magnus

Biceps femoris

Semitendinosus

Semimembranosus

Gastrocnemius

Soleus

S O FAR, ONLY SKELETAL MUSCLE HAS BEEN DESCRIBED, HOWEVER, THERE ARE TWO OTHER TYPES OF MUSCLE IN THE BODY: SMOOTH MUSCLE AND CARDIAC MUSCLE. DESPITE DIFFERENCES IN LOCATION AND FUNCTION, ALL THREE TYPES SHARE COMMON CHARACTERISTICS. ALL ARE MADE OF LONG CELLS, CALLED FIBERS, THAT ARE EXCITABLE—ABLE TO RESPOND WHEN STIMULATED BY A NERVE IMPULSE OR A HORMONE—AND CONTRACTILE—ABLE TO SHORTEN WHEN STIMULATED. MUSCLE FIBERS CONTAIN TWO TYPES OF PROTEIN FILAMENTS, CALLED **ACTIN** AND **MYOSIN**, THAT INTERACT WHEN THE FIBER IS STIMULATED TO MAKE IT SHORTEN. MUSCLE FIBERS ARE ALSO EXTENSIBLE—CAPABLE OF STRETCHING—AND ELASTIC—ABLE TO RECOIL.

TYPES OF MUSCLE

Key
1. Smooth muscle sheet
2. Smooth muscle fiber
3. Nucleus of smooth muscle fiber

Key
1. Nucleus
2. Striation (stripe)
3. Skeletal muscle fibre
4. Sarcomere

Key
1. Striation (stripe)
2. Intercalated disc
3. Cardiac muscle fiber
4. Nucleus
5. Branch of cardiac muscle fiber

An electron micrograph image of a cross section of skeletal muscle.

Smooth muscle (top): The fibers are composed of short, slightly rounded filaments aggregating to form muscular sheets.
Skeletal muscle (middle): Uniformly packed cylindrical filaments are bundled into long fibers; the regular arrangement of its smallest contractile units, sarcomeres, produces a banded or striped appearance.
Cardiac muscle (bottom): Striped but branched, cardiac fibers make junctions with one another at intercalated disks, which aid in propagating electrical impulses.

Skeletal muscle

Longest of the muscle fibers, skeletal muscle fibers have a striate (striped) appearance because of the arrangement of filaments inside them, and are also under conscious, voluntary control, hence their alternative names striate or voluntary muscle. Skeletal muscle fibers contract rapidly and powerfully, but tire easily. They are bound into bundles called **fascicles** by connective tissue called **perimysium**; fascicles are bound together by a protective connective tissue sheath, called the **epimysium**, to form a complete muscle.

Smooth muscle

Smooth muscle is found in the walls of hollow organs such as the small intestine, bladder, or blood vessels. Its fibers are short with tapering ends, do not have a striped appearance, and are typically arranged in sheets. Smooth muscle contraction is involuntary—hence its

A skeletal muscle consists of bundles of muscle fibers. The muscle is wrapped in a sheath called the epimysium. The fibers themselves are individual cells built from myofibrils—and are covered by a smaller layer called the perimysium. The long strands of muscle fiber are composed in turn of microscopic threads called sarcomeres. All the effort and energy expended by a skeletal muscle is devoted to contraction—it's a digital "on" or "off" situation; when in "off" mode, another muscle will be moving the limb in the opposing direction.

alternative name, involuntary muscle—and is controlled automatically by the autonomic nervous system *(see page 95).* Without a person being consciously aware of it, slow, sustained contractions of their smooth muscle, for example, move food along the intestines or squeeze urine out of the bladder.

Cardiac muscle

Cardiac muscle is found only in the heart. Its fibers are striated and branched. Cardiac muscle contracts and relaxes automatically without external stimulation, and never tires as it provides a lifelong service squeezing the heart wall to pump blood around the body. Its own inbuilt rhythm is speeded up or slowed by the autonomic nervous system, according to the body's needs; its rate cannot be consciously controlled by most people.

Muscle fibers   Perimysium   Epimysium

Fascicle

A cross section of skeletal muscle showing fat layers within the muscle fibers.

SKELETAL MUSCLE FUNCTION

Shown here is the effect of contracting the biceps muscle to raise the lower arm and fist. This is an example of flexion, in which the angle between the upper arm and the lower arm decreases.

Often, skeletal muscles act through leverage, that is, they cause a bone to turn around a fixed point called the **fulcrum**. The force of the effort, provided by the muscle and acting through a bone, is used to overcome another force, the load of a limb, for example, or an external object. Levers, in elementary physics, are said to be of three kinds: first class, with the fulcrum fixed between effort and load, like a seesaw; second class, where the load is between the fulcrum and effort, like a wheelbarrow; and third class, where effort is between fulcrum and load, picture a drawbridge. The majority of levering muscles fall into the third class, pulling on a bone somewhere along its length and pivoting it around a fulcrum, in this case the elbow joint, to move a load, which is the hand and forearm.

In relation to a specific motion, the muscle that causes it is termed an **agonist**. But because muscles work in one direction only, there is usually the need for another muscle to operate in the reverse sense, for example, to return a limb, a finger, or the neck to its original position—an **antagonist**. Muscles that work together to accomplish an action are **synergists**; and muscles that stabilize a bone or joint, so that it becomes a more or less fixed fulcrum, are termed **fixators**. The scapula, when involved in shoulder and arm movement, provides a particularly complex example of how muscles can work together, some holding it in place—as a properly positioned fulcrum—while others raise or lower the arm. At the same time, another group of fixators stabilizes the shoulder joint itself.

It may happen that nothing actually moves, that a muscle works to oppose another muscle or to resist some externally applied force. In other words, a muscle may not actually contract, or be allowed to contract, during its effort. This is called **isometric contraction**. The more straightforward action, in which muscle fibers shorten and thus move a load, is termed **isotonic contraction**.

Athletes' Advantage

Muscle fibers have different characteristics in terms of their speed of contraction. Some are fast fibers, designed for quick bursts of energy, while others are designed for endurance.

Coaches have learned that the number of "fast" fibers in particular muscles can be increased by specific training. In a typical healthy adult, fast fibers account for about half the fibers; in world class sprinters, they make up more than 80 percent of muscle content. Capable of contracting ten times faster than other muscle fibers, more fast fibers means quicker muscle contractions and a faster athlete.

The lighter muscle fibers are "fast".

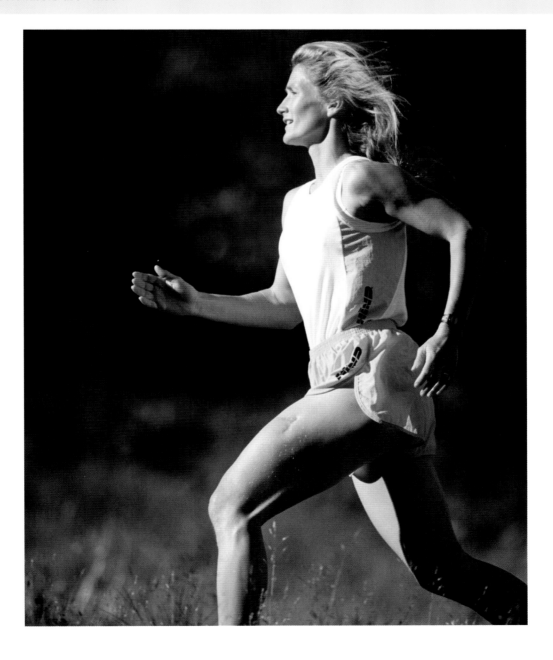

THE HEAD AND NECK CONTAIN MORE THAN 30 SMALL FACIAL MUSCLES. THESE MUSCLES PULL ON THE SKIN OF THE FACE, ENABLING A PERSON TO NONVERBALLY COMMUNICATE A WIDE RANGE OF EMOTIONS FROM PLEASURE TO ANGER. IN ADDITION, LARGER MUSCLES MOVE THE HEAD AND KEEP IT UPRIGHT, AND CLOSE THE LOWER JAW DURING SPEAKING AND EATING.

THE HEAD & NECK

Muscles visible in front view are the frontalis, which pulls the scalp forward to wrinkle the forehead and raise the eyebrows; orbicularis oculi, which surrounds the eye socket and closes the eye; levator labii superioris, which raises the upper lip and flares the nostril to indicate disgust; orbicularis oris, which surrounds the mouth and closes the lips; depressor anguli oris, which draws the corners of the mouth downward in a grimace; depressor labii inferioris, which draws the lower lip downward in a pout; and platysma, in the side of the chin and neck, which stretches the sides of the mouth downward.

Muscle shape and position

All skeletal muscles typically have the same basic features: the center of the muscle, called the belly, is attached by two ends to bones or other structures. However, the shape, power, and mobility of individual muscles depends on how their fascicles (bundles of fibers) are arranged.

• Parallel muscles—fascicles are arranged parallel to the long axis of the muscle. They can be fusiform, with a fleshy belly (e.g., biceps brachii in the upper arm), or straplike (e.g., sartorius in thigh).

• **Pennate** muscles—fascicles are arranged obliquely to a tendon running along the center of the muscle. These muscles can be **unipennate**, with fascicles attached to one side of the tendon (e.g., extensor digitorum longus in the lower leg), **bipennate**, with fascicles attached to both side of the central tendon like a feather (e.g., rectus femoris in the thigh), or **multipennate**, with many bipennate units (e.g., deltoid muscle in the shoulder).

• Circular—with concentric rows of fascicles, which form a **sphincter** controlling the closing of external body openings (e.g., orbicularis oculi around the eyes).

These muscles tug at the skin to alter the face's topography, thereby producing a wide range of facial expressions.

KEY

① Frontalis
② Orbicularis oculi
③ Nasalis
④ Zygomaticus major
⑤ Orbicularis oris
⑥ Depressor anguli oris
⑦ Platysma
⑧ Temporalis
⑨ Levator labii superioris
⑩ Zygomaticus minor
⑪ Depressor labii inferioris
⑫ Mentalis

THE HEAD & NECK

Large, powerful muscles in the head move the jaws during eating, while those in the neck support and move the head.

KEY

① Occipitalis

② Temporalis

③ Masseter

④ Sternocleidomastoid

⑤ Trapezius

⑥ Galea aponeurotica

⑦ Frontalis

⑧ Cartilage plates of external nose

⑨ Zygomaticus major

⑩ Buccinator

⑪ Depressor anguli oris

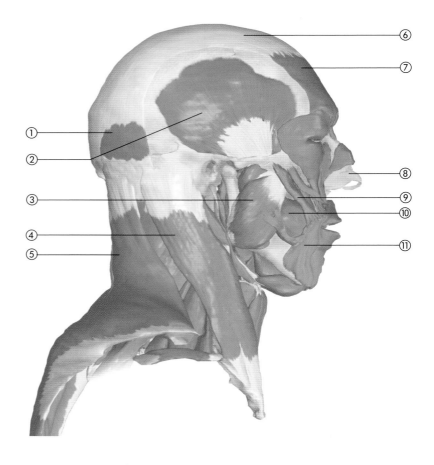

A side view of the head and neck reveals more of the muscles involved in facial expression and in supporting and moving the head and neck. The risorius pulls the corners of the lips laterally in smiling, while the zygomaticus raises the corners of the mouth in smiling and laughing. The buccinator, or cheek muscle, pushes the cheeks inward during sucking and forces food inward between the teeth during chewing. The temporalis and masseter are two powerful muscles that elevate the lower jaw to close the mouth during chewing, for example. The occipitalis, at the back of the skull, is linked to the frontalis by a flat tendon, the galea aponeurotica. Together, these two muscles move the scalp forward (frontalis) and backward (occipitalis). The sternocleidomastoids flex the head, pulling it toward the chest; acting individually, a sternocleidomastoid rotates the head to one side. The trapezius has an opposing action, and pulls the head and shoulders backward.

How muscle fibers contract

A single skeletal muscle fiber—which can range in length from 1 mm to 30 cm (¹⁄₂₅ in to 12 in)—is packed with thousands of parallel, rod-like **myofibrils** that extend for the entire length of the fiber. Each myofibril consists of a chain of linked units called **sarcomeres**. Inside each sarcomere are parallel arrays of contractile protein filaments: thin, actin filaments, attached to each end of the sarcomere, but not meeting in its center; and thick, myosin filaments, located in the center of the sarcomere. When the muscle is at rest, actin and myosin filaments partially overlap.

When stimulated by a nerve to contract, electrical signals pass to the muscle's constituent fibers, causing the actin filaments to slide toward the center of the sarcomere. This happens because actin and myosin filaments repeatedly make and break cross bridges between them; this energy-requiring action produces a ratchet-like effect, pulling the actin filaments towards the center of the sarcomere. As actin filaments slide, myofibrils and their fibers shorten, contracting the muscle. When nervous stimulation ceases, the actin filaments slide back, and the muscle relaxes.

OMINATING THE SUPERFICIAL MUSCLES AT THE FRONT OF THE THORAX IS THE PECTORALIS MAJOR, A LARGE, FAN-SHAPED MUSCLE WITH ITS ORIGINS IN THE CLAVICLE, STERNUM, AND THE COSTAL CARTILAGES OF RIBS 1 THROUGH 6. ITS INSERTION IS IN THE GREAT TUBERCLE AT THE TOP OF THE HUMERUS. THE PECTORALIS MAJOR FLEXES THE ARM AT THE SHOULDER SO THAT IT IS LIFTED ANTERIORLY (FORWARD). IT ALSO ADDUCTS THE ARM, PULLING IT INWARD TOWARD THE BODY, AND ROTATES THE ARM MEDIALLY (TOWARD THE BODY). THE PECTORALIS MAJOR IS USED IN ACTIVITIES SUCH AS CLIMBING, THROWING, AND PUSHING.

THE THORAX

The pectoralis minor muscle, which lies deep to (underneath) the pectoralis major, has its origin in the ribs and insertion in the scapula. With the ribs held stationary, it pulls the scapula forward and downward; with the scapula fixed, it helps elevate the ribs during forced breathing. The serratus anterior muscle, with its sawtooth appearance, plays an important part in raising the arm and in horizontal arm movements. Running obliquely between the ribs are the intercostal muscles that help to move the chest during breathing.

Muscle actions

Most skeletal muscles function as part of a lever system. A lever is a rigid rod that moves on a fixed point, called a **fulcrum**, when a force, the effort, is applied to overcome another force, called the load. Levers allow a heavier load to be moved with less of an effort than would normally be possible.

In the body, bones act as levers, a joint is the fulcrum, effort is provided by muscle contraction, and the load is that part of the body to be moved. There are three classes of levers, according to the relative positions of effort (E), load (L), and fulcrum (F).

- First class: F is between E and L, as in a seesaw or scissors. In the body, the trapezius (E) lifts the head (L), with F being the joint between atlas and skull.
- Second class: L is between F and E, as in a wheelbarrow. To put the body on tiptoe, calf muscles (E) pull the body upward (L) with the ball of the foot acting as F.
- Third class: E is between L and F, as in forceps (tweezers). Most skeletal muscles work in third class systems. In the elbow joint (F) the biceps brachii muscle (E) pulls the radius bone to lift the forearm and hand (L).

KEY

1. Deltoid
2. Sternocleidomastoid
3. Pectoralis major
4. Latissimus dorsi
5. Serratus anterior
6. Trapezius
7. Platysma
8. Costal cartilage of rib no. 1
9. Pectoralis minor
10. Position of intercostal muscles
11. Costal cartilage of rib no. 6

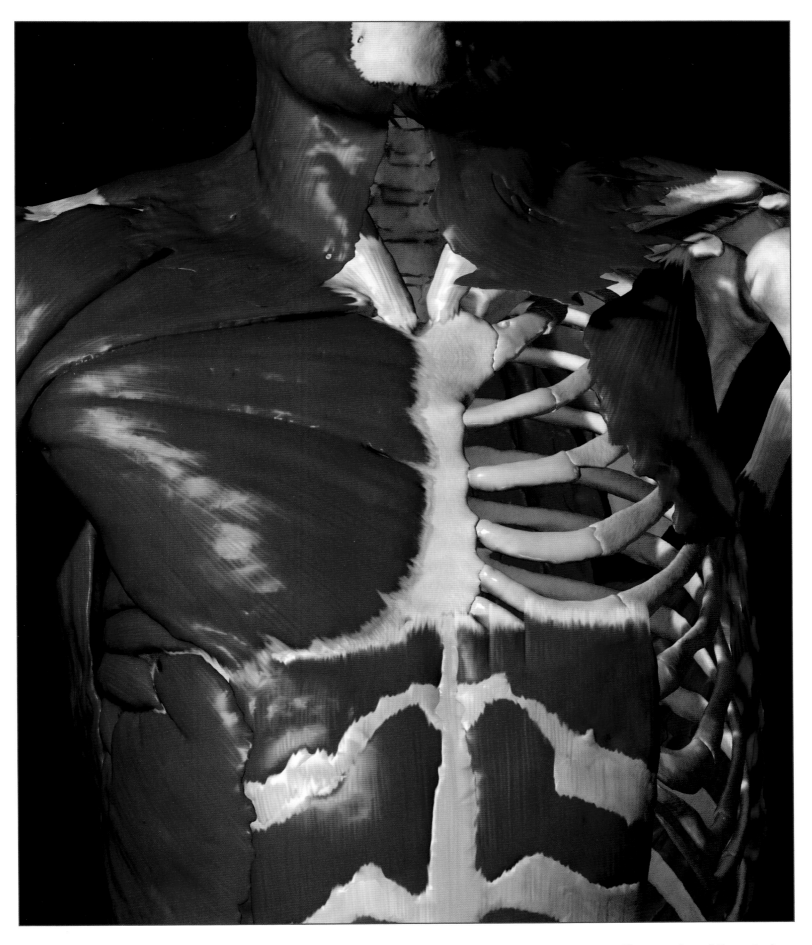

The muscles of the anterior thorax control movements of the shoulder and arm, are responsible for raising the ribs to facilitate breathing and provide stability for both the shoulder blade and shoulder joint.

THE SUPERFICIAL MUSCLES OF THE POSTERIOR THORAX MOVE THE ARMS AND STABILIZE THE SHOULDER. THE TRAPEZIUS HAS ITS ORIGIN IN THE SKULL AND VERTEBRAL COLUMN AND ITS INSERTION IN THE SCAPULA AND CLAVICLE. IT STABILIZES THE SCAPULA WHILE OTHER MUSCLES ARE ACTING, PULLS THE SHOULDERS UPWARD, AND HELPS TO SUPPORT THE HEAD. BOTH TERES MAJOR AND INFRASPINATUS HAVE THEIR ORIGIN IN THE SCAPULA AND INSERTION IN THE HUMERUS. THE TERES MAJOR EXTENDS, ADDUCTS, AND MEDIALLY ROTATES THE ARMS; THE INFRASPINATUS STABILIZES THE SHOULDER JOINT BY HOLDING THE HEAD OF THE HUMERUS IN PLACE, AND LATERALLY ROTATES THE ARM. THE LATISSIMUS DORSI ("WIDEST OF THE BACK") HAS A BROAD ORIGIN IN THE VERTEBRAL COLUMN AND PELVIS, AND ITS INSERTION IN THE HUMERUS. IT IS THE PRIME MOVER OF ARM EXTENSION (MOVEMENT OF THE ARM POSTERIORLY), AS WELL AS ADDUCTING AND MEDIALLY ROTATING THE ARM. THE LATISSIMUS DORSI SUPPORTS THE ARM WHEN IT IS HELD ABOVE THE HEAD, AND PULLS THE ARM DOWN IN A POWER STROKE DURING, FOR EXAMPLE, SWIMMING OR HAMMERING.

The powerful muscles of the posterior thorax, like those of the anterior thorax, move and stabilize the scapula and move the arm.

KEY

① Scapula
② Trapezius
③ Humerus
④ Latissimus dorsi
⑤ Lumbodorsal fascia
⑥ Spine of scapula
⑦ Deltoid
⑧ Infraspinatus
⑨ Teres minor
⑩ Teres major
⑪ Rhomboid major

THE THORAX

Muscle interactions

Most movements require several muscles working together in a group. Since muscles can only pull, and not push, some of these muscles pull a body part in one direction while others pull in the opposite direction. According to their role (or roles) muscles are divided into four groups.

• Prime mover or **agonist**—the muscle that provides the main force to achieve a specific movement. For example, the pectoralis major in the thorax is the prime mover of arm flexion.

• **Antagonist**—a muscle that opposes the action of a prime mover. For example, the antagonist of the biceps brachii, the prime mover of forearm flexion, is the triceps brachii, the prime mover of forearm extension.

• **Synergist**—a muscle that works with a prime mover to produce the same movement or to reduce any unnecessary movements that may occur when the prime mover contracts. For example, synergists stabilize the wrist joint while forearm flexor muscles—whose tendons pass over the wrist joint—bend the fingers.

• **Fixator**—this is a synergist that fixes a bone to stabilize the origin of the prime mover. For example, the scapula (which is only attached to the skeleton by muscles) is fixed by muscles such as the pectoralis minor and trapezius, while the prime mover, the deltoid, abducts the arm.

On the left side
the deltoid, the
infraspinatus, and the
teres major have been
removed to expose
the scapula and the
shoulder joint.

THE MUSCLES OF THE SHOULDER AND UPPER ARM ARE RESPONSIBLE FOR ARM MOVEMENT. MUSCLES THAT CROSS THE SHOULDER JOINT AND INSERT INTO THE HUMERUS, EITHER MOVE THE ARM OR STABILIZE THE SHOULDER JOINT, THE MOST FLEXIBLE BUT ALSO THE MOST UNSTABLE JOINT IN THE BODY. THE MUSCLES THAT FLESH OUT THE UPPER ARM AND CROSS THE ELBOW JOINT—A HINGE JOINT—TO INSERT ON THE BONES OF THE FOREARM, EITHER FLEX OR EXTEND THE FOREARM.

Shoulder muscles provide stability to the shoulder joint, a ball and socket joint that is highly mobile but also quite unstable.

THE SHOULDER & UPPER ARM

Bending and straightening of the elbow joint is achieved by the muscles of the upper arm.

KEY

1. Vertebral column (3rd cervical vertebra)
2. Trapezius
3. Clavicle
4. Deltoid
5. Pectoralis major
6. Triceps brachii
7. Latissimus dorsi
8. Biceps brachii
9. Serratus anterior
10. Brachialis
11. Brachioradialis
12. Rib

Of the nine muscles that cross the shoulder joint, seven have their origins on the scapula, while two—the pectoralis major and latissimus dorsi arise from the axial skeleton. One of these seven "scapular" muscles is the deltoid, which, like the pectoralis major and latissimus dorsi, is a prime mover of arm mobility. The deltoid wraps around the shoulder, provides its round contours, and is involved in

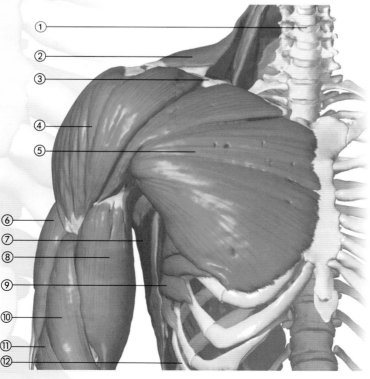

all arm movements. It is the prime mover of arm abduction (acting as an antagonist to the pectoralis major and latissimus dorsi, which both adduct the arm). Depending on which part of the deltoid is contracting, it either flexes (pulls anteriorly) and medially rotates the humerus, or extends (pulls posteriorly) the humerus and laterally rotates it. The other scapular muscles, apart from the coracobrachialis, are found posteriorly to the shoulder joint. The coracobrachialis is a small muscle that flexes and adducts the humerus.

The muscles of the anterior (front) part of the forearm cause the arm to bend at the elbow. The strong brachialis has its origin in the humerus and inserts on the ulna, pulling on the ulna to lift the forearm. It contracts at the same time as the biceps brachii, which both lifts and supinates the forearm. The less powerful brachioradialis, which has its origin in the distal humerus and insertion on the distal radius, acts as a synergist to the brachioradialis and the biceps brachii when they have already partially flexed the elbow joint.

A T THE REAR OF THE SHOULDER, FOUR OF THE SCAPULAR MUSCLES —THE SUPRASPINATUS, INFRASPINATUS, TERES MINOR, AND SUBSCAPULARIS—HAVE THEIR ORIGINS ON THE SCAPULA AND INSERTION ON THE HUMERUS. THEIR ASSOCIATED TENDONS AMALGAMATE EN ROUTE WITH THE FIBROUS CAPSULE SURROUNDING THE SHOULDER JOINT. KNOWN AS THE **ROTATOR CUFF MUSCLES,** THEY STABILIZE THE SHOULDER JOINT BY HOLDING THE HEAD OF THE HUMERUS IN ITS BALL AND SOCKET JOINT. THE TERES MAJOR EXTENDS, MEDIALLY ROTATES, AND ADDUCTS THE HUMERUS.

THE SHOULDER & UPPER ARM

The bulk of the posterior (rear) part of the upper arm is formed by the triceps brachii muscle, the prime mover of elbow extension. The triceps brachii has three heads: the long head has its origin on the scapula, and the lateral and medial heads on the humerus. The insertion is through a common tendon on the olecranon process of the ulna (the projection that can be felt at the posterior of the elbow).

Fast and slow twitch

How rapidly a muscle contracts, and how long it can stay contracted before it experiences fatigue (through a lack of energy necessary for contraction), varies from one muscle to the next. These variations are caused primarily by differences in muscle fibers. There are three basic types of fiber. These vary in the amount of the red pigment **myoglobin** they contain—myoglobin, like hemoglobin in the blood, stores oxygen needed to release energy—and in their speed of contraction.

- Red slow twitch (a twitch is a single muscle contraction) fibers are red in color, have plenty of myoglobin and contract slowly, have high endurance, and are fatigue-resistant, allowing them to contract for prolonged periods.
- White fast twitch fibers have little myoglobin and fatigue easily, contracting rapidly for short periods, and usually producing powerful contractions.
- Intermediate fast twitch fibers are red because of a high myoglobin content, but also contract rapidly and do not fatigue easily.

Most skeletal muscles contain a mixture of fibers, although relative proportions depend on the function of the muscle. Muscles in the neck, back, and legs that maintain posture, for example, contain more red slow twitch fibers; muscles, such as those in the arms, used from time to time to produce sudden strong actions such as throwing or lifting, contain more white fast twitch fibers; leg muscles, for example, involved in running contain more intermediate fast twitch fibers.

The "three headed" triceps brachii at the back of the arm acts as an antagonist to the biceps brachii by straightening the elbow.

KEY

1. Trapezius
2. Deltoid
3. Infraspinatus
4. Teres minor
5. Teres major
6. Rhomboid
7. Triceps brachii (long head)
8. Triceps brachii (medial head)
9. Biceps brachii
10. Brachialis
11. Latissimus dorsi
12. Tendon of triceps brachii
13. Medial epicondyle of humerus

78

THE BICEPS BRACHII—THE NAME MEANS "TWO HEADS IN THE ARM"—IN THE UPPER ARM IS THE MUSCLE COMMONLY FLEXED BY THOSE WISHING TO SHOW OFF THEIR MUSCULAR PROWESS BECAUSE IT BULGES VISIBLY DURING CONTRACTION. IT IS A FUSIFORM MUSCLE, SPINDLE-SHAPED WITH A FLESHY BODY TAPERING AT BOTH ENDS INTO TENDONS. THE TWO HEADS OF ITS NAME ARE AT ITS ORIGIN, WHERE TWO TENDONS ATTACH IT TO THE SCAPULA. ITS INSERTION IS IN THE RADIUS OF THE FOREARM. THE BICEPS BRACHII FLEXES THE ARM AT THE ELBOW AND ALSO HELPS TO SUPINATE THE FOREARM, TURNING THE FOREARM SO THE PALM OF THE HAND FACES UPWARD.

THE BICEPS BRACHII

Posterior view of the right shoulder, upper arm, and shoulder shows clearly the triceps brachii and its synergist, the anconeus, which assists in arm extension.

KEY

① Deltoid
② Scapula
③ Teres minor
④ Teres major
⑤ Triceps brachii
⑥ Brachialis
⑦ Brachioradialis
⑧ Lateral epicondyle of humerus
⑨ Extensor carpi radialis longus
⑩ Extensor carpi radialis brevis
⑪ Extensor digitorum
⑫ Medial epicondyle of humerus
⑬ Olecranon of ulna
⑭ Anconeus

The structure and function of tendons

Skeletal muscles are attached to bones by tendons. When the muscle contracts, the tendon pulls the bone to which it is attached, to make the bone move at its joint with another bone. Some tendons link muscles to other muscles, while others, such as those in the face, link the muscles that produce facial expression to the skin. Tendons also help to stabilize joints.

Tendons are an extension of the connective tissue sheaths that bind and surround muscle fibers. They are made of dense connective tissue that contains regularly arranged bundles of collagen (a type of protein) fibers running in parallel. This produces a white flexible tissue, which has considerable resistance to pulling forces.

The majority of tendons extend from the tapering ends of muscles like white cables. Extensions of the tendon's collagen fibers, called **Sharpey's fibers**, firmly anchor the tendon to its bone. These fibers penetrate the periosteum, the membrane covering the bone, and embed themselves in the layer of compact bone.

Long tendons, such as those in the hands and feet, are surrounded by tendon sheaths. These contain oily synovial fluid that lubricate the sliding tendons as the forearm muscles they are attached to pull on the fingers or toes. Some tendons, called **aponeuroses**, are flat rather than cablelike. Aponeuroses not only link muscles to bone but also muscles to muscles.

The right shoulder and upper arm seen from the right side showing the biceps brachii and the other arm flexors in the anterior upper arm, and the tripceps brachii, the prime mover of arm extension, in the posterior upper arm.

KEY

1. Deltoid
2. Triceps brachii
3. Lateral epicondyle of humerus
4. Olecranon process of ulna
5. Anconeus
6. Extensor carpi ulnaris
7. Flexor carpi ulnaris
8. Clavicle
9. Biceps brachii
10. Brachialis
11. Extensor carpi radialis longus
12. Extensor carpi radialis brevis
13. Extensor digitorum

THE HAND OWES ITS VERSATILITY AND FLEXIBILITY TO ITS FRAMEWORK OF SMALL BONES, AND TO THE MANY MUSCLES IN THE FOREARM AND HAND THAT MOVE THEM. MOST MOVEMENTS OF THE WRIST AND FINGERS ARE PRODUCED BY FOREARM MUSCLES. THESE HAVE THEIR ORIGIN AT THE ELBOW, THEN TAPER INTO LONG TENDONS THAT EXTEND INTO THE HAND, AND HAVE THEIR INSERTIONS IN THE WRIST OR FINGER BONES. THE TENDONS PASS UNDER FIBROUS STRAPS CALLED **RETINACULA** ("RETAINERS"), WHICH HOLD THEM IN PLACE, AND ARE SURROUNDED BY SLIPPERY SYNOVIAL SHEATHS THAT LUBRICATE THEM.

KEY

1 Brachioradialis
2 Flexor carpi radialis
3 Flexor digitorum superficialis
4 Flexor retinaculum
5 Abductor pollicis brevis
6 Palmaris longus
7 Flexor carpi ulnaris
8 Extensor carpi ulnaris
9 Extensor digiti minimi
10 Extensor carpi radialis brevis
11 Extensor digitorum
12 Abductor pollicis longus
13 Extensor retinaculum
14 Interosseous

THE FOREARM & HAND

Most muscles in the anterior (inner or underside) forearm are flexors. Their tendons are held in place by the flexor retinaculum. Among the superficial muscles the flexor digitorum superficialis flexes the fingers; the flexor carpi ulnaris flexes and adducts the wrist; the flexor carpi radialis flexes and abducts the wrist; and the palmaris longus flexes the wrist and tenses the palm. A deep muscle, the flexor pollicis longus, flexes the thumb. The pronator teres performs the important action of pronating the forearm, so that the palm turns downward. The brachioradialis is a synergist of the biceps brachii of the upper arm in forearm flexion.

Most muscles in the posterior (outer or upper side) forearm are extensors that act as antagonists to the flexors of the anterior forearm. Their tendons are held in place by the extensor retinaculum. Among the superficial muscles, the extensors carpi radialis longus and brevis extend and abduct the wrist; the extensor carpi ulnaris extends and adducts the wrist; and the extensor digitorum is the prime mover of finger extension. Other muscles include the extensors pollicis brevis and longus, which

extend the thumb; and the extensor digiti minimi, which extends the little finger.

Movements produced by the forearm muscles are assisted and made more precise by smaller muscles in the hand. These intrinsic muscles include the lumbrical and interosseus muscles between the metacarpals, which flex the metacarpophalangeal (knuckle) joints, but extend the fingers; thenar muscles, including the flexor pollicis brevis, which bends the thumb; and the abductor pollicis brevis, which abducts the thumb.

Palm upward view   **Palm downward view**

The superficial muscles of the right forearm and hand seen in anterior, palm upward view (left) and posterior, palm downward view (right).

NLIKE THE THORAX, THE WALLS OF THE ABDOMEN DO NOT HAVE THE SUPPORT OF A FRAMEWORK OF BONES. INSTEAD, THE ORGANS OF THE LOWER TRUNK ARE HELD IN PLACE AND PROTECTED BY ANTERIOR (FRONT) AND LATERAL (SIDE) WALLS MADE UP OF FOUR PAIRED, FLAT MUSCLES AND THEIR APONEUROSES (FLATTENED TENDONS). THESE MUSCLES ALSO PROMOTE MOVEMENT OF THE VERTEBRAL COLUMN TO FLEX THE TRUNK FORWARD AND TO THE SIDES, AND TO ROTATE IT; AND TO PREVENT HYPEREXTENSION OF THE BACKBONE (BENDING BACK TOO FAR).

THE ABDOMEN

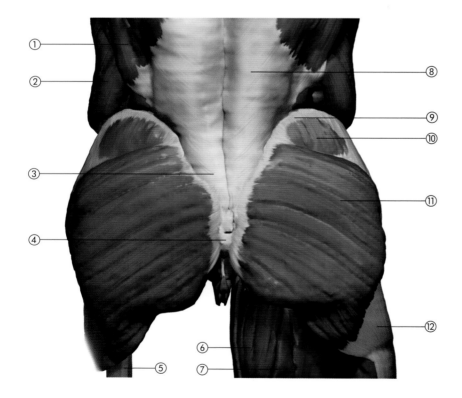

Posterior view of the muscles of the pelvis and thigh. The massive gluteal muscles act during forceful thigh extension; the thigh muscles extend the hip and flex the knee.

KEY

① Latissimus dorsi
② External oblique
③ Sacrum
④ Coccyx
⑤ Femur
⑥ Adductor magnus
⑦ Semimembranosus
⑧ Lumbodorsal fascia
⑨ Iliac crest
⑩ Gluteus medius
⑪ Gluteus maximus
⑫ Iliotibial tract

In the anterior section, the straplike rectus abdominis has its origin in the pubic bone of the pelvis and insertion in the sternum and ribs. It flexes and rotates the trunk, promotes anterior flexion of the trunk against resistance (as when a person does sit-ups), and pushes the abdominal organs inward. It is assisted in these roles by the lateral muscles that are layered on top of each other. On top, on each side, is the external oblique, whose fibers run downward and inward and which has its origin in the ribs and insertion via a broad aponeurosis and into the pelvic girdle. Below this lies the internal oblique, whose fibers run at 90° to the external oblique, and which has its origin in the posterior pelvis and insertion in the ribs, anterior pelvis, and linea alba, the tendinous seam that runs from sternum to pubic bone. Deep to the internal oblique is the transversus abdominis, whose fibers run horizontally, and which compresses the abdominal contents.

Isotonic and isometric contraction

Muscles do not always get shorter when they contract. Muscle contraction is an active process in which a force—called muscle tension—is generated. This muscle tension is exerted on part of the body. That body part, called the load, exerts an opposing force that resists the pull of the muscle.

During **isotonic contraction**, the familiar form of contraction already described, a muscle gets shorter and causes movement; the muscle tension generated is greater than the load. In **isometric contraction**, tension develops and the muscle exerts a pulling force, but it does not shorten because opposing forces are equal.

Most movements involve both isotonic and isometric contractions. However, contractions that cause clear movements, such as kicking or waving, are primarily isotonic, while those that maintain upright posture are primarily isometric.

Anterior view of the muscles of the pelvis and thigh. The size and strength of these muscles reflects the role of the lower limbs in movement and support.

KEY

① External oblique

② Iliopsoas

③ Pectineus

④ Tensor fasciae latae

⑤ Rectus femoris

⑥ Rectus abdominis

⑦ Anterior superior iliac crest (point of the hip)

⑧ Pubis of left coxal (hip) bone

⑨ Femur

⑩ Ischium of left coxal (hip) bone

⑪ Adductor longus

⑫ Sartorius

⑬ Gracilis

THE POSTERIOR (REAR) MUSCLES OF THE HIP AND THIGH EXTEND (STRAIGHTEN) THE HIP BY PULLING THE THIGH POSTERIORLY, ABDUCT THE LEG AND ROTATE IT, AND FLEX (BEND) THE LEG AT THE KNEE. THESE ACTIONS MAKE UP THE BACKWARD SWINGING PART OF WALKING.

THE PELVIS, THIGH & KNEE

The large, fleshy muscles of the posterior part of the thigh—the biceps femoris, semitendinosus, and semimembranosus—are collectively called the hamstrings. Their name derives from the habit, in times past, of butchers hanging pork legs by the tendons of this muscle group when making ham. The hamstring tendons can be felt behind the knee by sitting and tensing the leg. Antagonists of the quadriceps femoris, the hamstrings cross both hip and knee joints, and are the prime movers of hip extension and knee flexion. How the hamstrings act depends on which of two joints—hip or knee—is fixed. If the hip is fixed and extended, the hamstrings cause knee flexion; if the knee is fixed and extended, the hamstrings cause hip extension. All three hamstring muscles have their origin in the pelvic girdle, and all insert into the tibia, although the biceps femoris also inserts into the fibula. As well as extending the thigh and flexing the knee, the hamstrings also laterally rotate the thigh, especially when the knee is flexed.

The gluteus maximus, the largest muscle in the body, has its origins in the pelvic girdle and insertion in the femur and the iliotibial tract. It extends the thigh at the hip and rotates it laterally, especially when the knee is flexed. The gluteus maximus comes into its own when forceful thigh extension is needed in order to move it from the flexed position, such as during running or climbing stairs. The smaller gluteus medius and gluteus minimus, which with the gluteus maximus make up the bulk of the buttock, also run between pelvic girdle and femur. They abduct and medially rotate the thigh, an action that is important during walking in order to ensure that the foot of the leg that is swinging does not touch the ground.

The posterior hip and thigh muscles, shown here in the right leg, move the body and help to maintain its posture.

KEY

1. Sacrum
2. Adductor magnus
3. Gracilis
4. Semitendinosus
5. Semimembranosus
6. Sartorius
7. Gastrocnemius
8. Gluteus maximus
9. Iliotibial tract
10. Biceps femoris
11. Vastus lateralis
12. Tendon of biceps femoris

THE MUSCLES OF THE LOWER LEG AND FOOT MOVE THE FOOT AND TOES TO PROVIDE THE THRUST NEEDED TO PUSH THE BODY OFF THE GROUND DURING WALKING AND RUNNING, AND ALSO STABILIZE THE FOOT DURING STANDING. WHILE THE ARRANGEMENT OF LOWER LEG MUSCLES— TAPERING WITH LONG TENDONS—AND FOOT MUSCLES IS SIMILAR TO THAT OF THE HANDS, THE FEET ARE STRONGER AND LESS FLEXIBLE THAN THE HANDS. THIS REFLECTS THEIR ROLE IN SUPPORT AND MOVEMENT. AT THE ANKLE, A HINGE JOINT, MUSCLES PROMOTE **DORSIFLEXION** (BENDING OF THE FOOT UPWARD) AND **PLANTAR FLEXION** (EXTENSION OR STRAIGHTENING OF THE FOOT TO POINT THE TOES). OTHER MUSCLES FLEX AND EXTEND THE TOES, AND **INVERT** (TURNING THE SOLE OF THE FOOT INWARD) OR **EVERT** (TURNING THE SOLE OF THE FOOT OUTWARD) THE FOOT. WITHIN THE FOOT, INTRINSIC MUSCLES HELP TO MOVE THE TOES BUT, MORE IMPORTANTLY, ACT WITH THE LOWER LEG MUSCLES TO SUPPORT THE ARCHES OF THE FOOT.

THE LEG & FOOT

Right: the right ankle and foot seen from the underside; opposite: the right lower leg and foot in lateral (left) and anterior (right) views.

KEY

1. Flexor digitorum longus
2. Plantar aponeurosis
3. Flexor digitorum brevis
4. Abductor hallucis
5. Flexor hallucis longus
6. Flexor hallucis brevis
7. Hallux (great toe)
8. Calcaneal (Achilles) tendon
9. Calcaneus (heel bone)
10. Abductor digiti minimi
11. Flexor digiti minimi brevis
12. Lumbrical

In the anterior (front) part of the lower leg, extensor muscles dorsiflex the ankle and pull the foot upward. Dorsiflexion is not a powerful movement, but it prevents the toes dragging along the ground when the foot is lifted. Prime mover of dorsiflexion is the tibialis anterior, which also inverts the foot and supports the arch of the foot. Other anterior muscles that dorsiflex the foot are the extensor digitorum longus, which also extends the toes; the peroneus tertius, which also everts the foot; and the extensor hallucis longus, which also extends the hallux or great toe.

The muscles of the posterior (rear) of the lower leg plantar flex the foot. Plantar flexion is the most powerful movement of the ankle, necessary to provide thrust during the take-off phase of walking and running. The prime movers of plantar flexion are the gastrocnemius and soleus. Both insert via the large calcaneal (Achilles) tendon into the calcaneus or heel bone. The flexor digitorum longus and flexor hallucis longus plantar flex the foot and invert it; the former also flexes the toes, while the latter flexes the great toe. Toe flexion helps the foot "grip" the ground. On the lateral (outer) side of the lower leg, the peroneus longus and peroneus brevis also plantar flex the foot, and evert it to help keep the foot flat on the ground.

KEY

1. Gastrocnemius
2. Soleus
3. Peroneus longus
4. Peroneus brevis
5. Calcaneal (Achilles) tendon
6. Peroneus tertius
7. Fibula
8. Calcaneus (heel bone)
9. Extensor digitorum brevis
10. Tibialis anterior
11. Extensor digitorum longus
12. Extensor hallucis longus
13. Extensor hallucis brevis
14. Tendon of extensor digitorum longus
15. Tibia
16. Extensor retinacula

THE NERVOUS SYSTEM

Our body's high-speed communications network relies on trillions of interconnected neurons, or nerve cells. With incredible speed and layers of complexity, this system allows us to experience what we know as life.

THE NERVOUS SYSTEM

THE NERVOUS SYSTEM IS A COMMUNICATION NETWORK THAT CONTROLS AND COORDINATES MOST BODY ACTIVITIES. EVERY THOUGHT, MEMORY, EMOTION, OR SENSATION A PERSON HAS, AND EVERY ACTION SHE OR HE CARRIES OUT, IS A REFLECTION OF THE ACTIVITY OF THIS SYSTEM. IN ADDITION, THE NERVOUS SYSTEM WORKS UNNOTICED TO REGULATE A MULTITUDE OF INTERNAL EVENTS, SUCH AS MODULATING BODY TEMPERATURE OR ALTERING HEART RATE, IN ORDER TO MAINTAIN **HOMEOSTASIS**—THE STATE OF BALANCE AND STABILITY THAT EXISTS INSIDE A HEALTHY BODY REGARDLESS OF CHANGES IN THE EXTERNAL AND INTERNAL ENVIRONMENTS.

The nervous system extends throughout the body to provide a high speed co-ordination and control network. At its core are the brain and spinal cord, which receive and send out messages along the nerves.

Making up this communication network are trillions of interconnected **neurons**, or nerve cells, that extend throughout the body. These cells are unique in their ability to transmit electrical signals, called **nerve impulses**, at high speed, so that all the information needed to run the body can be collected, processed, and distributed in a split-second, and is constantly updated as the body's internal and external environments change.

Three linked functions drive the nervous system. Firstly, sensory input is provided by millions of sensory receptors that monitor changes—called stimuli—taking place inside and outside the body. Secondly, a processing and integration center analyzes, stores, and collates sensory input and makes decisions about what actions should be taken. Thirdly, a motor output activates effectors—either muscles or glands—resulting in a response. So, for example, seeing a charging elephant (sensory input) means danger (processing and integration) so the leg muscles are activated (motor output) to effect an escape.

Parts of the nervous system

The nervous system has two main parts. The central nervous system (CNS) consists of the brain and spinal cord, and it fulfills the function of processing and integration described above. The peripheral nervous system consists of cablelike nerves that are made

up of bundles of two types of neurons. **Sensory neurons** carry sensory input from receptors to the CNS, while **motor neurons** transmit motor output from the CNS to muscles and glands. Motor neurons fall into two groups. Those of the somatic nervous system carry signals to skeletal muscles in order to make them move. The motor neurons that make up the **autonomic nervous system** control involuntary activities, such as breathing rate and digestion, by activating glands and other organs.

Autonomic Nervous System

The autonomic nervous system is a division of the peripheral nervous system that, second by second, automatically controls involuntary functions in order to maintain homeostasis—a stable, internal environment—regardless of variations in internal or external conditions.

The ANS consists of motor neurons, arising from the brain stem and spinal cord, which carry instructions to smooth muscles in glands, blood vessels, the digestive and other organs, and the cardiac muscle. Receiving, directly or indirectly, information from the body's sensors that detect internal and external change, the ANS relays instructions to fine tune the body's response. For example, the smell of delicious food triggering salivation would be the work of the ANS.

① Brain
② Spinal cord
③ Paravertebral (chain) ganglion
④ Sympathetic trunk or chain
⑤ Oculomotor nerves (III)
⑥ Facial nerves (VII)
⑦ Glossopharyngeal nerves (IX)
⑧ Vagus nerves
⑨ Cranial parasympathetic outflow
⑩ Pelvic splanchnic nerves (sacral parasympathetic outflow)

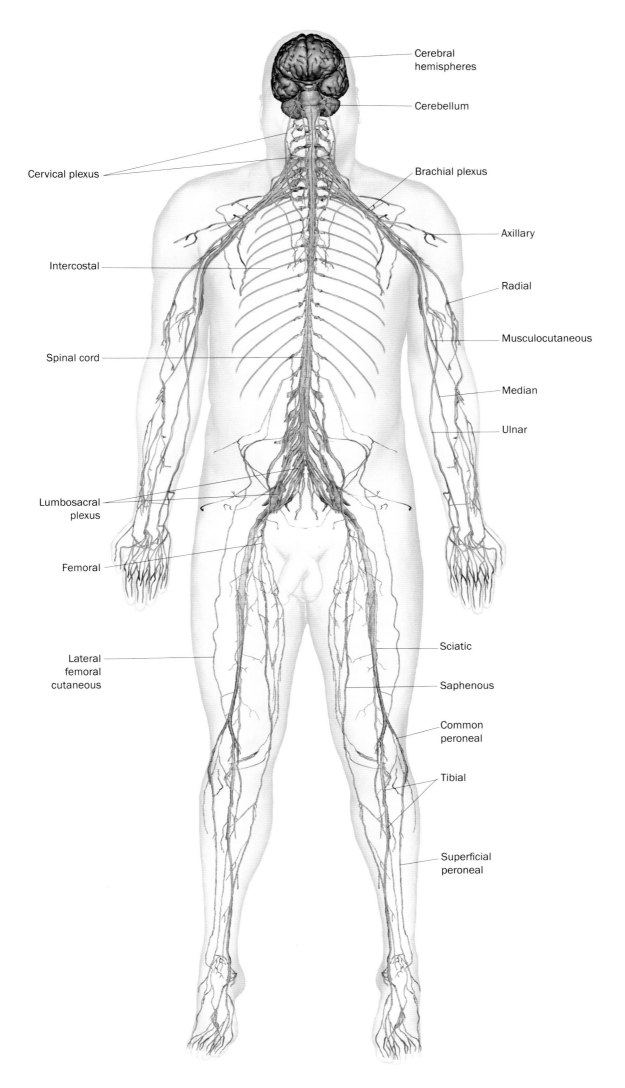

Cerebral
hemispheres

Cerebellum

Cervical plexus

Brachial plexus

Axillary

Intercostal

Radial

Musculocutaneous

Spinal cord

Median

Ulnar

Lumbosacral
plexus

Femoral

Sciatic

Lateral
femoral
cutaneous

Saphenous

Common
peroneal

Tibial

Superficial
peroneal

Neurons, the cells of the nervous system, are comprised of a number of parts, each with a specific function. The body of the cell includes a nucleus, which handles the basic tasks of keeping the cell alive. A series of armatures transmit and receive signals. The shorter dendrites receive incoming information, while the longer axons pass the information along to the next neuron in line. The axons are covered with an insulating sheath of myelin, a combination of fat and proteins.

HOW NERVE CELLS WORK

Dendrite

Nucleus

Cell body

Synaptic knob

Axon

Myelin sheath

Neurons and nervous transmission

The billions of neurons in the nervous system are long thin cells adapted for carrying electrical signals called nerve impulses, which form a communication system capable of transmitting information at high speed and permitting humans to think, feel, and act. Each neuron has a cell body, containing the **nucleus**; several branched processes, called **dendrites**, which carry impulses toward the cell body; and a long **axon**, or nerve fiber, which carries impulses away from the cell body toward another neuron or an effector, such as a muscle. There are three types of neurons. Sensory neurons carry sensory information from sense organs and other structures toward the CNS. Motor neurons carry nerve impulses away from the CNS to effectors, such as muscles and glands. Association neurons—which make up 90 percent of all neurons and are only found in the brain and spinal cord—relay nerve impulses between other neurons as well as sorting and analyzing them.

Where two or more neurons come into close contact, they do not touch but are separated at junctions called **synapses**. When a neuron is stimulated, a wave of electrical disturbance—the nerve impulse—sweeps along it at speeds of up to 100 meters (300 ft) per second. At the end of the axon of that neuron is a swelling, called the presynaptic terminal or synaptic knob. When the impulse arrives at the synaptic knob it causes the release of a chemical, called a **neurotransmitter**, which crosses the gap between the two neurons and causes the generation of a nerve impulse in the recipient neuron. This one-way process is how nerve impulses are transmitted through the nervous system.

Synaptic knobs where they meet dendritic receptors

As the nerve signal arrives at the presynaptic knob, synaptic vesicles, membranes containing neurotransmitters approach the synapse.

Neurotransmitters pass to the dendritic receptors in the postsynaptic membrane where they bind with receptors creating the reaction that passes the impulse along.

In the nervous system, the transmission of nerve signals is mediated by synapses. The nerve signal, or action potential, arrives at the presynaptic membrane of the synaptic end-bulb. This triggers release of chemical neurotransmitters stored in membrane-bound packets called synaptic vesicles. The neurotransmitter molecules then generate a response by stimulating receptors on the postsynaptic membrane, which in the central nervous system commonly belongs to a specialized structure called a dendritic spine.

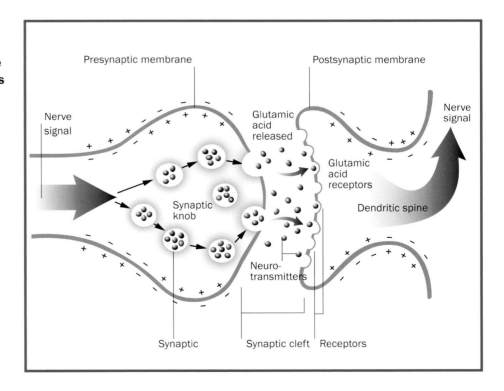

THE BRAIN

THE BRAIN IS THE CONTROL CENTER OF THE NERVOUS SYSTEM. THESE SUPERIOR AND LATERAL VIEWS REVEAL ITS MAIN PARTS. THE LEFT AND RIGHT CEREBRAL HEMISPHERES MAKE UP THE CEREBRUM, THE LARGEST PART OF THE BRAIN AND THE SITE OF THOUGHT, MEMORY, SENSATION, MOVEMENT, AND OTHER ASPECTS OF CONSCIOUS BEHAVIOR. THE CEREBELLUM MAKES UP ABOUT 10 PERCENT OF THE BRAIN AND ENSURES THAT THE BODY IS BALANCED AND THAT MUSCLE CONTRACTIONS PRODUCE SMOOTH, COORDINATED MOVEMENTS. THE BRAIN STEM, WHICH LINKS THE BRAIN TO THE SPINAL CORD, CONTROLS MANY VITAL FUNCTIONS INCLUDING HEART RATE, BREATHING RATE, AND BLOOD PRESSURE. THE **VENTRICLES** WITHIN THE BRAIN ARE FILLED WITH CLEAR, **CEREBROSPINAL FLUID** THAT HELPS TO NOURISH AND PROTECT THE BRAIN (AND THE SPINAL CORD).

Superior view of the brain showing the longitudinal fissure that divides the cerebrum into two hemispheres and, internally, the ventricles.

KEY

1. Inferior horn of LV
2. Lateral ventricle (LV)
3. Anterior horn of LV
4. Right cerebral hemisphere
5. Posterior horn of LV
6. Longitudinal fissure
7. Third ventricle
8. Left cerebral hemisphere

The human brain versus computer

Artificial Intelligence, or AI, has been the stuff of decades of science fiction and almost as many years of serious research. Just how does the human brain stack up against the most advanced computers? Computer scientists have been able to build machines that calculate faster than our brains and have far greater memory capacity – a scalable resource. That said, while a computer can calculate a complex equation thousands of times faster than even a gifted mathematician, the number of calculations for the myriad parallel tasks involved in something as simple as a child recognising a face or getting a glass of milk requires more processing power than we can achieve artificially. IBM's Blue Gene supercomputer has almost 150,000 parallel processors with about 1GB of memory each. The result allowed simulation of less than 5% of the human brain. IBM calculates that they will need to link about 900,000 processors to rival the power of our brains' 20 billion neurons and approximately 200 trillion synapses – a task they hope to achieve by 2019.

When and if the machines develop the computational horsepower to compete, there's still no sign of technology that can match the efficiency of our biochemical computer. The brain weighs in at an average of 3 lbs./1.3 kg, fits in our craniums with room to spare and uses about as much energy as a small flashlight. Today's most powerful supercomputer uses enough energy to run 10,000 homes and fills a warehouse. As a final note, IBM's Watson computer only won in the quiz show "Jeopardy" after the machine was given access to past *incorrect* answers of the contestants it was playing against; it was not just process of determining the right answers from a synthesis of knowledge.

KEY

1. Right cerebral hemisphere
2. Posterior horn of LV
3. Third ventricle
4. Cerebellum
5. Lateral ventricle (LV)
6. Anterior horn of LV
7. Interventricular foramen
8. Cerebral aqueduct
9. Fourth ventricle
10. Pons
11. Medulla oblongata

Inside the brain there are four cavities called ventricles filled with cerebrospinal fluid: two lateral ventricles and the third and fourth ventricles. Within the ventricles is a system of capillaries, the choroid plexus, which manufactures the cerebrospinal fluid which exits the fourth ventricle to bathe the entire spinal cord.

THE TWELVE PAIRS OF CRANIAL NERVES ARISING FROM THE UNDERSIDE OF THE BRAIN ARE CONCERNED MOSTLY WITH CARRYING SENSORY INPUT FROM THE SKIN AND SENSE ORGANS OF THE HEAD AND NECK, AND TRANSMITTING MOTOR OUTPUT TO THE MUSCLES OF THESE REGIONS. SOME CRANIAL NERVES ARE PURELY SENSORY, OTHERS ARE MIXED, CONTAINING BOTH SENSORY AND MOTOR NEURONS.

THE BRAIN

Cranial nerves are numbered (using Roman numerals) and typically named according to their primary functions.

- Olfactory nerve (I)—carries information about smells from the nasal cavity.
- Optic nerve (II)—carries visual signals from the retina of the eye.
- Oculomotor nerve (III) and trochlear nerve (IV)—control extrinsic muscles that move the eyeballs.
- Trigeminal nerve (V)—carries sensory input from eye, face, and teeth; controls chewing muscles.
- Abducens nerve (VI)—controls the muscle that turns the eyeballs laterally.
- Facial nerve (VII)—controls muscles of facial expression.
- Vestibulocochlear nerve (VIII)—carries sensory input from the ears about hearing and balance.
- Glossopharyngeal nerve (IX)—carries information about taste from tongue; controls swallowing.
- Vagus nerve (X)—extends into the thorax and abdomen to control many vital functions such as heart rate.
- Accessory nerve (XI)—controls movement of the head and shoulders, and is involved in voice production.
- Hypoglossal nerve (XII)—controls movements of the tongue.

The blood-brain barrier

The brain requires a constant, plentiful blood supply in order to deliver sufficient glucose and oxygen to meet its high energy demands. In fact, although making up just 2 percent of the body's mass, it receives 20 percent of the body's blood flow per unit of time. Starved of oxygen, the brain rapidly becomes comatose and dies. Despite this absolute requirement, the brain, more than any other tissue, must also be protected from fluctuating levels of blood and tissue fluid chemicals that occur, for example, after eating or exercise. Such fluctuations could cause the random firing of neurons and the breakdown of the control center. This protection is provided by the blood-brain barrier. Capillaries supplying brain tissues have walls that form a barrier to impede the flow of most substances, including many drugs. Generally, only small molecules such as glucose, oxygen, and carbon dioxide can pass through. However, some fat-soluble substances such as ethanol (alcohol), and nicotine can also pass through—hence their effects on the CNS—as well as anesthetics.

KEY

1. Optic nerve (II)
2. Optic chiasma
3. Trochlear nerve (IV)
4. Cerebellum
5. Right cerebral hemisphere
6. Olfactory nerve (I)
7. Oculomotor nerve (III)
8. Trigeminal nerve (V)
9. Abducens nerve (VI)
10. Facial (VII), vestibulocochlear (VIII), glossopharyngeal (IX), and vagus (X) nerves
11. Hypoglossal nerve (XII)
12. Accessory nerve (XI)
13. Medulla oblongata

A ventral view of the brain, with the anterior end pointing to the top of the page, showing the cranial nerves.

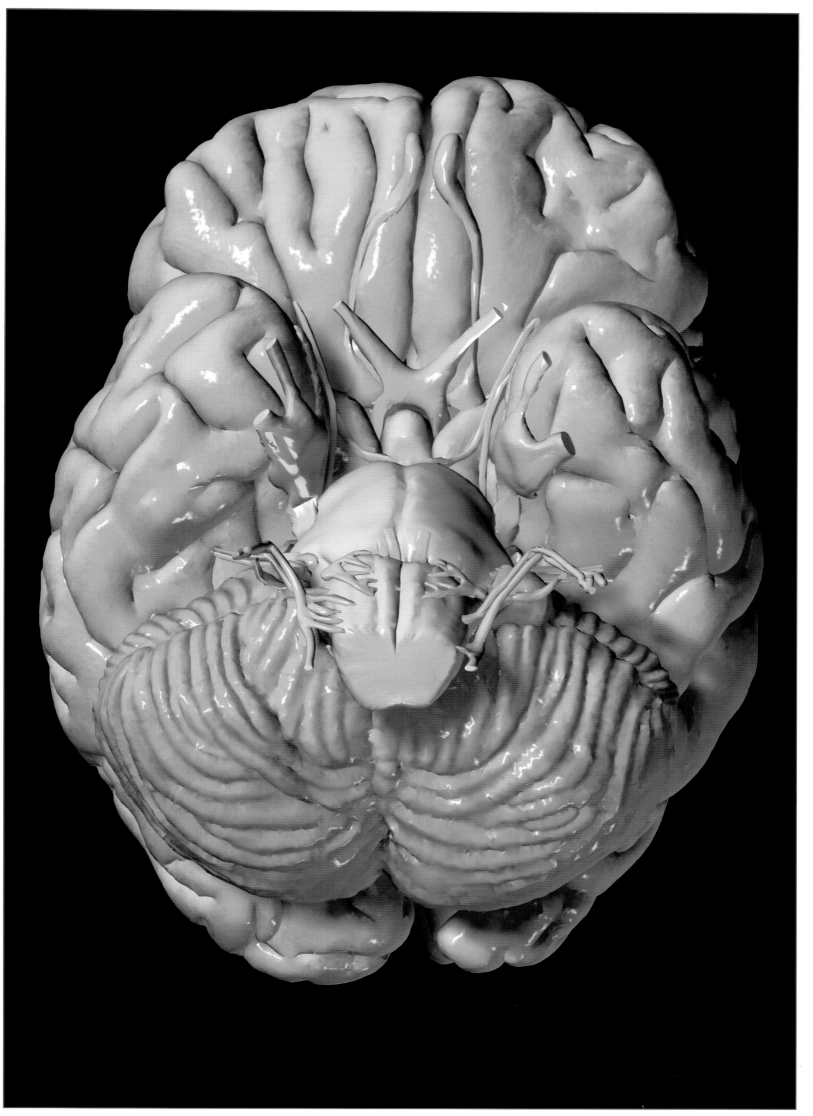

THE BRAIN

THE LARGEST PART OF THE BRAIN IS THE CEREBRUM, THE SEAT OF PERCEPTION AND CONSCIOUS BEHAVIOR. THE HUMAN CEREBRUM IS VERY LARGE, AND ITS SIZE HAS INCREASED WITH GREAT RAPIDITY DURING THE COMPARATIVELY BRIEF PERIOD OF HUMAN EVOLUTION. THE CEREBRUM HAS TWO HALVES, OR HEMISPHERES, EACH OF WHICH IS COVERED BY A THIN LAYER CALLED THE CEREBRAL CORTEX. DESPITE ITS THINNESS, THE CORTEX IS THE SITE OF ALL ELEMENTS OF CONSCIOUSNESS. THE WALNUT-LIKE APPEARANCE OF THE BRAIN SURFACE IS DUE TO ITS BEING FOLDED INTO **SULCI** (FOLDS) AND **GYRI** (BULGES). THIS ALLOWS A LARGE SURFACE AREA OF CORTEX TO BE SQUEEZED INTO THE LIMITED SPACE WITHIN THE SKULL. THE CORTEX OF EACH HEMISPHERE HAS FOUR LOBES: THE OCCIPITAL LOBE DEALS MAINLY WITH VISION; THE TEMPORAL LOBE IS INVOLVED WITH SOUND AND SPEECH; THE PARIETAL LOBE IS CONCERNED WITH MOVEMENT, TOUCH, AND RECOGNITION; AND THE FRONTAL LOBE DEALS WITH THINKING AND PLANNING.

brain and spinal cord and regulates basic functions such as heart rate and breathing rate.

Protection and cushioning of the brain

Brain tissue is soft and delicate and requires protection. Apart from the body covering provided by the skull, the brain is also surrounded and protected by three connective tissue membranes or **meninges**: the dura mater, the arachnoid mater, and, innermost, the pia mater. Beneath the arachnoid mater is a wide space that is filled with cerebrospinal fluid. This fluid forms a liquid cushion that reduces the weight of the brain and protects it from knocks and jolts. Derived from blood plasma, cerebrospinal fluid also helps to nourish the brain.

Linking the two cerebral hemispheres is a band of nervous tissue, called the corpus callosum, which permits the constant exchange of information between the two halves. Posterior to the cerebrum is the cerebellum, a "mini-brain" that controls movement and balance. In the space below the corpus callosum are the components of the limbic system, a more primitive system in evolutionary terms. The limbic system generates emotions and passes on information to the cerebral cortex; parts of it are also involved in memory and in maintaining homeostasis. The brainstem, the most primitive part of the brain, serves to relay information between

Anterolateral view of the brain from the right side with the grey matter (cerebral cortex) removed from the cerebrum.

KEY

1. White matter of right cerebral hemisphere
2. Cerebellum
3. Pons
4. Medulla oblongata

Anterolateral view of the brain from the left side showing the cerebral hemispheres, brain stem and cerebellum.

KEY

1. Superior sagittal sinus
2. Right cerebral hemisphere
3. Pituitary gland
4. Pons
5. Medulla oblongata
6. Left cerebral hemisphere
7. Cerebellum

THE BRAIN STEM

THE BRAIN STEM, WHICH LINKS THE SPINAL CORD TO THE THALAMUS, HYPOTHALAMUS, AND OTHER PARTS OF THE BRAIN, IS RESPONSIBLE FOR REGULATING AND CONTROLLING A NUMBER OF BODY FUNCTIONS. ITS ACTIVITIES PROCEED WITHOUT CONSCIOUS AWARENESS. IT CONSISTS OF THE MEDULLA OBLONGATA, ITS MOST INFERIOR PART, WHICH IS CONTINUOUS WITH THE SPINAL CORD; THE PONS, WHICH LINKS THE MEDULLA TO OTHER PARTS OF THE BRAIN; AND THE MIDBRAIN, THE UPPERMOST PART. THE MEDULLA OBLONGATA CONTROLS HEART AND BREATHING RATES, AS WELL AS OTHER ACTIVITIES INCLUDING SWALLOWING, SNEEZING, AND COUGHING. THE PONS WORKS WITH THE MEDULLA TO CONTROL BREATHING RATES, AND IT ALSO GIVES RISE TO SEVERAL CRANIAL NERVES THAT CONTROL FACIAL FUNCTIONS, SUCH AS CHEWING AND MOVEMENT OF THE EYEBALLS. THE MIDBRAIN CONTAINS THE SUBSTANTIA NIGRA, WHICH CONTROLS SUBCONSCIOUS MUSCLE ACTIVITIES; IT ALSO CONTROLS PUPIL SIZE AND LENS SHAPE IN THE EYE, AND SOME EYE MOVEMENTS.

The limbic system

A number of brain components—known collectively as the limbic system—encircle the brain stem close to the inner border of the cerebrum. These components include the hippocampus, the amygdala, the hypothalamus, and part of the thalamus and the fornix, which links these parts together. The limbic system is the "emotional brain," which deals with basic emotions such as fear, pain, pleasure, anger, sorrow, sexual excitement, and affection. It interacts closely with the cerebral cortex to produce a close relationship between feelings and thoughts; this interaction provides a conscious awareness of emotions and also enables us to control and limit the effects of basic and primitive emotional responses, and not express them under inappropriate circumstances. The hippocampus and amygdala also play a part in memory by converting new information into long-term memories. The hypothalamus, as well as playing a part in sexual arousal, also monitors and regulates many aspects of homeostasis, including temperature control and hunger.

Lateral view from the right side of the basal nuclei—caudate nucleus and lentiform nucleus—that play a vital role in controlling movement and parts of the limbic system.

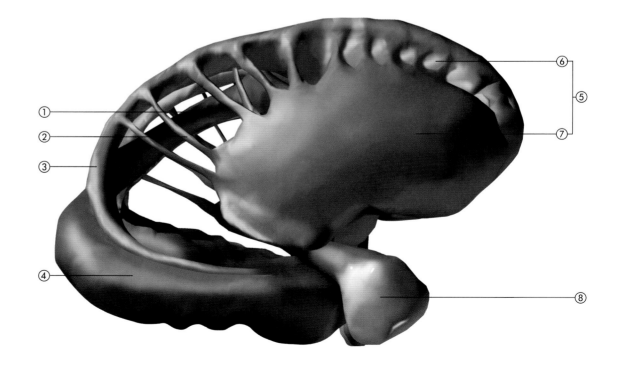

KEY

1. Fornix
2. Corona radiata
3. Tail of caudate nucleus
4. Hippocampus
5. Corpus striatum
6. Caudate nucleus
7. Putamen (lentiform nucleus)
8. Amygdala

KEY

① Caudate nucleus

③ Putamen (lentiform
   nucleus)

④ Hippocampus

⑤ Amygdala

⑥ Thalamus

⑦ Mammillary bodies

⑧ Lateral ventricle (posterior
   horn)

⑨ Lateral ventricle (anterior
   horn)

⑩ Hypothalamus

⑪ Pituitary gland

⑫ Pons

⑬ Medulla oblongata

**An inferior (from below) anterolateral view from the
right side of the corpus striatum with parts of the
limbic system (top), and with the ventricles and
brain stem (above).**

103

L INKED TO THE BRAIN BY THE BRAIN STEM, THE SPINAL CORD EXTENDS ABOUT 45 CM (18 IN) DOWN THE BACK FROM THE FORAMEN MAGNUM, THE LARGE OPENING IN THE BASE OF THE SKULL, TO THE LEVEL OF THE FIRST LUMBAR VERTEBRA. AT ITS MIDPOINT, THE SPINAL CORD IS ABOUT 1.8 CM (¾ IN) WIDE, NO MORE THAN THE WIDTH OF A FINGER. THE SPINAL CORD IS PROTECTED BY A BONY TUNNEL FORMED BY ADJACENT VERTEBRAE OF THE BACKBONE. ARISING FROM THE SPINAL CORD ARE 31 PAIRS OF SPINAL NERVES THAT PROTRUDE THROUGH GAPS BETWEEN THESE VERTEBRAE.

THE SPINAL CORD

Role of the spinal cord

The spinal cord relays information between the brain and the rest of the body by way of the spinal nerves. As well as forming a vital communication link, the spinal cord is also involved in many reflex actions. These are automatic split-second responses, many of which protect the body from hazards, such as automatically withdrawing the hand from a hot object.

Internal structure of the spinal cord

Internally, the spinal cord is composed of a central, H-shaped core of gray matter, that consists of association neurons, the endings of sensory neurons, and the cell bodies of motor neurons. Surrounding the gray matter is white matter, which is made up of nerve fibers, and arranged in bundles called tracts that pass up and down the spinal cord. Ascending tracts carry information about sensory input, arriving through the sensory neurons of spinal nerves, to the brain. Descending tracts carry instructions from the brain that will travel along the motor neurons of spinal nerves to muscles and glands.

Nerve structure

Nerves are creamy-colored, glistening cords that form the body's "wiring" or peripheral nervous system. Both cranial nerves, which arise from the brain, and spinal nerves, which arise from the spinal cord, share the same structure. A nerve contains bundles of neurons—or, more specifically, the long nerve fibers (axons) of neurons—called **fascicles**. Each fascicle is surrounded by a sheath of connective tissue, called **perineurium**, while several fascicles, and the nerve's blood vessels, are bound together by **epineurium**, the outer connective tissue coating of the nerve. Most nerves are mixed, carrying both sensory and motor neurons.

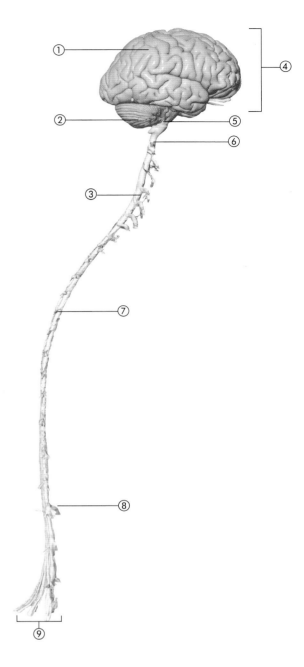

The brain and spinal cord from the right side. The curvature of the spinal cord follows that of the vertebral column, which normally surrounds and protects it.

KEY

① Right cerebral
   hemisphere
② Cerebellum
③ Spinal cord
④ Brain
⑤ Brain stem
⑥ Cervical spinal nerve
⑦ Thoracic spinal nerve
⑧ Lumbar spinal nerve
⑨ Cauda equina

Vision is the most important of the body's five senses. It provides a means of understanding the world around, as well as facilitating communication. The visual sense organs are the eyes: they detect light and send nerve impulses to the brain that are interpreted as "seen" images.

Only one sixth of the eyeball can actually be seen—the rest is protected by bone and tissue.

THE EYE

Only a small portion of each eye, or eyeball, is visible; the rest of the hollow, spherical organ lies enclosed and protected by a cushion of fat within the bony orbit formed by certain skull bones. The eyeball has three layers. The outer fibrous layer consists mostly of the tough, white, protective sclera; at the front of the eye it forms a clear window—the cornea—through which light is admitted. Extrinsic muscles attached to the sclera and orbit move the eyeball. The middle vascular layer forms the iris, the colored part of the eye that surrounds the pupil, as well as the suspensory ligaments that hold the focusing lens in place. The inner layer, the retina, contains over 70 percent of the body's sensory receptors. These **photoreceptors** detect the patterns produced by light reflected from objects outside the body and send messages to the brain.

Vision and the visual cortex

The conscious perception of visual images—seeing—happens in the **primary visual cortex** located in the occipital lobe of left and right cerebral hemispheres. Nerve fibers from the retina, the light-detecting layer inside the eye, travel along the optic nerves to the primary visual areas. En route, certain fibers cross over so that the left primary visual area receives visual images from the right side of the object in view, and the right primary visual area receives visual images from the left side.

KEY

1. Frontal bone
2. Sclera
3. Sphenoid bone
4. Temporal bone
5. Cornea
6. Nasal bone
7. Orbit
8. Maxilla
9. Infraorbital foramen
10. Zygomatic bone

Different centers within each primary visual cortex process information about the shape, color, movement, and location of the object being looked at. Because each primary visual area receives a slightly different view of the object, information from both areas is "pooled" to produce **binocular** or three-dimensional vision that enables a person to perceive depth. Surrounding the primary visual areas are the **visual association areas**. Here, incoming visual information is compared to previous visual experiences so that, for example, a person can recognize a familiar face or object.

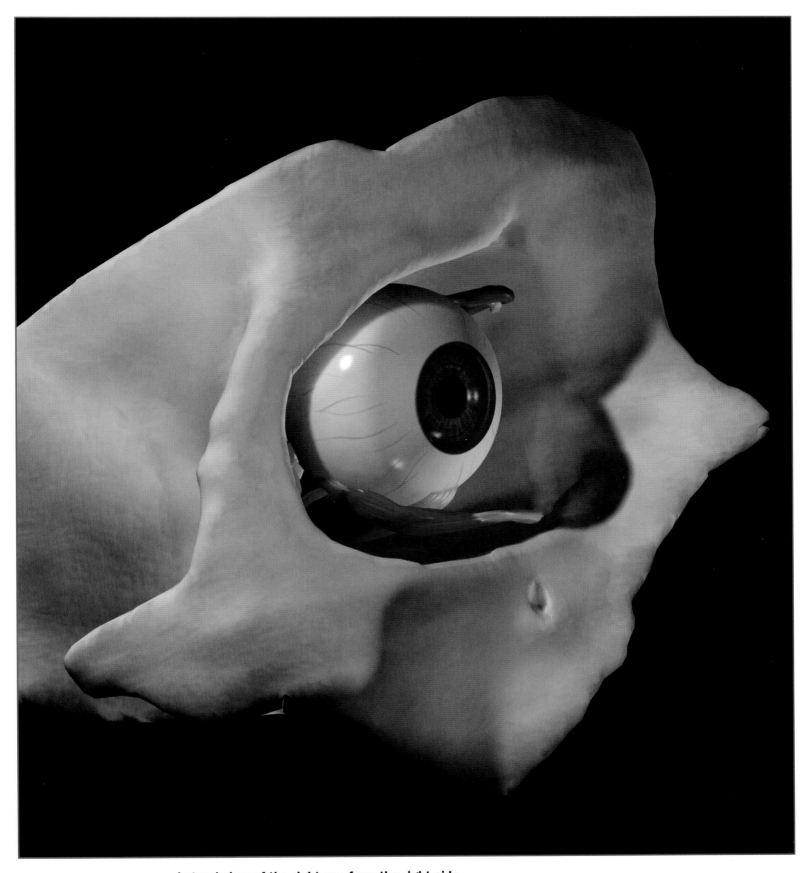

Lateral view of the right eye from the right side with the facial muscles removed. The eye is protected by the bony orbit.

THE VISUAL INFORMATION THE EYES GATHER IS ANALYZED BY THE BRAIN IN ORDER TO PROVIDE A CONSTANTLY UPDATED VIEW OF THE OUTSIDE WORLD. EACH SPHERICAL EYEBALL LIES PROTECTED WITHIN ITS ORBIT, A BONY SOCKET IN THE SKULL. EXTERNALLY, THE EYEBROWS PROTECT THE DELICATE SURFACE OF THE EYE FROM DRIPPING SWEAT AND EXCESS LIGHT, WHILE THE EYELASHES ENSURE THE REFLEX CLOSURE OF THE EYELIDS IF THEY ARE STIMULATED BY A GUST OF WIND OR IF THEY ARE TOUCHED.

THE EYE

Lateral view of the right eye showing the extrinsic muscles that move the eyeball and the optic nerve that conveys impulses from the eye to the visual areas of the brain.

KEY

1. Superior rectus muscle
2. Optic nerve
3. Lateral rectus muscle
4. Inferior rectus muscle
5. Inferior oblique muscle
6. Lacrimal gland

Lacrimal glands

Lacrimal glands, which lie within the orbit above the lateral end of each eye, continuously secrete a liquid known familiarly as tears. This dilute saline solution bathes the cornea and the conjunctiva—the thin membrane covering the rest of the front of the eye and the lining of the eyelids—so that the eyeball remains moist and lubricated. Tears also wash away dust particles, and contain an antibacterial substance called lysozyme. Released from the lacrimal glands through ducts, tears are swept across the eyeball every time blinking occurs. Tears drain from the eye through two medial openings, called lacrimal puncta, into paired lacrimal ducts, which drain into the nasal cavity through the nasolacrimal duct.

Extrinsic eye muscles

Each eyeball is moved by six extrinsic (external) muscles—four rectus muscles and two oblique muscles—that have their origins in the orbit and insert into the sclera of the eyeball. The rectus muscles, arranged at right angles to each other, move the eyeball up and down, and from side to side. The function of each is indicated by its name: the superior rectus (upward), inferior rectus (downward), lateral rectus (to the side), and medial rectus (toward the nose). The oblique muscles move the eyeball diagonally. The inferior oblique pulls the eyeball upward and laterally. The superior oblique, which inserts via a pulley-like loop of cartilage called the trochlea, swivels the eyeball downward and laterally. The eye muscles produce two types of movements: scanning movements enable the eye to follow moving objects even when the head is moving; saccades are short, jerky movements that allow the eye to scan the visual field rapidly when the head is still.

A view from the right side of the eyeball within the socket, showing the extrinsic muscles that move it.

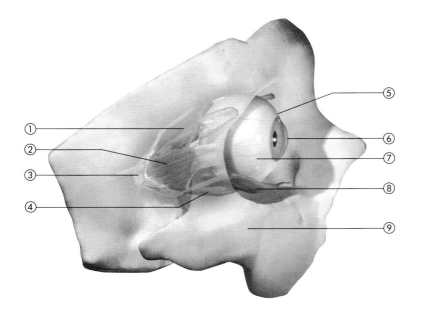

KEY

1. Superior rectus muscle
2. Lateral rectus muscle
3. Optic nerve
4. Inferior rectus muscle
5. Eyeball
6. Cornea
7. Sclera
8. Inferior oblique muscle
9. Skull

THE EYE HAS TO FUNCTION EFFICIENTLY AS A LIGHT SENSOR OVER A WIDE RANGE OF DIFFERENT LIGHT INTENSITIES. THE COLORED PART OF THE EYE, THE IRIS, CHANGES THE SIZE OF THE PUPIL, THEREBY CONTROLLING THE AMOUNT OF LIGHT ENTERING THE EYE. THE IRIS HAS RADIALLY AND CIRCULARLY ARRANGED SMOOTH MUSCLE FIBERS. A REFLEX ACTION ENSURES THAT, IN DIM LIGHT, THE RADIAL FIBERS CONTRACT, AND THE PUPIL DILATES (WIDENS); IN BRIGHT LIGHT, THE CIRCULAR FIBERS CONTRACT, AND THE PUPIL CONSTRICTS (SHRINKS).

THE EYE

KEY

1. Eyeball
2. Inferior oblique muscle
3. Lateral rectus
4. Optic nerve
5. Trochlea of the superior oblique muscle
6. Superior oblique muscle
7. Medial rectus
8. Superior rectus

Inferior view of the right eye showing the extrinsic muscles that are inserted into the bony orbit and which move the eyeball.

How light is focused on the retina

During their passage through the eye, light rays are refracted, or bent, in order to focus them on the retina and produce a clear image. Light is focused by the cornea and lens. The cornea, the transparent zone at the front of the eye, provides most light **refraction** but its refractory powers are unchanging. The fine tuning required to focus light from objects regardless of whether they are near or distant is provided by the lens. This **biconvex**, transparent, elastic structure lies just behind the iris suspended by a ring-shaped suspensory ligament that links the lens to the ciliary body. Within the ciliary body is a circular mass of smooth muscle, the ciliary muscle. To focus light from distant objects, the ciliary muscle relaxes and the suspensory ligament is pulled taut, making the lens thinner. To focus light from near objects, the ciliary muscle contracts, the suspensory ligament becomes slack, and the lens recoils and gets fatter.

Rods and cones

Internally, the back of the eye is lined by the retina, a thin layer of about 130 million **photoreceptors**—cells sensitive to light—that fire off impulses along the optic nerve to the brain when they are stimulated. There are two types of photoreceptors: the majority are **rods**, which work best in dim light, generate **monochrome** images, and provide **peripheral vision**; the remainder are called **cones**, photoreceptors that work best in bright light, provide color vision, and which are mostly concentrated in a small area—the **macula lutea**—directly behind the lens.

Impulses from photoreceptors travel along nerve fibers in the optic nerve to the visual cortex at the back of each cerebral hemisphere. Here, different areas process different features—such as color, shape, size, distance, and movement—in order to produce an image.

KEY

1. Optic nerve
2. Superior rectus
3. Lateral rectus
4. Medial rectus
5. Superior oblique muscle
6. Trochlea of the superior oblique muscle
7. Eyeball

Superior view of the right eye showing the extrinsic muscles and the optic nerve.

THE PROCESS OF SEEING

Vision is arguably the most important of the senses. It is certainly one of the most complex, a delicate chemical system that transforms light into nerve impulses. Once images are converted to impulses the raw data needs to be filtered through association centers to allow us identify and interpret the images.

Your eyes work a lot like a camera.

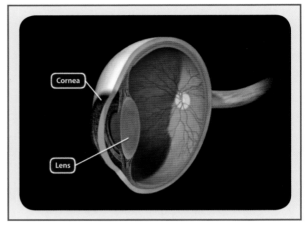

Just as the lens of a camera focuses light onto the film inside, the cornea and lens in the front of the eye focus light onto the back.

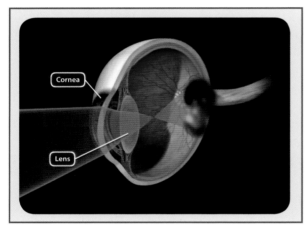

The image captured by the eye is projected to the retina, the light-sensitive tissue at the back of the eye.

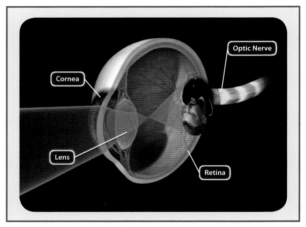

When the retina receives an image, it sends a signal through the optic nerve to the brain for the image to be "developed" or recognized.

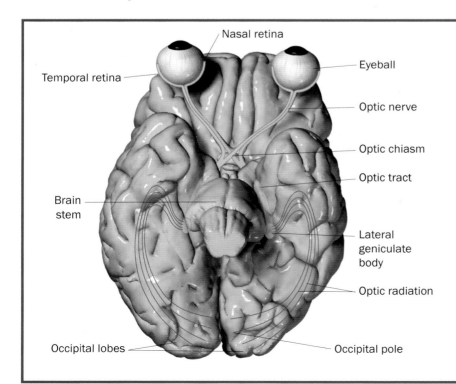

Nasal retina

Eyeball

Temporal retina

Optic nerve

Optic chiasm

Optic tract

Brain stem

Lateral geniculate body

Optic radiation

Occipital lobes

Occipital pole

VISION AND THE VISUAL CORTEX

The conscious perception of visual images—seeing—happens in the primary visual cortex located in the occipital lobe of the brain. Impulses from rods and cones—photoreceptors that form the retina—travel along nerve fibers in the optic nerves to the primary visual areas at the back of the brain. En route, certain fibers cross over so that the left primary visual area receives visual images from the right side of the object in view, and the right primary visual area receives visual images from the left side. The primary visual areas process different features—such as color, shape, size, distance, and movement—in order to produce an image. Information from both areas is then "pooled" to produce binocular or three-dimensional vision.

Surrounding the primary visual areas are the visual association areas. Here, incoming visual information is compared to previous visual experiences so that, for example, a person can recognize a familiar face or object.

Each eye has over 125 million photoreceptors – the rod and cone shaped neurons that process raw images and pass them along.

Surrounding the lens are ciliary muscles that change the shape of the lens allowing the eye to focus on near or far objects.

For viewing objects far away, the muscles relax allowing the lens to flatten.

When viewing objects up close, the muscles contract to round out the lens.

Nearsightedness occurs when the eyeball is is too long or the muscles over-contract, focusing the image of distant objects too far in front of the retina. Concave lenses correct the problem.

Farsightedness is the opposite. The eyeball is too short or the muscles are not strong enough to contract the lens, focusing the image of near objects behind the retina. Convex lenses correct the problem.

CONDITIONS & DISEASES OF THE EYES

The importance sight plays is demonstrated by the fact that over half of the brain's cerebral cortex is devoted to interpreting visual information. The simple act of misplacing our eyeglasses reminds us of how difficult it is to make our way through the world with less than good eyesight.

Vision in older adults may be impaired by Age-related macular degeneration or AMD. This painless disease damages the macula, which is in the center of the retina in the back part of

The macula helps you see fine details in the center of your vision. AMD takes two forms, wet and dry. Both result in a blind spot around the center of vision that makes it difficult to read, drive, and recognize faces.

Presbyopia is another condition that occurs with age as the lens of the eye becomes less elastic. Light rays focus behind, rather than directly on, the retina, making close objects appear out of focus.

Cataracts are a condition where the clear lens of the eye becomes more and more opaque. At first vision will only be impaired, losing contrast and definition as the cloudy lens spreads light across its surface, the way glare obscures our view through a dirty window.

When the lens becomes too opaque, cataracts can be treated either by removing part of the lens or by replacing the lens with a plastic intraocular implant that stays in the eye permanently.

GLAUCOMA

Glaucoma is a group of eye conditions in which high pressure inside your eye damages the optic nerve, impairing its ability to transmit visual information to the brain. The eye's inner pressure depends on the amount of fluid in the eye.

Increased interocular pressure in glaucoma usually results from a build up of fluid called aqueous humor. Normally, production and removal of this fluid is in balance. It is produced by ciliary bodies in the area behind the iris called the posterior chamber.

Aqueous humor flows up the back of the iris, through the pupil, into the area in front of the iris called the anterior chamber. It leaves the eye at the angle where the cornea and iris meet, flowing through spongy tissue called the trabecular network into a channel that is part of the venous system.

In closed-angle Glaucoma, the iris bulges forward and blocks the fluid from reaching the network. The fluid builds up and interocular pressure increases, usually suddenly.

In open-angle glaucoma, the trabecular network is partially blocked so the fluid drains out too slowly.

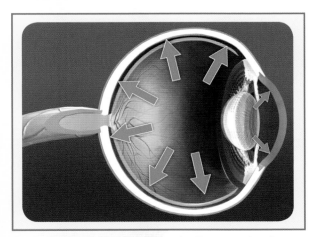

As fluid backs up, pressure in the eye slowly increases. There may be substantial vision loss before the problem is identified.

THEIR SENSE OF HEARING ENABLES HUMANS TO HEAR OVER 400,000 DIFFERENT SOUNDS PRODUCED BY THEIR SURROUNDINGS. SOUNDS ARE DETECTED BY THE EARS, WHICH ALSO PLAY AN IMPORTANT ROLE IN BALANCE, OR EQUILIBRIUM. THE STRUCTURES OF THE EAR FUNCTION AS A CONDUCTION SYSTEM THAT CONVEYS SOUND WAVES—PRESSURE WAVES IN THE EAR—TO THE FLUID-FILLED INNER PART OF THE EAR WHERE THEY ARE DETECTED BY VIBRATION-SENSITIVE RECEPTORS THAT SEND NERVE IMPULSES TO THE BRAIN WHERE THEY ARE INTERPRETED AS SOUNDS.

THE EAR

The ear is divided into three sections: the outer, the middle and the inner. The pinna, or flap, of the outer ear is the only visible part of the ear. Its shape helps conduct sound vibrations in the air along the ear canal, through to the eardrum, across the ossicles, and through the oval window into the inner ear.

The auditory cortex

The arrival of sound waves in the ear causes the production of vibrations in the fluid filling the snail shell-shaped cochlea of the inner ear. Within the cochlea, **mechanoreceptors** sense the vibrations and send nerve impulses along the cochlear division of the vestibulocochlear nerve to the brain by way of the thalamus, an area of the brain that processes most sensory input and relays it to the cerebral cortex.

Nerve impulses carried by the vestibulocochlear nerve arrive in the primary auditory area of the brain located in the superior margin of the temporal lobe. Some nerve fibers "cross over" on their journey from the ears, so that each **primary auditory area** receives impulses from both ears. The primary auditory area distinguishes sounds in terms of their basic characteristics: pitch, rhythm, and loudness. The **auditory association area**, posterior to the primary auditory area, determines whether these sounds are speech, music, or noise so that they are perceived, or heard.

Most of the ear is concealed and protected within the temporal bone of the skull; only the external ear, the pinna, is visible.

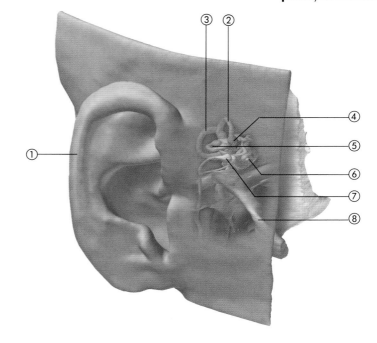

KEY

① Pinna (ear flap)
② Anterior semicircular canal
③ Posterior semicircular canal
④ Ampulla of semicircular canal
⑤ Lateral semicircular canal
⑥ Cochlea
⑦ Ossicles
⑧ Zygomatic process of temporal bone

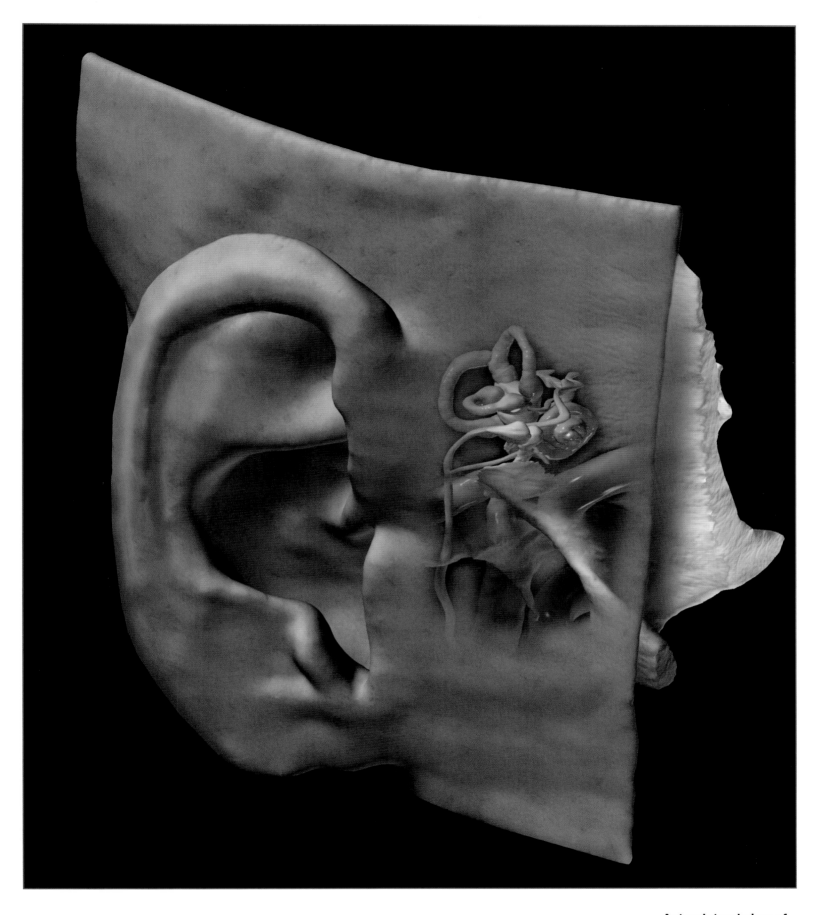

**Anterolateral view of
the head with part
of the temporal bone
removed to reveal the
component parts of
the right ear.**

THE EAR

Most of the ear lies hidden within the temporal bone of the skull. When incoming sound waves arrive from an external source they are directed into the auditory canal by the pinna or ear flap. When they reach the end of the auditory canal they make the eardrum, the taut skin stretched over the end of the canal, vibrate. This, in turn, sets up vibrations in the three tiny ossicles that traverse the air-filled middle ear. The ossicles move back and forth as they vibrate, and the innermost, the stirrup (stapes), acts like a piston pushing the oval window—the boundary between middle and inner ears—in and out. This movement sets up vibrations in the fluid of the inner ear, and these vibrations are detected by hair cells in the **organ of Corti**, part of the coiled, tubular cochlea. If these cells are stimulated—by having their projecting hairs distorted by vibrations—they send nerve impulses to the auditory area of the cortex, along the cochlear part of the vestibulocochlear nerve where they are interpreted as sounds.

The ear as an organ of balance

As well as detecting sounds, the ear also supplies the brain with information about the body's position. This is used to achieve balance or equilibrium when moving or standing still. At the base of each of the three fluid-filled semicircular canals in the inner ear is a small swelling called an **ampulla**. This contains sensory hairs embedded in a jellylike cupula. When the head moves, the fluid moves in the opposite direction and deflects the **cupula**, resulting in the hair cells, to which sensory hairs are attached, sending nerve impulses to the brain. Since the three semicircular canals are set at right angles to each other, the brain is aware of head movements in any direction. In the **vestibule** there are two further balance detectors, the **utricle** and **saccule**. These contain sensory hairs embedded in a jelly that is "weighed down" with crystals of calcium carbonate. The saccule detects whether the head is upright, tilted or upside down, and the utricle detects linear acceleration and deceleration. The brain combines the information obtained from these sensors with information from the eyes, feet, and muscles to ensure that balance is maintained.

Frontal view of the right ear with skin and muscles removed.

KEY

1. Ossicles
2. Tympanum (eardrum)
3. Semicircular canal
4. Vestibulocochlear nerve
5. Cochlea

**Superior view of the internal parts of the right ear from the
right side (above) and a frontal view of the ossicles (right).**

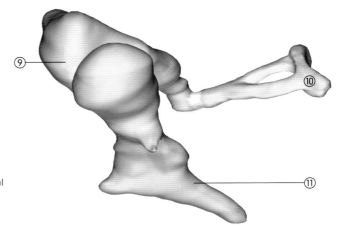

KEY

1. Internal carotid artery
2. Posterior semicircular canal
3. Cochlear nerve
4. Vestibular nerve
5. Cochlea
6. Anterior semicircular canal
7. Facial nerve
8. Lateral semicircular canal
9. Incus
10. Stapes
11. Malleus

119

HOW THE EAR WORKS

The ear detects sound waves in the air, transforming them into nerve impulses that are ultimately interpreted by the brain as sound. The vestibular system of the ear also gives us our sense of balance.

Incoming sound waves are directed into the auditory canal by the pinna of the outer ear.

The canal is connected to the tympanic membrane, or eardrum, which vibrates as sound waves enter the ear.

The eardrum's vibrations are transmitted to the malleus, the first of the series of three tiny bones in the middle ear called ossicles.

The ossicles amplify the energy of the sound waves' vibrations as they transmit them to the inner ear.

The third and innermost ossicle, called the stapes, or stirrup (because of its shape), vibrates against an oval window that serves as the boundary between the middle ear and the fluid-filled inner ear.

In the inner ear the vibrations are transmitted to the organ of Corti as waves of pressure.

Here, chambers contain the columnar cells that serve as auditory receptors.

The cells convert the waves of pressure into electrical signals which are carried to the part of the brain that perceives sound.

Repeated exposure to high levels of sound can shear the hair cells so that they tear and shrivel. This is a primary cause of hearing loss in situations where there is too much noise in the environment.

Inside the ear canal, wax is created to remove dust particles from the air before they reach the eardrum. But wax buildup can also block sound waves.

Infections can cause fluid to build up in the middle ear. This can cause bulging of the eardrum and dampen the vibrations that would normally be passed to the ossicles.

Semicircular canals

Balance

Each of the three semicircular canals of the ear are aligned to sense motion from a different axis: forward and backwards rotationally or from side to side. As we move, hairs within fluid sacs in the canals relay this information to the brain. Motion sickness occurs when these signals are contradicted by information received visually.

THE NOSE PROVIDES A PASSAGEWAY FOR AIR DURING BREATHING; WARMING, MOISTENING, AND FILTERING AIR AS IT IS BEING INHALED. IT ALSO HOUSES SMELL DETECTORS. THERE ARE TWO PARTS TO THE NOSE. THE EXTERNAL NOSE IS SUPPORTED BY A FRAMEWORK PROVIDED BY THREE OF THE SKULL BONES— THE NASAL AND FRONTAL BONES, AND THE MAXILLA—AND BY FLEXIBLE PLATES OF CARTILAGE.

THE NOSE

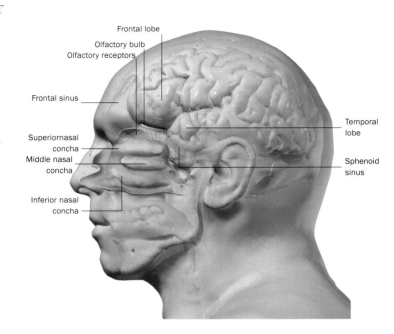

Frontal lobe
Olfactory bulb
Olfactory receptors
Frontal sinus
Superiornasal concha
Middle nasal concha
Inferior nasal concha
Temporal lobe
Sphenoid sinus

Behind the external nose is the nasal cavity. Its roof is formed by the ethmoid and sphenoid bones, and its floor by the palate, which separates it from the mouth. Vertically, the nasal cavity is divided into left and right halves by the nasal septum. The external opening of the nasal cavity is through the nostrils, or external nares. Posteriorly, the nasal cavity opens into the upper pharynx (throat) through the internal nares. The nasal cavity is lined with a mucous membrane that secretes watery mucus, which moistens incoming air, dissolves chemicals so that they can be detected by smell receptors, and traps dirt and bacteria.

Smelling, the olfactory cortex, and the limbic system

In the upper part of each side of the nasal cavity is a postage-stamp sized area of mucous membrane called the **olfactory epithelium**, which contains more than 10 million olfactory (smell) receptors. Specifically, these are **chemoreceptors** that can detect airborne chemicals that dissolve in the watery mucus. The olfactory chemoreceptors can detect

more than 10,000 different smells. When stimulated, the receptors send nerve impulses along fibers of the olfactory nerve, which pass through holes in the ethmoid bone, and into the olfactory bulbs that project anteriorly on the underside of the brain.

Olfactory tracts within the bulbs lead to the olfactory cortex on the lateral and medial surfaces of the temporal lobe of the brain. This primitive region of the cortex, which forms part of the limbic system—the part of the brain responsible for emotions and memory—is the primary olfactory area, where the conscious awareness of smells occurs. Some smell information from the nose travels to other parts of the limbic system and also the hypothalamus, provoking subconscious emotional and memory-linked responses to smells, such as the odor of a particular food evoking memories of childhood.

Side view of the head with the concha exposed showing the olfactory receptors and olfactory nerve, the first of the cranial nerves.

THE ENDOCRINE SYSTEM

While the nervous system controls activities of the body via electrical impulses, the endocrine system controls functions including growth, sexual development and response to danger using hormones transmitted by the bloodstream.

A model of Human Growth Hormone (HGH), also known as somatropin.

TWO SYSTEMS ENSURE THAT THE BODY WORKS IN A CONTROLLED AND COORDINATED MANNER. ONE IS THE NERVOUS SYSTEM; THE SECOND IS THE ENDOCRINE, OR HORMONAL, SYSTEM, WHICH CONSISTS OF ENDOCRINE GLANDS LOCATED IN THE HEAD AND TRUNK. AMONG THE MANY BODY ACTIVITIES IT COORDINATES ARE THE PRODUCTION OF SECONDARY SEXUAL CHARACTERISTICS (SUCH AS BREASTS AND PUBIC HAIR), REPRODUCTION, AND GROWTH.

THE ENDOCRINE SYSTEM

The endocrine and nervous systems—a comparison

The endocrine and nervous systems work together to coordinate body activities, but each works in a very different way. The endocrine system releases chemicals into the blood in order to alter the metabolic activities of cells. It works relatively slowly and typically has long-lasting effects. The nervous system, on the other hand, uses electrical impulses that travel at high speed along neurons in order to alter the activities of muscles and glands, and has immediate, short-term effects.

This comparison of the male and female pelves reveals the difference between the male and female endocrine systems. The female pelvis (above, top) contains the ovaries, while below the male pelvis (above, bottom) are the testes.

Endocrine glands

Glands are organs, or groups of cells, that release substances called secretions into or onto the body. There are two types of glands. Exocrine glands release their secretions via ducts within or outside the body—examples are the salivary glands releasing saliva into the mouth or sweat glands releasing sweat onto the skin.

Endocrine glands lack ducts and release their secretions, called **hormones**, directly into the bloodstream. The main endocrine glands are the pituitary, pineal, thyroid, parathyroids, and adrenal glands. The pancreas, ovaries, and testes also contain endocrine sections.

How hormones work

Each hormone travels in the bloodstream to deliver a chemical message to a specific target area on which it has an effect. Some hormones may target all or most body cells, while others affect only one particular tissue. When a hormone reaches a target cell it locks onto a specific receptor site. This action either increases or decreases the rates of certain chemical reactions going on inside the cell, altering the cell's activity.

The major endocrine organs found in the male body. The hypothalamus is a part of the brain that controls the activity of the pituitary gland. The kidneys are included here because the adrenal glands "sit" on top of them.

KEY

1. Hypothalamus
2. Pituitary gland
3. Thyroid gland (parathyroid gland on posterior surface)
4. Pancreas
5. Adrenal gland
6. Kidneys
7. Testes

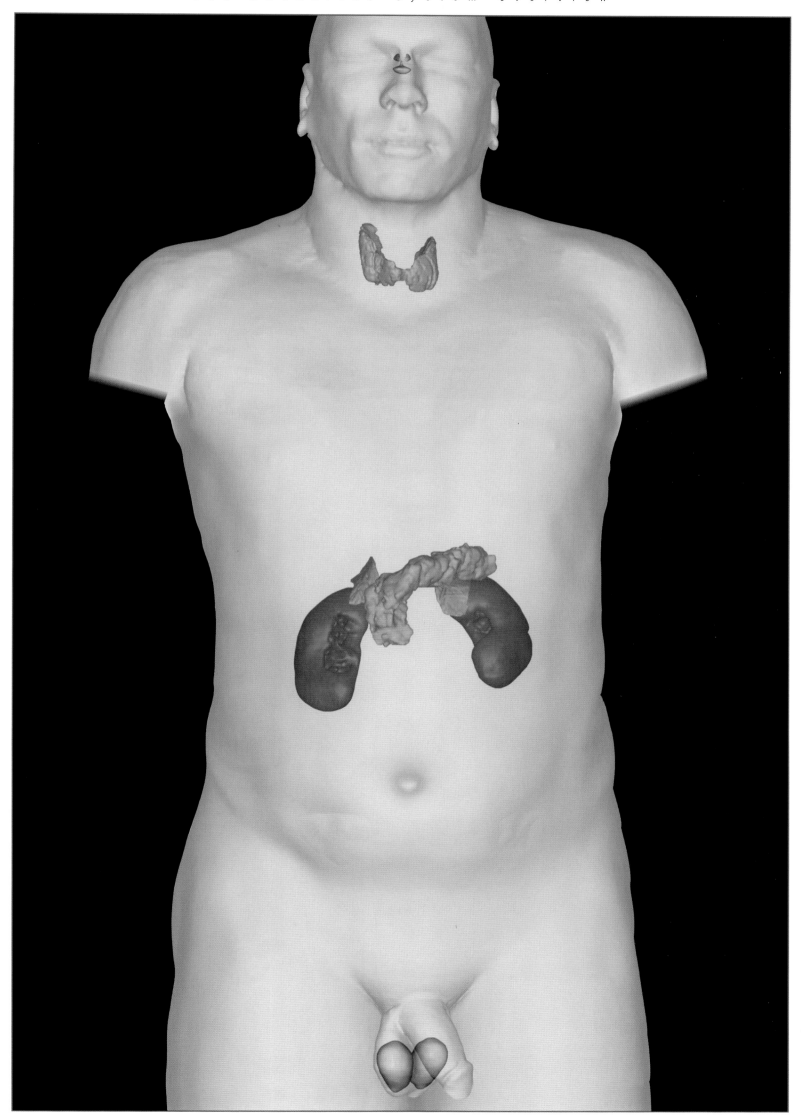

RESEMBLING A PEA, THE PITUITARY GLAND LIES JUST BELOW THE BRAIN. IT IS CONNECTED BY A STALK TO THE HYPOTHALAMUS, A SMALL AREA OF THE BRAIN THAT MONITORS AND REGULATES MANY OF THE BODY'S ACTIVITIES. THE PITUITARY GLAND RELEASES MORE THAN EIGHT HORMONES, MANY OF WHICH CONTROL OTHER ENDOCRINE ORGANS. FOR THAT REASON, IT IS REGARDED AS THE MOST IMPORTANT ENDOCRINE GLAND. HOWEVER, THE DRIVING FORCE BEHIND THE PITUITARY GLAND IS THE HYPOTHALAMUS.

THE HYPOTHALAMUS & PITUITARY

The pituitary gland has two parts. The larger anterior lobe produces most pituitary hormones. It is controlled by the hypothalamus which secretes its own hormones, called **releasing factors**, in order to stimulate the release of pituitary hormones. The smaller posterior lobe releases two hormones, **oxytocin** and **antidiuretic hormones** (ADH), which are made by the hypothalamus and carried by special nerve fibers to the posterior lobe.

Pituitary gland hormones

The anterior lobe hormones are:
- **Growth hormone**, which stimulates growth during childhood and adolescence.
- **Thyroid-stimulating hormone** (TSH), which stimulates the release of thyroid hormone by the thyroid gland.
- **Adrenocorticotropic hormone** (ACTH), which stimulates release of glucocorticoid hormones by the adrenal glands.
- **Follicle-stimulating hormone** (FSH), which stimulates egg maturation in, and release of **estrogen** by, the ovaries; and stimulates sperm production in the testes.

- **Luteinizing hormone** (LH), which stimulates **ovulation** and **progesterone** production in the ovaries; and **testosterone** production in the testes.
- **Prolactin**, which stimulates milk production by the mammary glands.

The posterior lobe hormones are:
- **Oxytocin**, which stimulates the uterus to contract during childbirth, and the mammary glands to release milk.
- **ADH**, which acts on the kidneys to reduce the volume of urine released.

The control of hormone levels

Hormone levels must be carefully controlled so that they do not have too great, or too little, effect. In most cases control is achieved by a negative **feedback** system that automatically reverses an unwanted change. For example, low levels of thyroid hormone are detected by the hypothalamus, which secretes a releasing factor that stimulates the pituitary gland to secrete thyroid stimulating hormone (TSH). In turn, this causes the thyroid gland to secrete more thyroid hormone. High levels of thyroid hormone, on the other hand, stop secretion of the releasing factor and slow the production of TSH, thereby reducing levels of thyroid hormone.

A view of the head from the left side to show the position of the pituitary gland. It lies just below the brain, between the temporal lobes of the two cerebral hemispheres. Most of the hormones released by the anterior pituitary gland control the secretions of other endocrine glands.

KEY

1. Position of the hypothalamus
2. Position of the pituitary gland
3. Left cerebral hemisphere of brain
4. Left temporal lobe

THE BUTTERFLY-SHAPED THYROID GLAND IS FOUND IN THE FRONT OF THE NECK, OVERLYING THE TRACHEA AND JUST BELOW THE LARYNX. HOLLOW FOLLICLES INSIDE THE THYROID RELEASE THREE HORMONES: **TRIIODOTHYRONINE** AND **THYROXINE**, BOTH OF WHICH CONTAIN IODINE AND ARE KNOWN COLLECTIVELY AS THYROID HORMONE;, AND CALCITONIN.

THE THYROID & PARATHYROIDS

The largest pure endocrine gland in the body, the thyroid gland consists of two lateral lobes linked by a narrow isthmus. On the posterior surface of each lobe are embedded two yellow-brown parathyroid glands.

KEY

① Neck
② Thyroid cartilage
③ Larynx
④ Cricoid cartilage
⑤ Right lateral lobe
⑥ Thyroid gland
⑦ Isthmus
⑧ Head
⑨ Left lateral lobe
⑩ Trachea

Thyroid hormone acts as the body's "accelerator pedal." It speeds up **metabolic rate**, the rate of chemical reactions inside cells. Among its other roles, thyroid hormone also promotes growth during childhood and adolescence, and ensures the normal functioning of both heart and nervous system. The release of thyroid hormone is controlled by thyroid stimulating hormone (TSH), which is produced by the pituitary gland.

The third thyroid hormone, calcitonin, helps to control levels of calcium in the blood. The most abundant mineral in the body, calcium is essential for building bones and teeth, the transmission of nerve impulses, muscle contraction, and blood clotting. It is vitally important, therefore, to maintain stable levels of calcium in the blood. Calcitonin decreases calcium levels in the blood by slowing down the rate at which bone—the body's major storehouse of calcium—is resorbed or broken down, and speeding up the uptake of calcium to make more bone matrix. If calcium levels in the blood increase, so does calcitonin secretion by the thyroid gland. Precise control of blood calcium levels depends on calcitonin working with a hormone that has opposing effects. This hormone is released by the parathyroid glands.

Parathyroid glands

Four tiny parathyroid glands are embedded in the posterior part of the thyroid gland. They release **parathyroid hormone** (PTH), which raises calcium levels in the blood by increasing the rate at which bone is broken down, by stimulating the uptake of calcium from digested food in the small intestine, and by increasing the resorption of calcium into the bloodstream via the kidneys. Release of PTH is triggered by low levels of calcium, and inhibited by high levels of calcium in the blood.

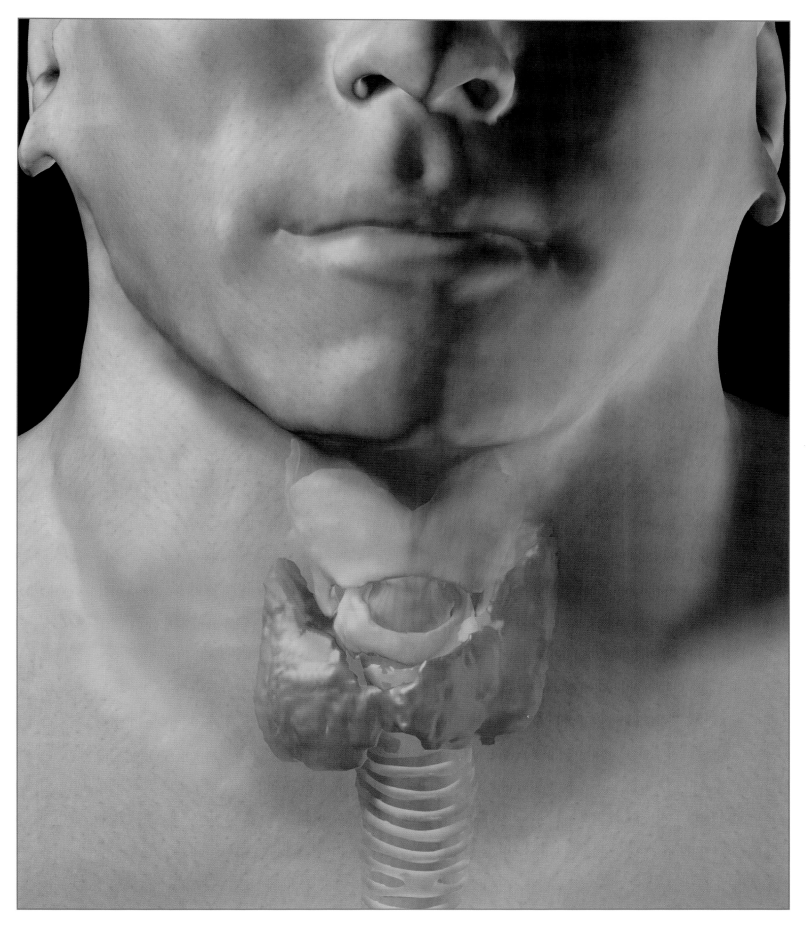

Iodine is the principle chemical element of the thyroid hormones. It is vitally important that sufficient iodine is obtained from the diet otherwise the thyroid gland will enlarge in an attempt to increase and maintain normal levels. Enlargement of the thyroid gland causes a characteristic swelling of the neck known as a goiter.

The two, pyramid-shaped adrenal glands resemble "hats" that are perched on top of the kidneys. Each gland has two distinct sections. The outer zone, or cortex, produces steroid hormones called **CORTICOSTEROIDS**. The inner zone, or medulla, produces two hormones—**EPINEPHRINE** (**ADRENALINE**) and **NOREPINEPHRINE** (**NORADRENALINE**)—that trigger the "fight-or-flight" response when the body is exposed to danger or stress.

THE ADRENAL GLANDS

The two adrenal glands are located in the posterior part of the upper abdomen, perched on top of the kidneys. Each adrenal gland is surrounded and protected by a fibrous capsule and a cushioning layer of fat.

KEY

① Right adrenal gland
② Right kidney
③ Left adrenal gland
④ Left kidney

Three groups of corticosteroid hormones are made by the adrenal cortex. Mineralocorticoids, such as aldosterone, control the levels of sodium and potassium in blood and other body fluids. Maintaining balanced and stable levels of sodium and potassium is essential for regulating blood pressure and blood volume; both minerals are also vital for the conduction of nerve impulses and for muscle contraction. Aldosterone acts on the kidneys by preventing the loss of sodium in the urine.

Glucocorticoids, notably cortisol, help the body adapt to changing conditions by stabilizing blood glucose levels and influencing cell metabolism. Cortisol release is stimulated and regulated by the pituitary hormone, **adrenocorticotropic hormone** (ACTH). During times of stress resulting from, for example, surgery, bleeding, trauma, or infection, cortisol sets various processes in motion that help the body overcome its crisis.

Gonadocorticoids are principally male sex hormones or **androgens**. In men, the amount of androgen produced by the adrenals is minute compared to that released by the testes. In women, however, adrenal androgens stimulate the growth of pubic and axial (armpit) hair, as well as promoting sex drive and other sexual behaviors.

The "fight-or-flight" reaction and stress

Faced with the threat of short-term stress or danger, the body prepares itself to stay and fight, or to run away. This fight-or-flight reaction is mediated by epinephrine and norepinephrine, whose release is stimulated by the autonomic nervous system *(see page 95)*. Unlike other hormones, epinephrine and norepinephrine are fast acting and short-lived in their effects. They act rapidly to increase heart and breathing rates (extra oxygen), increase levels of glucose in the blood (extra fuel), and to direct more blood to skeletal muscles (extra energy for muscle contraction) so that the body is geared up to either fight or run.

Each adrenal gland has two main parts, an outer cortex and an inner medulla. The outer cortex produces the glucocorticoids, the gonadocorticoids, and the mineralocorticoids, while the inner medulla produces epinephrine (adrenaline) and norepinephrine (noradrenaline).

L YING HORIZONTALLY BELOW AND BEHIND THE STOMACH, THE PANCREAS CONSISTS OF A HEAD, NECK, AND TAIL, THE HEAD BEING TUCKED INTO THE CURVE FORMED BY THE DUODENUM, THE FIRST PART OF THE SMALL INTESTINE. THE PANCREAS IS ACTUALLY TWO GLANDS IN ONE: PART EXOCRINE AND PART ENDOCRINE. NINETY-NINE PERCENT OF ITS MASS CONSISTS OF TINY EXOCRINE GLANDS CALLED ACINI THAT RELEASE A DIGESTIVE JUICE INTO THE DUODENUM. SCATTERED AMONG THE ACINI ARE BETWEEN ONE AND TWO MILLION TINY CLUSTERS OF ENDOCRINE CELLS CALLED PANCREATIC ISLETS, OR ISLETS OF LANGERHANS.

THE PANCREAS

The pancreas is a mixed gland: most of its tissues are involved in producing and secreting enzymes that are released into the duodenum to digest food; but part of it secretes two hormones that between them control the level of glucose in the blood.

KEY

1. Liver
2. Gallbladder
3. Head of pancreas
4. Duodenum
5. Pancreas
6. Spleen
7. Tail of pancreas
8. Body of pancreas

Pancreatic islets produce two hormones—glucagon and insulin—that ensure the body has sufficient fuel, in the form of the sugar glucose, to supply its cells with the energy they need to function normally. Glucose levels in the bloodstream must be kept relatively stable regardless of whether a person has not eaten for several hours, or whether glucose from a recently eaten meal is flooding into the bloodstream. Too little or too much glucose in the blood inhibits glucose uptake by cells. In the case of the brain, fluctuating glucose levels can result in confusion, convulsions and, possibly, coma.

Glucagon and insulin have opposing effects and balance each other to maintain stable blood glucose levels. If blood glucose levels are low, more glucagon is released by **alpha cells** in the pancreatic islets. This hormone stimulates the liver to turn the **glycogen**—a complex carbohydrate reserve made up of glucose molecules—stored inside its cells into glucose, which passes into the bloodstream to restore normal glucose levels.

The level of blood glucose rises after a meal, which stimulates the beta cells of the pancreatic islets to release insulin. Insulin reduces blood glucose levels by storing the excess to meet future demands. It has three major targets. It encourages skeletal muscles to take up` glucose from the bloodstream and either store it as glycogen, or use it to release the energy needed for movement. It stimulates **adipose** (fat) cells to use glucose as an immediate energy source or to store it as fat. Finally, it encourages liver cells to remove glucose from the blood and convert it into glycogen.

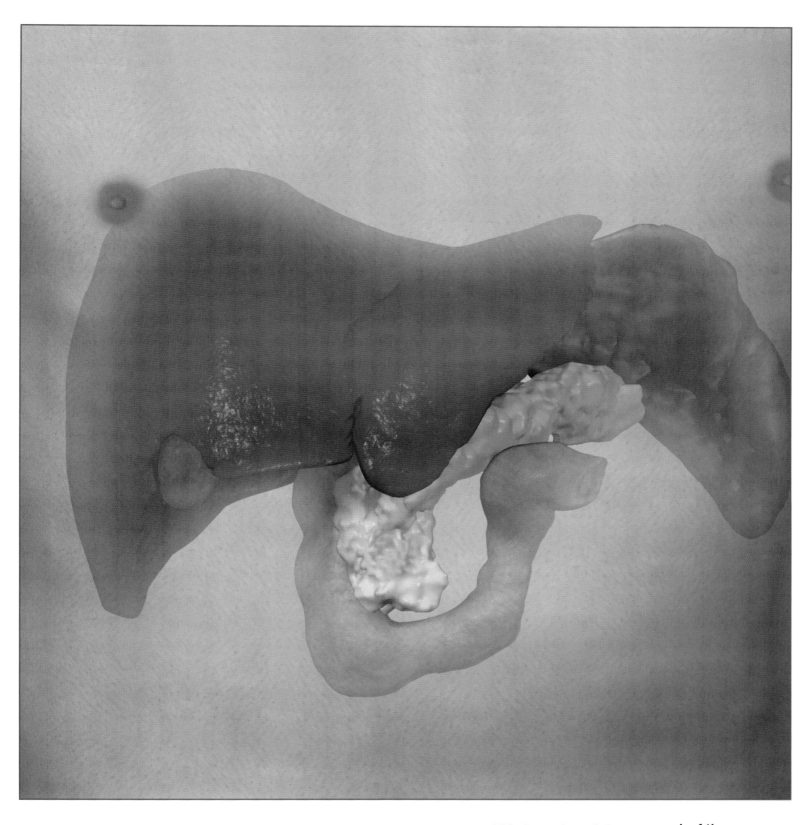

This front view of the abdomen shows the pancreas extending along the duodenum and under the liver and spleen. The larger head of the pancreas tapers into its body and ends in its tail, both of which lie behind the stomach. While much of the pancreas is involved in the production of digestive enzymes, dotted within the pancreas are thousands of cell groups called the islets of Langerhans. These are responsible for the production of insulin.

THE TWO ALMOND-SHAPED OVARIES LIE ONE ON EITHER SIDE OF THE UTERUS. AS THE PRIMARY FEMALE SEX ORGANS, OVARIES SERVE A DUAL PURPOSE. AS STOREHOUSES OF EGGS OR **OOCYTES**, THE OVARIES RELEASE ONE MATURE OOCYTE, OR **OVUM**, EACH MONTH BETWEEN **PUBERTY** AND **MENOPAUSE**. IF FERTILIZED BY A SPERM, THE OVUM WILL DEVELOP INTO A BABY. AS ENDOCRINE ORGANS, THE OVARIES RELEASE TWO SEX HORMONES—ESTROGEN AND PROGESTERONE—THAT MAINTAIN THE REPRODUCTIVE SYSTEM AND PREPARE THE BODY FOR PREGNANCY.

KEY

① Pelvic girdle
② Right coxa (hip bone)
③ Right ovary
④ Uterus
⑤ Left coxa (hip bone)
⑥ Left ovary
⑦ Vagina

THE OVARIES

The ovaries, the primary female sex organs, lie within the pelvic cavity, one on each side of the uterus. As endocrine glands, the ovaries release the hormones that control the ovarian and menstrual cycles and maintain female secondary sexual characteristics.

Estrogen first exerts its effects at puberty. It causes the reproductive system to mature and start working, and stimulates the production and maintenance of secondary female sexual characteristics, which include the growth of breasts; the development of a female body through characteristic fat deposition; the broadening of the pelvis; and the pattern of hair growth on the face and body. Estrogen also works with growth hormone to promote rapid growth during puberty. Each month between puberty and the menopause, estrogen stimulates the thickening of the endometrium, the lining of the uterus, so that it can receive an ovum if it is fertilized. Progesterone acts with estrogen to thicken the endometrium.

The release of both estrogen and progesterone is controlled by two other hormones—the **gonadotropins** FSH and LH—released by the pituitary gland. The gonadotropins also control the maturation and release of an ovum from an ovary each month. As levels of estrogen and progesterone increase they inhibit the release of gonadotropins. However, if fertilization does not occur, the secretion of estrogen and progesterone by the ovaries decreases and levels of gonadotropins increase. As sex hormones and gonadotropins interact with each other, and their levels fluctuate, they synchronize two events or cycles that follow the same sequence on a monthly basis: the **ovarian** cycle, which releases an ovum from the ovary; and the **menstrual** cycle, which thickens the endometrium and prepares the uterus to receive the fertilized egg and then, if fertilization does not occur, causes the endometrium to break down. If fertilization does occur, high levels of estrogen and progesterone are maintained in order to inhibit the release of gonadotropins and prevent either ovarian or menstrual cycles occurring during the pregnancy.

The ovaries are not fully functional at birth, only producing a few hormones. At the onset of puberty, a sudden increase in the levels of sex hormones occurs, causing the initiation of the reproductive cycle and the development of secondary sexual characteristics.

T HE PAIRED, OVAL TESTES LIE IN A SKIN POUCH, CALLED THE SCROTUM, THAT HANGS BETWEEN THE LEGS. THE TESTES ARE A MAN'S PRIMARY SEX ORGANS, AND LIKE THE OVARIES—THE FEMALE PRIMARY SEX ORGANS—THEY HAVE TWO ROLES. FIRSTLY, COILEDTUBULES, CALLED SEMINIFEROUS TUBULES, INSIDE THE TESTES ARE RESPONSIBLE FOR THE MANUFACTURE OF HUNDREDS OF MILLIONS OF SEX CELLS, CALLED SPERM, THROUGHOUT LIFE FROM ABOUT THE AGE OF FOURTEEN. SECONDLY, THE TESTES ARE ENDOCRINE ORGANS THAT RELEASE MALE SEX HORMONES CALLED ANDROGENS INTO THE BLOODSTREAM.

THE TESTES

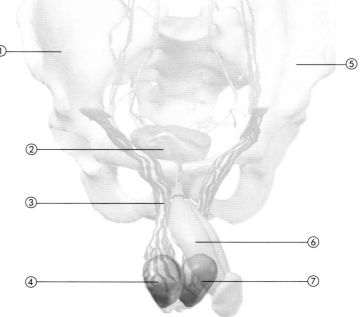

The testes, the primary male sex organs, lie outside and below the pelvic cavity, and produce hormones that stimulate sperm production and maintain male secondary sexual characteristics. The spermatic cord contains the blood vessels that convey hormones away from the testes.

KEY

1. Right coxa (hip bone)
2. Urinary bladder
3. Spermatic cord
4. Right testis
5. Left coxa (hip bone)
6. Penis
7. Left testis

Androgens, most notably the hormone testosterone, are secreted by endocrine cells called **interstitial**, or **Leydig**, cells that surround the seminiferous tubules. When a boy reaches puberty, testosterone secretion increases and stimulates the growth and maturation of the reproductive system, works with growth hormone to cause rapid growth, and causes the appearance of secondary sexual characteristics. In males, these characteristics include the growth of skeletal muscles and bones to produce a typical male body shape with wide shoulders and narrow hips; the appearance of facial, pubic, axial (armpit), and chest hair; and the growth of the larynx, which results in the voice "breaking" and deepening. In adults, testosterone maintains the secondary sexual characteristics, promotes sperm production, and powers the sex drive or **libido**. (Sex drive and the appearance of pubic hair in women are also controlled by testosterone, but the hormone is released by the adrenal glands.

Testosterone release is controlled by another hormone, a gonadotropin called LH, released by the pituitary gland. LH stimulates interstitial cells to release testosterone. The whole system is overseen by a feedback mechanism that controls testosterone release: if there is too much testosterone in the bloodstream it inhibits the release of LH by the pituitary gland; too little testosterone has the opposite effect. In this way, testosterone levels in the blood remain relatively stable, unlike the cyclical fluctuations of female sex hormones. Another gonadotropin, FSH, released by the pituitary gland, works with testosterone to stimulate the seminiferous tubules to manufacture sperm.

The production of androgens by the testes stimulates the maturation of the male reproductive system and the development of secondary sexual characteristics, such as the development of a typical body shape, the growth of facial, armpit, and chest hair, and the "breaking" of the voice, caused by the growth of the larynx.

THE CARDIOVASCULAR AND LYMPHATIC SYSTEM

DOZENS OF MILES OF ARTERIES, VEINS, CAPILLARIES, AND LYMPH VESSELS SUPPLY EVERY PART OF THE BODY WITH NOURISHMENT AND OXYGEN WHILE TAKING AWAY WASTE AND TOXINS.

THE HUMAN BODY IS MADE UP OF TRILLIONS OF CELLS. THESE CELLS ARE SURROUNDED BY TISSUE FLUID, OR **INTERSTITIAL FLUID**, FROM WHICH THEY CONSTANTLY EXTRACT THE OXYGEN, NUTRIENTS, AND OTHER SUBSTANCES THEY NEED IN ORDER TO STAY ALIVE, AND INTO WHICH THEY DEPOSIT WASTE MATERIAL PRODUCED BY THE CHEMICAL REACTIONS OF METABOLISM. FOR CELLS TO STAY ALIVE, TISSUE FLUID STOCKS OF NUTRIENTS AND OXYGEN MUST BE CONSTANTLY REPLENISHED, AND WASTE MUST BE REMOVED BEFORE CELLS ARE POISONED BY THEIR OWN POLLUTION. THESE DELIVERY AND REMOVAL FUNCTIONS ARE PERFORMED BY THE CARDIOVASCULAR, OR CIRCULATORY, SYSTEM. IT HAS THREE MAIN ELEMENTS: BLOOD, BLOOD VESSELS, AND THE HEART.

THE CARDIOVASCULAR SYSTEM

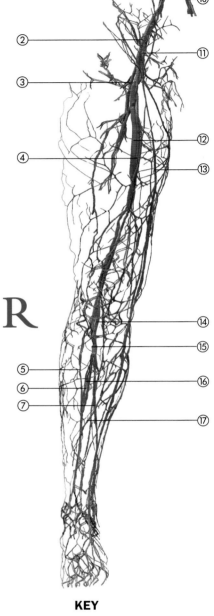

Blood is the liquid transport medium that carries oxygen, nutrients, waste matter, and many other substances. It also contains cells, called white blood cells, which are involved in tracking down and destroying microorganisms, such as bacteria and viruses, before they can infect the body and cause disease.

Blood vessels are living, flexible tubes that form a network that channels blood to and from every part of the body apart from the hair, nails, the outer layer of skin, the corneas of the eyes, and tooth enamel.

There are three main types of blood vessels: **arteries** carry blood away from the heart; **veins** carry blood to the heart; **capillaries** link arteries and veins, and carry blood through the tissues where nutrients and oxygen pass into cells via tissue fluid, and wastes pass in the opposite direction into the blood.

At the core of the system is the heart. This muscular pump has two sides—left and right—that simultaneously pump blood in a figure-of-eight path

Anterior view of the lower pelvis and right leg showing the main arteries and veins. These blood vessels serve the muscles, bones, and skin of the thigh, leg and foot.

through two circuits of blood vessels. In the **pulmonary** circuit, the right side of the heart pumps oxygen-poor blood to the lungs along the pulmonary artery, and oxygen-rich blood returns to the left side of the heart along the pulmonary vein. In the systemic circuit, the left side of the heart pumps oxygen-rich blood along the aorta, which divides into smaller arteries that supply the body's organs where oxygen is consumed. Veins from these organs merge to form the superior vena cava and inferior vena cava, which empty oxygen-poor blood into the right side of the heart, thereby completing the circuit.

KEY

① Inferior vena cava
② External iliac artery
③ Deep femoral artery
④ Femoral artery
⑤ Anterior tibial artery
⑥ Peroneal vein
⑦ Posterior tibial artery
⑧ Descending aorta
⑨ Common iliac artery
⑩ Common iliac vein
⑪ External iliac vein
⑫ Femoral artery
⑬ Great saphenous vein
⑭ Popliteal vein
⑮ Popliteal artery
⑯ Peroneal artery
⑰ Anterior tibial vein

KEY

1. Common carotid artery
2. Internal jugular vein
3. Right subclavian artery
4. Right subclavian vein
5. Brachiocephalic vein
6. Superior vena cava
7. Brachial artery
8. Cephalic vein
9. External carotid artery
10. Left subclavian artery
11. Brachiocephalic artery
12. Aortic arch
13. Pulmonary arteries
14. Heart
15. Abdominal aorta
16. Inferior vena cava
17. Celiac trunk
18. Renal artery
19. Renal veins
20. Common iliac vein
21. Common iliac artery

Anterior view of the heart and the main arteries and veins of the head, right upper limb, and the trunk.

ARTERIES, VEINS, AND CAPILLARIES FORM A TUBULAR DISTRIBUTION SYSTEM THAT TOTALS SOME 150,000 KM (93,000 MILES) IN LENGTH. SHARING THE SAME BASIC STRUCURE, ARTERIES AND VEINS DIFFER IN THE RELATIVE THICKNESS OF THEIR WALLS. THE WALLS OF ARTERIES AND VEINS HAVE THREE LAYERS OR COATS THAT ENCLOSE THE **LUMEN**, THE INNER CHANNEL THAT CARRIES BLOOD. THE INNERMOST LAYER, THE **TUNICA INTIMA,** CONSISTS OF A LINING OF **ENDOTHELIUM**—A SINGLE LAYER OF SMOOTH, FLATTENED CELLS IN CONTACT WITH BLOOD—UNDERPINNED BY SUPPORTING TISSUE. THE **TUNICA MEDIA** CONSISTS OF SMOOTH MUSCLE AND ELASTIC FIBERS. THE OUTERMOST **TUNICA ADVENTITIA** CONTAINS TOUGH COLLAGEN FIBERS AND PROTECTS THE BLOOD VESSEL.

THE ARTERIAL SYSTEM

A network of arteries distributes nutrients and oxygenated blood throughout the body. An additional, shorter pathway, the pulmonary circuit, delivers oxygen-depleted blood to the lungs. Typically, they have thick walls (especially the tunica media) enabling them to withstand the high pressure created when the heart pumps blood along them. As blood is forced into an artery, it expands and then recoils in order to push blood onward.

This means that blood flows in a continuous stream even when the heart relaxes between contractions. This expansion and recoil can be felt as a pulse where arteries pass near the surface of the skin, such as in the wrist. The smaller artery branches that supply organs and tissues divide to form thin-walled arterioles, that are less than 0.3 mm in diameter, which divide to form capillaries.

The main arteries leaving the heart branch into smaller arteries, and into still smaller arteries and then—within an organ or other tissue—into thin-walled arterioles, with diameters of about 0.3 mm (1/100 in). Arterioles further divide into a meshwork of smaller channels called capillaries,

Capillaries, the smallest blood vessels, form extensive networks, called capillary beds, in tissues and organs. Each capillary is about 0.008 mm in diameter, just wide enough for red blood cells to squeeze through. The wall consists of a layer of endothelium one cell thick. Nutrients and oxygen pass across the capillary wall into tissue fluid and, in return, waste is carried in the reverse direction. Where tissues are infected or inflamed, white blood cells squeeze between endothelial cells and pass into the infected tissues in order to destroy pathogens.

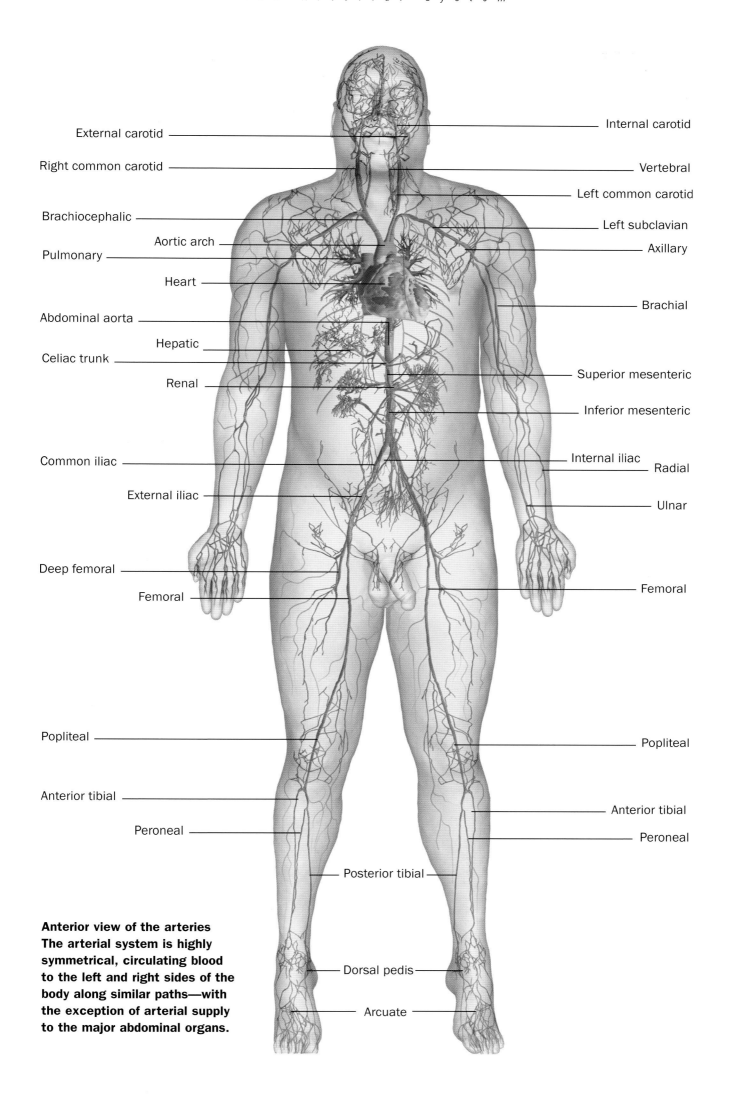

External carotid

Right common carotid

Brachiocephalic

Aortic arch

Pulmonary

Heart

Abdominal aorta

Hepatic

Celiac trunk

Renal

Common iliac

External iliac

Deep femoral

Femoral

Popliteal

Anterior tibial

Peroneal

Internal carotid

Vertebral

Left common carotid

Left subclavian

Axillary

Brachial

Superior mesenteric

Inferior mesenteric

Internal iliac

Radial

Ulnar

Femoral

Popliteal

Anterior tibial

Peroneal

Posterior tibial

Dorsal pedis

Arcuate

**Anterior view of the arteries
The arterial system is highly
symmetrical, circulating blood
to the left and right sides of the
body along similar paths—with
the exception of arterial supply
to the major abdominal organs.**

THE BODY'S INTERSTITIAL FLUID CARRIES CONSTANTLY RENEWED SUPPLIES OF OXYGEN AND NUTRIENTS; IT ALSO ACCUMULATES CELLULAR WASTE, INCLUDING CARBON DIOXIDE. IN THE CAPILLARY BEDS, THESE METABOLIC PRODUCTS PASS INTO THE BLOOD, AND FROM THERE INTO VENULES, THEN ON TOWARDS THE HEART IN LARGER RETURNING STREAMS, THE VEINS. BLOOD IN THE VENOUS SYSTEM IS IN A SENSE "SPENT." IT HAS LOST A GOOD DEAL OF ITS PROPELLING PRESSURE, NEEDS RECHARGING WITH OXYGEN, AND MAY CARRY A BURDEN OF RAW NUTRIENTS AS WELL AS THE ORDINARY BYPRODUCTS OF CELLULAR ACTIVITY.

THE VENOUS SYSTEM

Although the veins have thinner walls than arteries, they are usually somewhat larger in channel diameter, or **lumen**. Because veins conduct fluid at a lower pressure than arteries, vein walls need not be as strong. To lessen the effort needed to return blood to the chest, many veins have several one-way valves along their lengths (very small and very large veins, such as the brachiocephalic and pulmonary veins do not). These valves are flexible, pouchy structures that purse tightly by any backward flow, closing the vein to any surge in that direction.

The major veins occur more or less as matching return loops with the major arteries and usually bear matching names: a femoral vein, and its tributary venules, drains the capillary beds and the arteriole network supplied by the femoral artery, and so forth. Exceptions, however, are not uncommon: blood from the head is returned by the jugular veins (not by carotid veins). Also, more major veins than major arteries appear to run through the limbs. In the limbs, generally, blood is supplied deep to the tissues and works through capillary beds towards the surface, where it must be collected over a wider area, from many superficial veins. So, for example, in the leg, the great saphenous vein (the longest vein in the body) and small saphenous vein have no exact arterial counterparts.

The veins eventually converge at the right atrium of the heart in two main trunks: the superior and inferior vena cava. Blood is pushed onward by the right ventricle, through the pulmonary arteries and lungs, and directly then to the left side of the heart through the pulmonary veins. The distinction between vein and artery is always in relation to the direction of blood flow: oxygenated blood flows in the pulmonary veins, towards heart (its left side) and oxygen-poor blood flows in the pulmonary arteries, away from the heart (its right side).

Portal circulation

When blood is collected and carried by vessels from one capillary bed to another before being returned to the heart, the intervening circulation is called portal. Most commonly this refers to circulation between the gastrointestinal tract (and spleen) and liver—through the portal vein. Blood that has recently absorbed a heavy load of nutrients, and perhaps some toxins, from digestive processes cannot circulate without first being processed in the liver, through its dense meshwork of venules and capillaries. Leaving the liver, blood flows via the hepatic veins directly into the inferior vena cava.

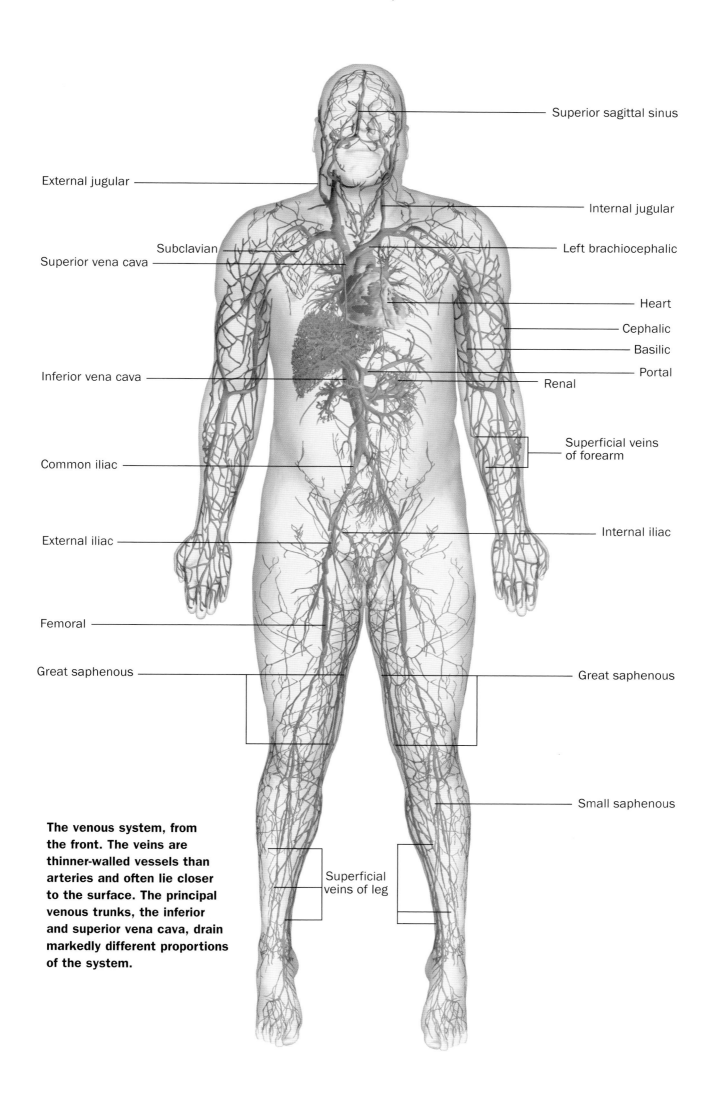

Superior sagittal sinus

External jugular

Internal jugular

Subclavian

Superior vena cava

Left brachiocephalic

Heart

Cephalic

Basilic

Portal

Inferior vena cava

Renal

Superficial veins
of forearm

Common iliac

External iliac

Internal iliac

Femoral

Great saphenous

Great saphenous

Small saphenous

Superficial
veins of leg

**The venous system, from
the front. The veins are
thinner-walled vessels than
arteries and often lie closer
to the surface. The principal
venous trunks, the inferior
and superior vena cava, drain
markedly different proportions
of the system.**

THE FIST-SIZED, CONE-SHAPED HEART IS A POWERFUL MUSCULAR PUMP THAT CONTRACTS TO MOVE BLOOD AROUND THE BODY. TIPPED SLIGHTLY TO THE LEFT, THE HEART LIES ANTERIOR TO THE BACKBONE AND POSTERIOR TO THE STERNUM, AND IS LATERALLY SURROUNDED, AND PARTIALLY OVERLAPPED BY, THE TWO LUNGS. THE HEART IS MADE PRIMARILY FROM CARDIAC MUSCLE, A TISSUE UNIQUE TO THE HEART THAT CAN CONTRACT CEASELESSLY WITHOUT TIRING. DAILY, THE HEART BEATS SOME 100,000 TIMES. IN A LIFETIME OF 70 YEARS, IT WILL BEAT 2.5 BILLION TIMES WITHOUT STOPPING.

THE HEART

Externally, the heart is surrounded and protected by a tough double membrane, the pericardium. Internally, the heart is divided into left and right sides by a muscular septum. Each half has a smaller chamber called an atrium that receives blood and pumps it to the larger, thicker-walled ventricle below. The right atrium receives oxygen-poor blood from the body through the inferior and superior venae cavae; the left atrium receives oxygen-rich blood from the lungs through the pulmonary veins. The ventricles contract to push blood out of the heart. The right ventricle pumps oxygen-poor blood through the pulmonary trunk and arteries to the lungs; the left ventricle pumps oxygen-rich blood to the body through the aorta.

Heart valves

Heart valves play a vital role in ensuring that blood flows in the right direction when the heart contracts and relaxes. **Atrioventricular valves** between each atrium and ventricle—the **mitral valve** on the left, and the **tricuspid** on the right—open to permit blood to flow from atria to ventricles, but close when the ventricles contract to stop blood flowing backward into the atria. The **semilunar valves** are located where the pulmonary trunk and the aorta, respectively, exit the heart. These valves permit blood to leave the heart when the ventricles contract, but close to prevent backflow when the ventricles relax.

KEY

1. Aortic arch
2. Superior vena cava
3. Right atrium
4. Right ventricle
5. Inferior vena cava
6. Pulmonary trunk
7. Fatty tissue
8. Left ventricle

Anterior view of the heart showing the main blood vessels through which blood enters and leaves the heart. Fatty tissue, which underlies the pericardium, covers the coronary blood vessels.

Superior view of the heart with fatty tissue removed reveals the coronary blood vessels that supply the cardiac muscle in the heart wall with fuel and oxygen.

KEY

1. Left common carotid artery
2. Brachiocephalic artery
3. Superior vena cava
4. Aortic arch
5. Right atrium
6. Right coronary artery
7. Right ventricle
8. Left subclavian artery
9. Pulmonary trunk
10. Left atrium
11. Left coronary artery
12. Left ventricle
13. Apex

WHILE A HEARTBEAT MAY FEEL LIKE A SINGLE CONTRACTION, IT IS ACTUALLY MADE UP OF THREE PHASES THAT OCCUR IN A PRECISELY TIMED SEQUENCE CALLED THE CARDIAC CYCLE. EACH CYCLE TAKES ABOUT 0.8 SECONDS WHEN A PERSON IS AT REST. THE THREE PHASES ARE **DIASTOLE**, **ATRIAL SYSTOLE**, AND **VENTRICULAR SYSTOLE**.

THE HEART

Lateral view of the heart from the left side shows the coronary blood vessels that cover the heart like a crown and provide its muscles with the fuel and oxygen they need to keep contracting.

KEY

1. Brachiocephalic trunk
2. Common carotid artery
3. Aortic arch
4. Pulmonary trunk
5. Left atrium
6. Left coronary artery
7. Right ventricle
8. Subclavian artery
9. Left pulmonary artery
10. Descending aorta
11. Circumflex artery (branch of left coronary artery)
12. Pulmonary veins
13. Left ventricle
14. Inferior vena cava

• Diastole—the atria and ventricles relax, blood enters the atria, and some flows into the ventricles. The semilunar valves close, and the atrioventricular valves are open.

• Atrial systole—the two atria contract and squeeze blood into the ventricles.

• Ventricular systole—the two ventricles contract and pump blood out of the heart. The atrioventricular valves slam shut, and the semilunar valves open.

When the valves close they produce the characteristic heart sounds used by doctors to diagnose possible heart problems. The closing of the atrioventricular valves produces a longer, louder "lub" sounds while the closing of the semilunar valves produces a shorter, sharper, "dup" sound.

Controlling heart rate

The timing and sequence of the cardiac cycle is controlled from within the heart. The **sinoatrial (SA) node** located in the wall of the right atrium produces regular bursts of electrical impulses and acts as a natural pacemaker. These impulses spread through the atria causing them to contract (atrial systole). They then reach the atrioventricular (AV) node, just above the tricuspid valve, which delays the signal for about 0.1 seconds to give time for the atria to contract. The electrical signals are then carried into the ventricle walls by specialized conduction tissue and the ventricles contract (ventricular systole).

Following diastole, another electrical signal is sent out by the SA node.

While the generation of the heartbeat is internal, heart rate itself is controlled by the autonomic nervous system (ANS) and adjusted according to the body's demands. Two centers in the medulla oblongata in the brain stem monitor changes in blood composition and pressure, and send out signals to alter heart rate accordingly. The **cardioaccelaratory center** sends impulses along sympathetic fibers to speed up heart rate—during exercise or stress, for example, when extra oxygen is needed by muscles—while the **cardioinhibitory center** sends impulses along parasympathetic fibers to slow the heart when the body is at rest. These two branches of the ANS exert their effects by altering the rate of "firing" of the SA node.

Posterior view of the heart with the superior and inferior venae cavae removed. The right and left pulmonary veins, which empty oxygen-rich blood into the left atrium, can be seen clearly. The coronary sinus (part of the cardiac circulation) collects oxygen-poor blood from heart muscle and empties it into the right atrium.

KEY

1. Descending aorta
2. Aortic arch
3. Left pulmonary artery
4. Left pulmonary veins
5. Circumflex artery
6. Coronary sinus
7. Left atrium
8. Left common carotid artery
9. Brachiocephalic artery
10. Superior vena cava
11. Right pulmonary artery
12. Inferior vena cava
13. Right atrium
14. Right ventricle

HEART FUNCTION

The heart is divided into two sides and four chambers. The top two chambers, the atria, are collection chambers for blood. The bottom two chambers, the ventricles, receive blood from the atria and pump it to the lungs and the body. The chambers are separated by valves which control the direction of blood flow. There are four valves: tricuspid, pulmonic, mitral and aortic. The series of images below shows the blood flow and valve function of a beating heart.

A heartbeat is made up of three phases that occur in a precisely timed sequence called the cardiac cycle. Each cycle takes about 0.8 seconds at rest. The three phases are diastole, atrial systole, and ventricular systole.

(A) Diastole—the atria and ventricles relax, blood enters the atria, and some flows into the ventricles. The semilunar valves close, and the atrioventricular valves are open.

(B) Atrial systole—the two atria contract and squeeze blood into the ventricles.

(C) Ventricular systole—the two ventricles contract and pump blood out of the heart. The atrio-ventricular valves shut, and the semilunar valves open.

An electric system transmits signals throughout the heart to control its pumping. The electrical signal begins in the sinoatrial or SA node, in the top of the right upper chamber or atrium.

The electrical signal passes down towards the ventricles, the lower chambers of the heart, via the atrioventricular or AV node. This controls the signals so the atria contract before the ventricles.

When the signals reach the ventricles they contract, which then pumps blood out to the lungs and the rest of the body.

Heart attacks occur when blood flow to the heart muscle is blocked. The most common cause is plaque; fatty deposits in the coronary arteries. As we age, protein, cholesterol, white blood cells and calcium are also deposited, increasing the buildup. If the plaque buildup breaks open, the body tries to repair it by forming a clot, which can stop the blood flow to the point where the heart muscle dies.

A minimally invasive procedure called angioplasty can clear blocked arteries using a balloon catheter. A thin flexible tube is inserted into the artery and a balloon at the end of the tube inflates dilating the vessel's lumen. If that does not provide sufficient passage, a mesh stent is placed around the catheter. The balloon is deflated and the catheter removed, leaving the mesh stent in place.

REPAIRING THE HEART

While new and minimally invasive techniques for heart repair are always being introduced, there are still many procedures that can successfully repair heart problems that involve traditional surgery where the chest is opened.

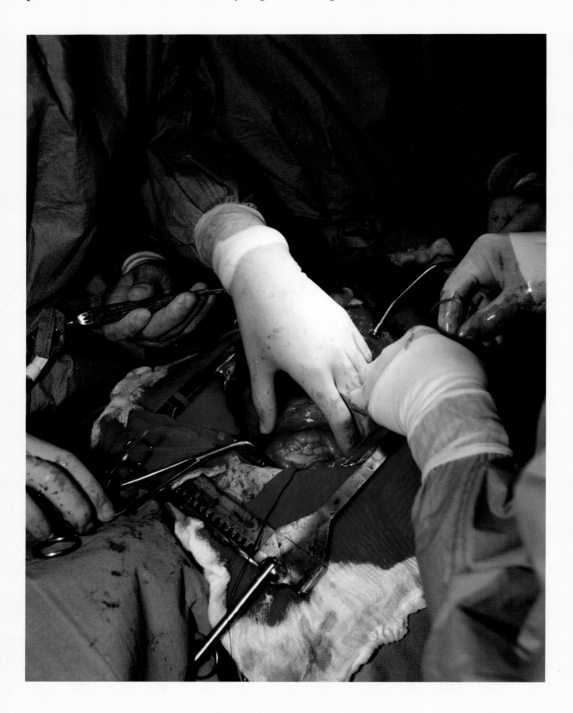

OPEN CHEST PROCEDURES INCLUDE:

• **repair or replacement of valves**

• **bypassing or widening blocked or narrowed arteries**

• **repairing aneurysms (bulges) in the aorta**

• **implanting devices to regulate the heart's rhythm**

• **neutralizing tissue that disturbs the electrical flow through the heart**

• **replacing a damaged or diseased heart with one from a donor.**

Here a damaged mitral valve is exposed. If the valve is too damaged to repair, it must be replaced.

The new valve can be made of animal tissue or it can be a prosthetic valve, as shown above.

Often, the heart must be stopped for the surgery to be performed. The heart is usually stopped with chemicals, and the patient is connected to a heart-lung machine which takes over the functions of the heart, keeping oxygenated blood supplied to the body while the heart is "off line."

While the heart-lung machine is supplying blood to the body, care must be taken with the heart tissue itself. A bath of cold water, and sometimes ice is used to lower the heart's temperature, and so its metabolic rate.

The heart-lung machine removes the blood from the body, adds oxygen, and returns it via the aorta.

In cases where the heart's arteries are too clogged to be cleared by a stent, a bypass can be performed where an artery or vein from another part of the body can be used to build a detour for blood flow.

BLOOD, THE LIFEGIVING LIQUID THAT CIRCULATES THROUGHOUT THE BODY, IS A LIVING TISSUE— ITS COMPLEX CELLULAR CONSTITUENTS JUST HAPPEN TO BE MOBILE INSTEAD OF FIXED WITHIN A FIBROUS OR BONY FRAMEWORK. AS WELL AS OXYGEN, THE BLOOD ABSORBS OR DISTRIBUTES A LARGE NUMBER OF SUBSTANCES THAT REQUIRE TRANSPORT AROUND THE BODY: NUTRIENTS, PROTEINS, METABOLIC BYPRODUCTS, HORMONES, AND, UNFORTUNATELY, PATHOGENS. BLOOD ALSO HAS AN IMPORTANT ROLE TO PLAY IN TEMPERATURE REGULATION, TAKING HEAT UP AND CONDUCTING IT WITHIN AND AROUND THE BODY, OR CLOSER TO THE SURFACE FOR COOLING.

OUR LIFE'S BLOOD

Blood makeup

The volume of blood in an average adult lies in the range of 8–10 pints (4–5 liters) for a female, and 10–12 pints (5–6 liters) for a male. About 55 percent of it is plasma, a clear and slightly yellowish fluid, which is mostly water in which are dissolved over 100 substances including nutrients, hormones, antibodies, and waste substances.

The composition of blood constantly changes as substances enter or leave the bloodstream. Various **homeostatic** mechanisms—mostly parts of the endocrine system— monitor and control certain basic blood properties, maintaining proper volume, density, pH, and chemical reactivity. Any serious disturbance, for example, of blood's osmotic potential, might cause **interstitial fluid** to be pulled into the circulation with consequent injury to cells. A continual balance among ions—principally of sodium, but also potassium, calcium, and phosphate—is achieved through several fine-control mechanisms.

Blood cells

The remaining 45 percent of blood consists of two distinct cell types—red and white—plus platelets. Of the three, only the white cells (leucocytes) possess nuclei within their cellular envelopes. The red blood cells (erythrocytes) carry oxygen; trillions of red cells circulate at any one time and they make up 99 percent of the blood cell population. Within the red cells are large proteins, **hemoglobin**, that attach oxygen where concentration is high and release it where oxygen presence is low.

White blood cells identify and attack invading pathogens (but may also be stirred by false alarms, causing hypersensitivity reactions). There are three kinds of white blood cells, and several subtypes of each:

- **Granulocytes**: These cells are active against pathogens, both detecting and destroying cells that are sensed to be alien or defective in some way.
- **Monocytes**: They are the largest of the white cells and the least numerous, making up 3–6 percent of all leucocytes. They are voracious; after engulfing a suspect intruder, they can also trigger a lymphocyte response.

Monocytes circulate in the blood and lymph, but the **macrophage** (so-called "big eater") variety migrates into tissues.

- **Lymphocytes**: These are of two major types, T-cells and B-cells, present both in blood and lymph. A third type, NK ("natural killer"), is also often distinguished, as its origin and action differ from T cell types. B cells produce large protein molecules called **antibodies**, which are patterned to disable specific pathogens—hence B cells are the key element in what is termed "specific immunity." (A group of about 20 circulating proteins, collectively called complement, assist in destruction after an antibody has attached itself to its target.) T cells destroy pathogens, but also modulate the immune system's response, activating or deactivating B cells and other T cells. NK cells identify possible targets differently, which makes them more successful than other types against threats such as viruses or tumor cells—where the cause of concern may lie inside a cell that is outwardly normal enough to pass lymphocyte scrutiny.

Blood clotting

Platelets, or thrombocytes, operate in blood clotting: They stick together immediately at the site of a wound but also stage the clotting process with the aid of plasma components such as calcium, and several proteins and enzymes that are together known as clotting factors. In clotting, a plasma protein, **fibrinogen**, is altered (to **fibrin**) and formed into a barricade net across the site of injury. Platelets are shed in great numbers from large parent cells in the marrow; about a billion are circulating at any time.

Normal clotting occurs where there is an injury to the blood vessel.

Sometimes clotting can grow too large. When a piece of the clot breaks off and eventually enters a smaller vessel, blocking its blood supply, it is called an embolus.

When a clot grows large enough to partially or completely block a vessel, it is called a thrombus.

Blood types

While blood is made of the same basic elements, not all blood is alike. There are eight different common blood types, which are determined by the absence or presence of certain antigens – substances that trigger an immune response to foreign bodies. Some antigens can trigger a patient's immune system to attack transfused blood, which is why safe blood transfusion depends on careful blood typing and cross-matching.

There are four major blood groups determined by the presence or absence of two antigens – A and B – on the surface of red blood cells:

Group A – has only the A antigen on red cells (and B antibody in the plasma)
Group B – has only the B antigen on red cells (and A antibody in the plasma)
Group AB – has both A and B antigens on red cells (but neither A nor B antibody in the plasma)
Group O – has neither A nor B antigens on red cells (but both A and B antibody are in the plasma)

There is a further antigen called Rh factor which can either be present (+) or absent (-).

A white blood cell

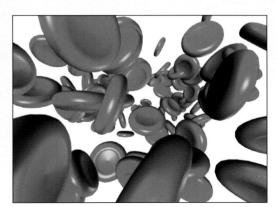

On average, red blood cells survive for about 120 days, so their replacement is a continuing activity of the bone marrow.

THE LYMPHATIC SYSTEM

L IKE THE CARDIOVASCULAR SYSTEM, THE LYMPHATIC SYSTEM CONSISTS OF A NETWORK OF TUBES, OR VESSELS, THAT REACH ALL PARTS OF THE BODY. UNLIKE BLOOD VESSELS, THESE LYMPHATIC VESSELS ARE BLIND-ENDING, AND THERE IS NO HEART TO PUMP FLUID THROUGH THEM. THE LYMPHATIC SYSTEM ALSO INCLUDES ASSOCIATED LYMPHATIC ORGANS, SUCH AS LYMPH NODES AND THE SPLEEN. THE LYMPHATIC SYSTEM HAS TWO DISTINCT YET OVERLAPPING ROLES: TO DRAIN FLUID THAT HAS ACCUMULATED IN THE TISSUES AND RETURN IT TO THE BLOODSTREAM SO THAT ITS VOLUME AND CONCENTRATION REMAIN CONSTANT; AND TO DEFEND THE BODY BY DESTROYING PATHOGENS (DISEASE-CAUSING MICRO-ORGANISMS).

Consider the drainage function first. As blood flows along blood capillaries, fluid oozes out through the capillary walls to bathe the cells of the surrounding tissue. This fluid delivers essentials such as nutrients and oxygen to cells, and removes waste before returning to the bloodstream. However, about one-sixth of the fluid does not return through the capillary wall, remaining instead in the tissues as tissue fluid. Permeating the tissues are tiny, blind-ending lymph capillaries. Excess tissue fluid—now called lymph—passes through tiny valves in these capillaries, which then remove it. Lymph capillaries merge to form larger and larger lymph vessels which eventually form lymphatic trunks that empty via two lymphatic ducts into the left and right subclavian veins. Lymph is pushed along by the contraction of skeletal muscles that surround lymph vessels; as with veins, valves help prevent backflow.

Lymph is a clear fluid that also contains debris and pathogens, such as bacteria and viruses. Lying along the lymphatic vessels are swellings called lymph nodes. As lymph passes through them, large numbers of lymphocytes and macrophages detect and destroy pathogens, kill cancer cells, and remove debris, and by doing so filter the lymph before it returns to the bloodstream. The defensive white blood cells—lymphocytes, which release killer chemicals called antibodies and macrophages that engulf and destroy pathogens—found in the circulatory and lymphatic systems together comprise the immune system. Other lymphatic organs such as the spleen and tonsils also play a part in the body's immune response.

The spleen

The spleen is one of the major "housekeeping" organs and the largest lymphatic organ. It is draped by the diaphragm, nestling to the rear against the lower ribs on the left side. The spleen has significant immune system functions and removes worn-out red blood cells from the circulation, recycling some components and disposing of other cellular debris. A fibrous capsule encloses the spleen and sends strands into the interior to support its tissues. A **hilum** (a hollow) on the spleen's underside receives its blood vessels, the splenic artery and splenic vein. Splenic tissues are of two main types: patchy nodes of white pulp, surrounded by red pulp.

Lymph is a clear fluid that also contains debris and pathogens, such as bacteria and viruses. Lying along the lymphatic vessels are swellings called lymph nodes. As lymph passes through them, large numbers of lymphocytes—which release killer chemicals called antibodies and macrophages that engulf and destroy pathogens—detect and destroy pathogens and cancer cells, and remove debris, and filter the lymph before it returns to the bloodstream. The defensive white blood cells—lymphocytes—found in the circulatory and lymphatic systems together comprise the immune system. Other lymphatic organs such as the spleen and tonsils also play a part in the body's immune response.

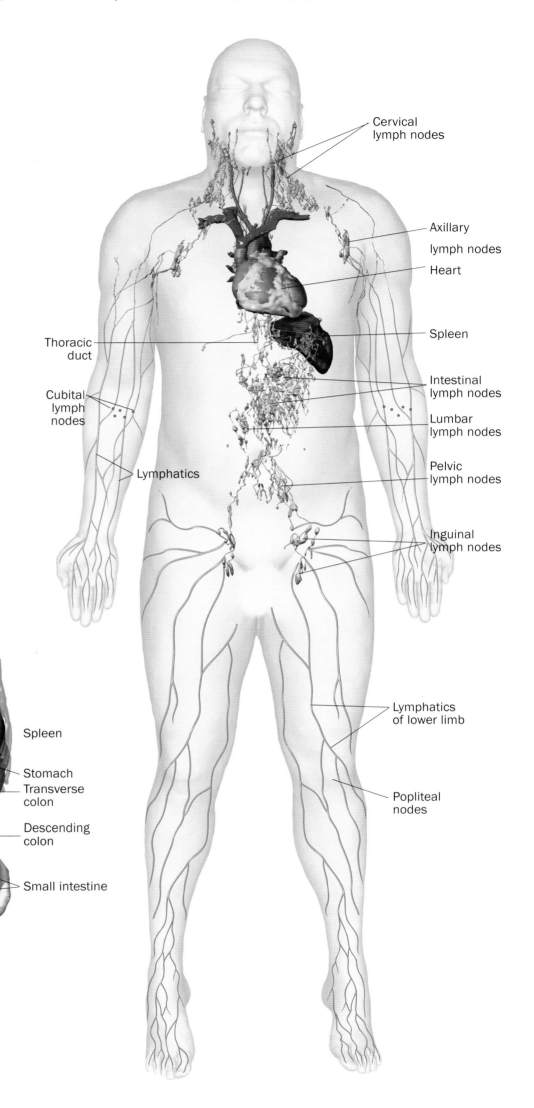

Cervical lymph nodes

Axillary lymph nodes

Heart

Spleen

Thoracic duct

Intestinal lymph nodes

Cubital lymph nodes

Lumbar lymph nodes

Lymphatics

Pelvic lymph nodes

Inguinal lymph nodes

Lymphatics of lower limb

Popliteal nodes

Liver

Spleen

Gallbladder

Stomach

Transverse colon

Intestinal lymph nodes

Descending colon

Ascending colon

Small intestine

THE FIST-SIZED SPLEEN LIES ON THE LEFT SIDE OF THE ABDOMINAL CAVITY JUST
BELOW THE DIAPHRAGM. AT 12 CM (5 IN) LONG, THE SPLEEN IS THE LARGEST
OF THE LYMPHATIC ORGANS AND HAS TWO MAJOR FUNCTIONS: AS PART OF
THE BODY'S IMMUNE SYSTEM; AND IN CLEANSING THE BLOOD. IN THE FETUS, THE SPLEEN
MANUFACTURES RED BLOOD CELLS, A FUNCTION THAT CEASES AFTER BIRTH. THE SPLEEN
IS SURROUNDED BY A PROTECTIVE, FIBROUS CAPSULE, AND HAS A **HILUS**, OR INDENTATION,
ON ONE SIDE THROUGH WHICH ITS BLOOD VESSELS ENTER. SERVING THE SPLEEN ARE THE
SPLENIC ARTERY, A BRANCH OF THE CELIAC TRUNK, ITSELF A BRANCH OF THE AORTA;
AND THE SPLENIC VEIN THAT EMPTIES INTO THE HEPATIC PORTAL VEIN . THERE IS NO
AFFERENT LYMPHATIC SUPPLY INTO THE SPLEEN SO
THAT, UNLIKE LYMPH NODES, THE SPLEEN DOES NOT
"FILTER" LYMPH.

KEY

1. Stomach
2. Spleen
3. Transverse colon
4. Kidney
5. Descending colon
6. Jejunum
7. Ileum
8. Sigmoid colon

THE SPLEEN

Lateral view of the abdomen showing the spleen and kidneys in position relative to the stomach and intestines.s

Inside the spleen there are two distinct tissue types. Around smaller branches of the splenic artery there are clusters of what is termed **white pulp**. This consists of lymphocytes suspended on fibers, and is the part of the spleen involved in the immune response. Here, **B-lymphocytes** proliferate and generate the antibody-producing plasma cells that target specific pathogens and mark them for destruction.

Forming a "sea" around the "islands" of white pulp is red pulp, a zone of connective tissue and blood spaces that is rich in **phagocytic** cells, called **macrophages**, and red blood cells. Macrophages remove blood-borne **pathogens**, such as **bacteria** and **viruses**, by engulfing and digesting them. They also play a vital role in maintaining the quality of circulating blood by removing worn-out red blood cells and **platelets** (the spleen also stores platelets), as well as cellular debris and toxins. The macrophages also store salvaged breakdown products from red blood cells, such as iron, in order that they can be used again by bone marrow for the purpose of making new blood cells.

Anterior view of the abdominal cavity. With the liver, stomach, and intestines removed the spleen and kidneys can easily be seen.

KEY

1. Abdominal aorta
2. Inferior vena cava
3. Right kidney
4. Ureter
5. Pelvis
6. Spleen
7. Renal artery
8. Renal vein
9. Left kidney
10. Vertebral column
11. Common iliac artery
12. Common iliac vein

161

THE
RESPIRATORY
SYSTEM

THE BODY'S MAIN METHOD OF CONVERTING ITS STORES OF FUEL TO ENERGY

IS AEROBIC METABOLISM—A PROCESS THAT USES OXYGEN AND PRODUCES

CARBON DIOXIDE AS WASTE.

THE RESPIRATORY SYSTEM FULFILLS AN ESSENTIAL SERVICE BY PROVIDING THE BODY WITH A CONSTANT SUPPLY OF OXYGEN FROM THE AIR. OXYGEN IS USED BY ALL BODY CELLS TO RELEASE ENERGY FROM FUELS, SUCH AS GLUCOSE, IN A PROCESS CALLED AEROBIC RESPIRATION. RESPIRATION ALSO RELEASES A WASTE PRODUCT, CARBON DIOXIDE, WHICH MUST BE REMOVED FROM THE BODY BY THE RESPIRATORY SYSTEM BEFORE IT CAUSES ANY HARMFUL EFFECTS.

THE RESPIRATORY SYSTEM

Energy released by respiration is used inside cells to power the many chemical reactions—known collectively as metabolism—that keep them functioning as living units. An absolute requirement for oxygen is something that humans share with most other living organisms. The smallest of these— flatworms, for example—take in oxygen directly across their body surface by **diffusion**, and lose carbon dioxide as it passes in the opposite direction. Larger animals, including humans, lack sufficient surface area to take in enough oxygen through their skin to supply the large internal volume made up of trillions of cells. Instead, humans have a respiratory system that consists of two parts: a respiratory tract, or airway, which carries air in and out of the body; and a pair of lungs in the thorax (chest), where oxygen diffuses into, and carbon dioxide diffuses out of, the bloodstream. The respiratory tract consists of the nose, mouth, throat, and trachea (windpipe). The trachea divides at its lower end to form two bronchi (sing. bronchus), one for each lung.

Development of the respiratory system

During normal fetal life, the lungs are filled with fluid and do not take part in gas exchange. That role is performed by the **placenta**, the organ attached to the wall of the **uterus** across which oxygen passes

from the maternal blood supply to the fetal blood supply. By the time the baby is ready to be born, the airways in the respiratory tract and lungs have been drained of fluid. At birth, as the oxygen supply from the placenta ceases, rising carbon dioxide levels in the baby's blood are detected by the part of the brain that controls breathing, and this stimulates the baby to take its first breath, so that gaseous exchange takes place in the lungs.

KEY

① Cartilage plates of external nose
② External nares (nostrils)
③ Mouth
④ Pharynx (throat)
⑤ Larynx (voicebox)
⑥ Trachea (windpipe)
⑦ Right lung
⑧ Fissure
⑨ Frontal sinus
⑩ Maxillary sinus
⑪ Cartilage ring of trachea
⑫ Left lung

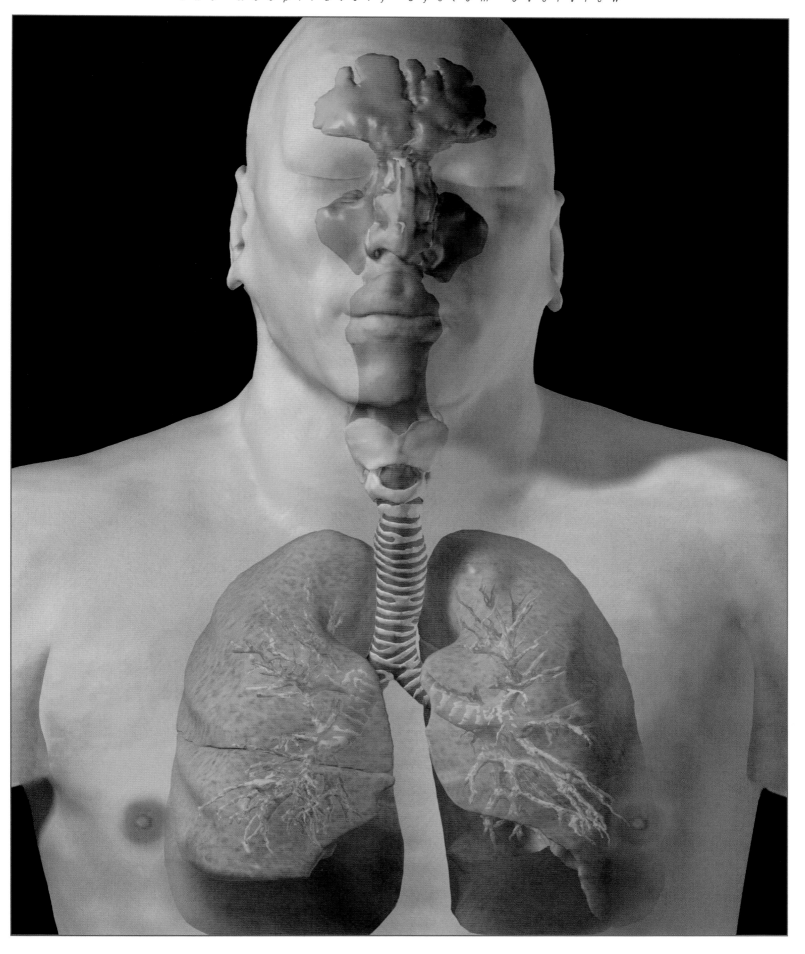

Anterior view of the head and thorax showing the respiratory system and the paranasal sinuses, hollows in skull bones that help to warm and moisten inhaled air.

THE RESPIRATORY TRACT—THE MOUTH, NOSE, PHARYNX (THROAT), LARYNX, AND TRACHEA—PROVIDES AN AIRWAY ALONG WHICH AIR IS CONDUCTED INTO AND OUT OF THE LUNGS. IT ALSO "PROCESSES" AIR AS IT IS BREATHED IN BY WARMING, MOISTENING, AND FILTERING IT: AIR THAT IS COLD, DRY, AND LADEN WITH DIRT AND GERMS DAMAGES DELICATE LUNG TISSUES.

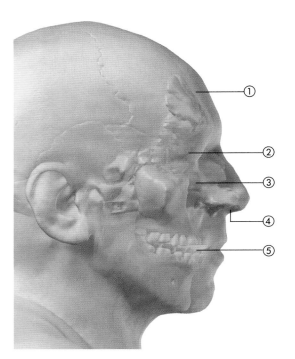

THE MOUTH, NOSE & THROAT

In the nose, hairs lining the nostrils trap larger particles in the air; the mucous membrane that lines the nasal cavity (and much of the respiratory system) moistens and warms the air; while sticky mucus traps dust, dirt, and bacteria. Tiny hair-like **cilia** covering the mucous membrane sway rhythmically, like a field of wheat, pushing dirt-laden mucus to the throat where it can be swallowed and digested by stomach acids. Paranasal sinuses—membrane-lined cavities in the bones surrounding the nasal passage—help Insulate sensitive structures like dental roots and eyes from rapid temperature fluctuations and produce high concentrations of nitrous oxide, which is toxic to bacteria, fungi, and viruses. They also produce mucus and help with warming and moistening the air. This continues in the pharynx and trachea which has cilia that pushes dirty mucus upward towards the throat where it can be swallowed.

Speech and the larynx

Speech plays a vital role in communication that is unique to humans. Sounds are produced by the larynx, or voice box, a funnel-shaped arrangement of cartilages that links the pharynx to the trachea.

Stretched across the larynx, from front to back, is a pair of membranes called vocal cords. During normal breathing the vocal cords are wide open so that air flow is not impeded. During speech, muscles in the larynx pull the vocal cords together—rather like pulling drapes across a window—making them more taut. When exhaled air passes in controlled bursts through the closed vocal cords they vibrate and produce sounds. These sounds are amplified by the throat, mouth, nasal cavity, and paranasal sinuses, and are turned into recognizable speech by the tongue and lips. The tighter the vocal cords are pulled, the higher the pitch of the sounds; the greater the force of the exhaled air, the louder the sound. Men have longer, thicker vocal cords that vibrate more slowly and produce lower pitched sounds.

Sinuses—cavities within the skull bones surrounding the nasal passage—perform valuable functions treating and conditioning the air we breathe.

KEY

① Frontal sinus
② Sphenoid sinus
③ Maxillary sinus
④ Nasal vestibule
⑤ Oral cavity

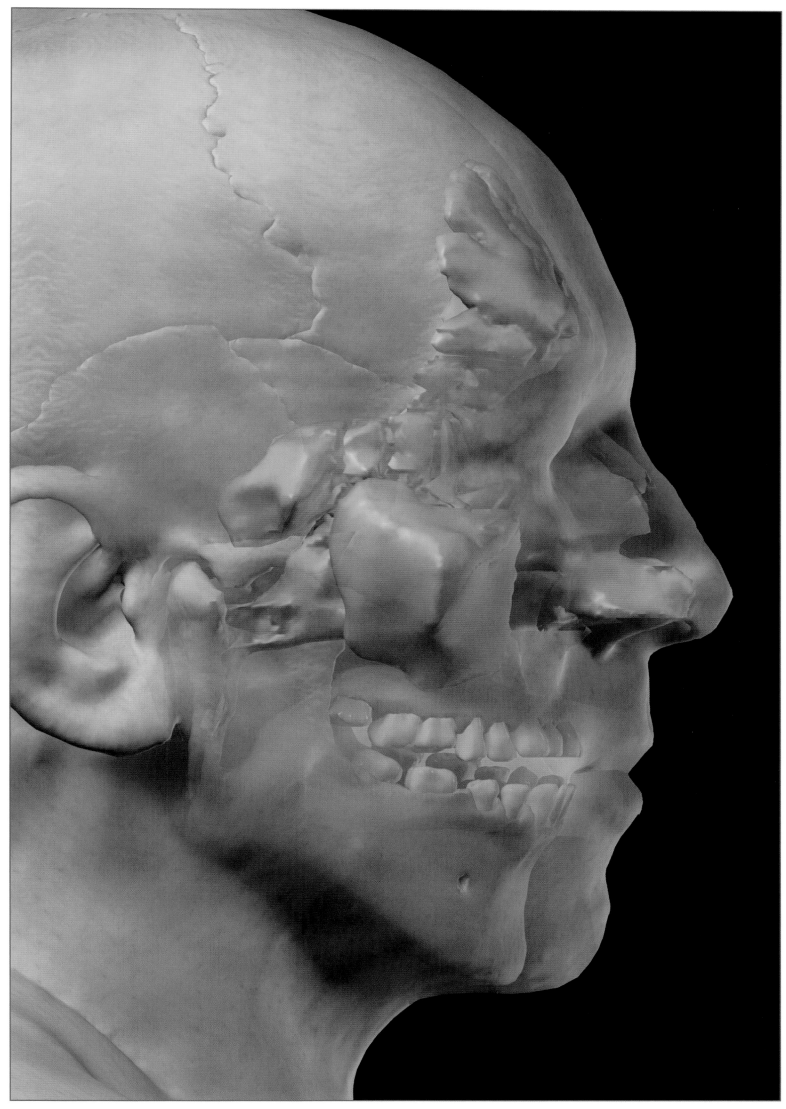

O CCUPYING MOST OF THE THORACIC CAVITY, THE TWO LUNGS ARE SOFT, SPONGY ORGANS THAT CONTAIN SOME 300 MILLION AIR SACS, CALLED ALVEOLI, IN WHICH GASEOUS EXCHANGE TAKES PLACE: OXYGEN PASSES INTO THE BLOODSTREAM AND WASTE CARBON DIOXIDE PASSES INTO THE AIR FOR ELIMINATION. THE REMAINING LUNG TISSUE CONSISTS MAINLY OF ELASTIC CONNECTIVE TISSUE THAT ENABLES THE LUNGS TO EXPAND AND RECOIL DURING BREATHING.

THE LUNGS

The trachea and its branches are referred to as the "bronchial tree" because they resemble an upside-down tree.

KEY

1. Thyroid cartilage
2. Cricoid cartilage
3. Trachea
4. Superior lobe of left lung
5. Left primary bronchus
6. Oblique fissure
7. Inferior lobe of left lung
8. Arytenoid cartilage
9. Superior lobe of right lung
10. Right primary bronchus
11. Inferior lobe of right lung

Internally, the lungs consist of a network of tubes and sacs, sometimes called the "bronchial tree" because of its resemblance to an upside down tree with the trachea as the trunk. Inside the lungs, the two bronchi arising from the trachea divide repeatedly to form smaller and smaller bronchi, which in turn divide to form terminal bronchioles that branch further to form microscopic respiratory bronchioles at the end of which are the alveoli, the site of gaseous exchange.

Gaseous exchange

The interchange of life-giving oxygen for waste carbon dioxide takes place through the alveoli. Air breathed into the lungs contains about 21 percent oxygen, while air breathed out contains about 16 percent; the remaining 5 percent passes through the alveoli into the bloodstream. Exhaled air contains over 100 times more waste carbon dioxide than inhaled air.

The lungs contain around 300 million microscopic alveoli, grouped in clusters like bunches of grapes. These alveoli have an internal surface area of about 70 square meters (750 square feet), equivalent to 35 times the surface area of skin covering the body squeezed into the thorax. This large surface area is essential to ensure that enough oxygen is taken in to the body in the fastest possible time to meet the body's demands.

Alveoli are surrounded by a network of blood capillaries that deliver oxygen-poor blood to the alveoli and remove blood enriched with oxygen. Together, alveolar and capillary walls form a thin respiratory membrane, the interface between air and blood—just 0.001 mm (0.00004 in) thick—across which gaseous exchange takes place. Oxygen diffuses across the respiratory membrane from the alveoli, where there is a high concentration of oxygen, to a low concentration in the bloodstream. Carbon dioxide diffuses in the opposite direction. The inner surface of the alveoli is covered by a fluid film in which oxygen dissolves before it diffuses across the respiratory membrane, thereby speeding up the process.

Highly branched airways inside the lungs terminate in microscopic sacs in which oxygen is exchanged for carbon dioxide.

KEY

① Larynx
② Trachea
③ Superior lobe of right lung
④ Right primary bronchus
⑤ Fissure
⑥ Middle lobe of right lung
⑦ Inferior lobe of right lung
⑧ Superior lobe of left lung
⑨ Left primary bronchus
⑩ Secondary (lobar) bronchus
⑪ Tertiary (segmental) bronchus
⑫ Inferior lobe of left lung

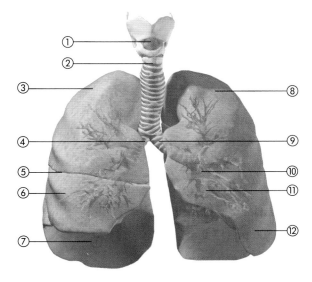

This anterior view of the lungs shows the right lung is divided into three lobes by two fissures, while the left lung has just two lobes.

169

THE LUNGS REST ON THE DIAPHRAGM, A DOME-SHAPED SHEET OF MUSCLE THAT SEPARATES THE THORAX FROM THE ABDOMEN, AND ARE SURROUNDED BY A "CAGE" FORMED BY THE RIBS, STERNUM, AND BACKBONE. MOVEMENT OF THE RIBS AND DIAPHRAGM—KNOWN AS BREATHING OR VENTILATION—FORCES AIR IN AND OUT OF THE LUNGS ABOUT 20,000 TIMES EACH DAY IN ORDER TO PROVIDE A CONTINUOUS SUPPLY OF FRESH AIR.

THE LUNGS

Ventilation

Ventilation, or breathing, moves air in and out of the lungs so that fresh supplies of oxygen can be brought in and waste carbon dioxide can be eliminated into the atmosphere. Air is taken in—inhaled—and pushed out—exhaled—by the lungs through the action of the diaphragm and the intercostal muscles. These muscles alter the volume of the thoracic cavity, changes that are followed passively by the lungs.

During inhalation, the diaphragm contracts and pushes the abdominal organs downward, while the external intercostal muscles contract to pull the ribs upward and outward. Together these actions increase the volume inside the thoracic cavity—and, therefore, inside the lungs. The pressure in the thorax and lungs decreases and air is sucked in from outside. During exhalation, the diaphragm relaxes and is pushed upward into a dome shape by the abdominal organs, and the ribcage moves downward and inward. This decreases the volume of the thoracic cavity and the lungs, and increases air pressure inside the lungs so that air is squeezed out. During forced breathing, the internal intercostal muscles contract to pull the ribcage downward. At rest, about 500 ml (17 fl oz) of air is taken in with each breath. The lungs never empty of air; inhaled air serves to refresh the air that is already there. During exercise, both the rate and depth of breathing increase.

Nervous control of breathing

Breathing rate and depth are controlled by the respiratory centers in the brain stem. The inspiratory center sends out regular "bursts" of nerve impulses along the phrenic and intercostal nerves that, respectively, cause the diaphragm and intercostal muscles to contract. When the thorax has expanded, the inspiratory center ceases activity, the muscles relax, and exhalation takes place. Regular emissions from the respiratory center produce a breathing rate between 12 and 18 breaths per minute. During exercise, increased carbon dioxide levels in the blood are detected by chemoreceptors, while increased muscle activity is detected by stretch receptors. These receptors send "messages" to the brain stem, which cause the inspiratory center to increase its activity so that breathing rate rises.

Posterior view of the lungs, trachea and heart reveals that the cartilage rings of the trachea do not extend to its posterior surface where it is attached to the esophagus.

KEY

① Left lung
② Trachea
③ Heart
④ Right lung

Anterior view of the lungs, trachea, and heart. The left lung has two lobes, while the right lung has three. The left lung is smaller than the right; a concavity in the left lung, the cardiac notch, accommodates the heart which is tilted to the left.

KEY

1. Trachea
2. Right lung
3. Aortic arch
4. Superior lobe
5. Horizontal fissure
6. Middle lobe
7. Oblique fissure
8. Inferior lobe
9. Cartilage ring
10. Left lung
11. Heart
12. Cardiac notch

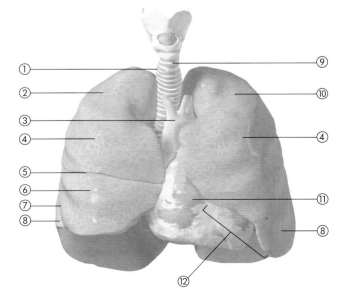

171

LUNG FUNCTION

The rhythmic filling and expulsion of air from the lungs – breathing – takes place about 12-16 times each minute, or an average of 20,000 times a day.

When relaxed, the diaphragm bulges upward, forming a dome over the abdominal organs beneath. As it contracts, it pushes the organs down, creating space in the thoracic cavity above.

At the same time, external intercostal muscles lift the ribs up and out. Atmospheric pressure expands the lungs to fill the enlarged volume. As the muscles relax, the chest and abdomen fall back into place, pushing air from the lungs.

Air travels through the primary bronchi which divide many times into smaller bronchi—and then into even narrower bronchioles.

The bronchioles end in tiny air exchange glob-ules called alveolar sacs, whose ultimate offshoots have diameters of about 5/100 in (1 mm) or less.

Inside the sacs are short ducts that lead to the bunched pouchings of alveoli. There are about 300 million alveoli in the lungs with a working surface of about 750 sq. ft. (70 sq m).

Capillary beds surround the alveoli, exposing oxygen-depleted blood to fresh air across a membrane wall that is only 40 millionths of an inch thick (0.001 mm). A fluid film coats the inner surfaces, aiding diffusion across the thin barrier between blood and the atmosphere.

LUNG DAMAGE

Bronchial walls are made of cartilage, with a good deal of elastic fiber, underlain by intersecting strands of muscle. On the interior is a constantly moist mucosal layer. In the bronchioles there is no cartilage and little muscle fiber; collagen with some elastic reinforcement comprises most of the wall. This delicate machine works in a highly efficient way, but its fragile structure is easily damaged by airborne pollutants like cigarette smoke. The sequence below shows this shows Chronic Obstructive Pulmonary Disease (COPD), most commonly caused by smoking.

Air, along with cigarette smoke, enters the airways.

Goblet cells, which are located in these larger airways, are enlarged and produce much more mucus.

The airway walls are damaged and thickened, narrowing the passage further.

The small airways respond to the noxious particles and gases. They swell and fill with macrophages, T-cells and neutrophils. These cells release further streams of inflammatory products into the walls of the small airways and into the air spaces.

We also see widespread alveolar wall destruction. Alveolar wall destruction leads to a reduction in lung elastic recoil. The remaining alveoli increase in size.

The devastating effect of reduced elastic recoil becomes more apparent as we look at a cross section of the small airways. Small airways normally lack cartilaginous support. When they are no longer held open by the elastic recoil of intact alveoli, the small airways collapse.

THE
DIGESTIVE
SYSTEM

WE NEED TO BE ABLE TO EFFICIENTLY ABSORB NUTRIENTS FROM A WIDE RANGE OF FOODS—OFTEN IN LESS THAN IDEAL QUANTITIES AND COMBINATIONS—AND DISPOSE OF THEIR RESIDUE, WHILE STILL MAINTAINING THE BODY'S STASIS.

FOOD IS ESSENTIAL FOR LIFE. THE NUTRIENTS CONTAINED IN FOOD KEEP THE BODY'S CELLS FUNCTIONING BY PROVIDING THEM WITH ENERGY AND THE RAW MATERIALS FOR GROWTH AND REPAIR. THE ONLY PROBLEM IS THAT MOST OF THESE ESSENTIAL NUTRIENTS ARE LOCKED INSIDE THE FOOD WE EAT. COMPLEX FOOD MOLECULES MUST BE BROKEN DOWN, OR DIGESTED, IN ORDER TO LIBERATE THE SIMPLE NUTRIENTS SUCH AS GLUCOSE AND AMINO ACIDS THAT CAN BE USED BY THE BODY. THIS PROCESS IS THE FUNCTION OF THE DIGESTIVE SYSTEM.

THE DIGESTIVE SYSTEM

Most foods, such as a slice of bread or a piece of chicken, consist of a mixture of different nutrients, particularly carbohydrates, proteins, fats, vitamins, minerals, and fiber. Carbohydrates include simple sugars, such as glucose, and complex carbohydrates, such as starch, which consist of chains of sugar molecules. During digestion, complex carbohydrates are broken down to release simple sugars that provide energy. Proteins are broken down into their constituent molecules, amino acids, which are used by cells to make new proteins. These are used for the growth and repair of cells, and to make **enzymes** *(see box on page 136)*. Fats are broken down during digestion into fatty acids and glycerol, which can be used as a fuel, or reassembled to form fats that are used to insulate the body. Vitamins, such as vitamin C, and minerals, such as calcium and iron, are essential for the normal functioning of the chemical reactions of metabolism. Finally, indigestible strands of vegetable tissue, called fiber, ensure that the intestines work efficiently.

The digestive process

Processing of food by the digestive system takes between 24 and 48 hours and consists of four basic stages.

- **Ingestion** is the taking in of food and drink through the mouth.
- **Digestion** is the breaking down of a wide range of foods into a few simple nutrient molecules. Digestion can be mechanical, such as the chewing action of teeth or the crushing action of the stomach walls; or chemical, by the action of enzymes.
- **Absorption** is the movement of simple nutrient molecules into the bloodstream, which carries them to where they are needed.
- **Egestion** is the elimination of undigested food in the form of **feces** through the anus.

KEY

① Liver
② Gallbladder
③ Large intestine
④ Pelvis
⑤ Esophagus
⑥ Spleen
⑦ Stomach
⑧ Pancreas
⑨ Small intestine
⑩ Rectum

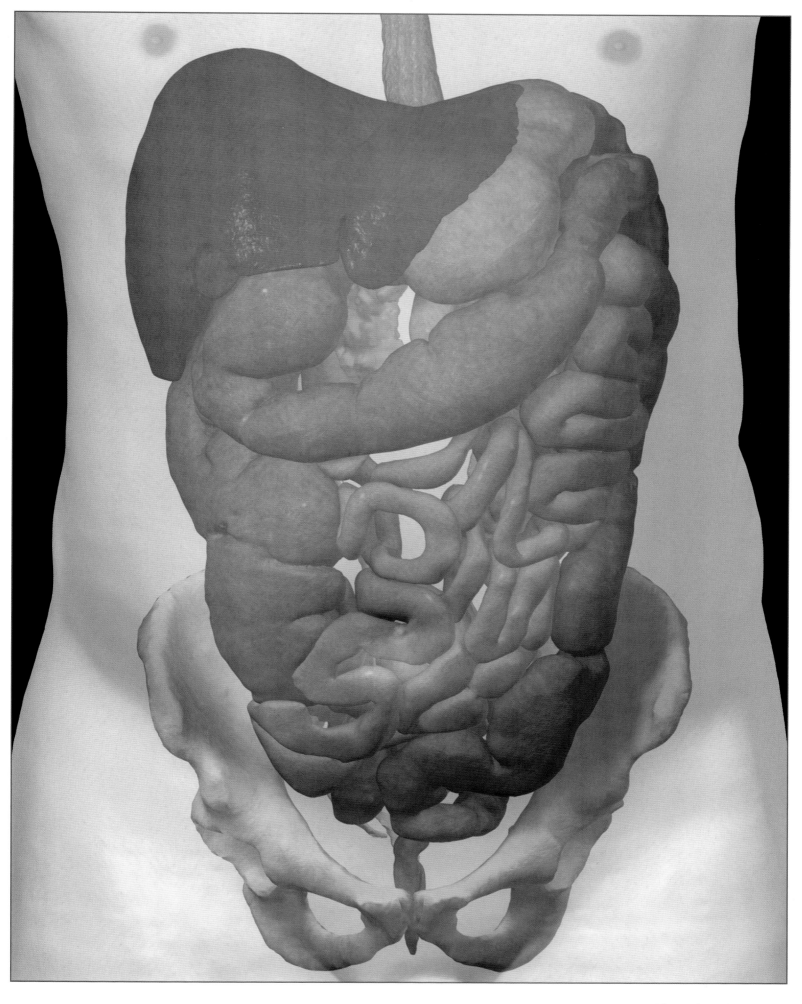

Most digestive organs are located in the abdomen, as revealed by this anterior abdominal view with the organs *in situ*.

DIGESTION

Digestion is the process of breaking food down so that nutrients can be absorbed by cells. The complex process selects and extracts what the body can use – either for energy or for creating new tissue – and processes what remains into solid and liquid waste.

The majority of the space in the abdominal cavity is taken up by organs of digestion.

In your stomach, food is churned and mixed with acid and enzymes to break it down.

The semi-liquid food, called chyme, is then pushed into the first part of the small intestine where most digestion and absorption takes place.

To aid its absorption, chyme is mixed with bile which is produced by the liver and stored in the gallbladder. Carried into the duodenum, the first part of the small intestine, via ducts bile reduces the high acidity of the stomach contents and helps to emulsify fats to aid in their digestion.

After leaving the small intestine, waste material moves upwards through the ascending colon and then across and downwards towards the rectum.

The interior of the intestine is lined with nodes called villi which increase the surface area of the interior by at least 50 times.

The finger-like villi help absorb nutrients, providing digested food molecules with the maximum surface area for transferring nutrients to capillaries in the intestinal walls.

Some nutrients—like amino acids and glucose—enter the bloodstream directly. Others are carried up through the portal vein into the liver for further processing and storage.

Almost all nutrients have been absorbed by the time digested food leaves the small intestine and enters the colon; there water and salt are extracted, leaving solid waste for elimination.

After leaving the small intestine, waste material moves upward through the ascending colon and then downwards toward the rectum. Throughout, the body absorbs water and salts, solidifying the stool. Diarrhea is caused by too little water being removed; if too much water is removed the result is constipation.

CHOLESTEROL & FAT

While too much cholesterol can be deadly, it is also one of the essential building blocks of life. Most of the cholesterol in your body is made in your liver from carbohydrates, proteins, and fats. About 25% comes from animal proteins you eat that contain cholesterol, like meat and egg yolks. Low density lipoproteins (LDL) have a higher fat to protein makeup and carry cholesterol from the liver to cells of the body. LDLs are sometimes referred to as the "bad cholesterol"and can adhere to the sides of the arteries forming plaque that can inhibit blood flow to the heart and brain. High density lipoproteins (HDL) collect cholesterol from the body's tissues and bring it back to the liver. HDLs are sometimes referred to as the "good cholesterol" since they help the liver in the process of eliminating cholesterol through secretion as bile acids. Bile helps your body digest fats.

Fats, or lipids, are broken down into particles that can be absorbed by the small intestine's lining. Cells within the lining reconfigure cholesterol into droplets within a layer of protein-forming lipoproteins called chylomicrons.

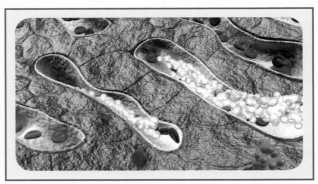

The chylomicrons are released into the lymphatic system which transports them to the blood stream and on to the liver where they are absorbed by cells called hepatocytes.

Inside the hepatocytes, the cholesterol is repacked into forms the body can use. These packages, called lipoproteins, are composed of proteins, lipids and cholesterol.

Released into the bloodstream, the lipoproteins distribute fat throughout the body – where it is used to build cell membranes - and to collect fat to be returned to the liver for processing.

The liver is usually a rich red color, but excess lipids stored in its cells can change it to a whitish color. This is known as fatty liver disease.

A buildup of lipids is closely associated with obesity, particularly central obesity involving the omentum, the fatty pad that hangs down from the stomach. Consuming too much fat adds to its size, producing a large waistline.

Fat is carried by the blood vessels in the process of providing oxygen and nutrients to all our tissues. Specialized cells are designed to store this fat.

As more fat is stored, the cells become larger.

As fat cells grow the red nucleus may be pushed to the side and the enlarged cells begin to touch each other.

The massed cells ultimately grow their own blood vessels in order to sustain their growth.

The Roux-en-Y gastric bypass is a common surgical procedure for extreme obesity. The upper stomach is divided and stapled forming a small pouch.

The small intestine is segmented – the lower section is connected directly to the new pouch, bypassing the upper section which is reconnected to the lower section.

The result is a smaller capacity in terms of food intake and reduced absorption of what is ingested with the bypassing of the highly absorptive upper section of the lower intestine.

In gastric banding procedures the upper portion of the stomach is restricted by a band that can be adjusted after surgery by adding saline to an injection port placed under the skin.

THE ALIMENTARY CANAL & ACCESSORY ORGANS

THE ALIMENTARY CANAL IS A LONG TUBE CONSISTING OF LINKED ORGANS—THE MOUTH, PHARYNX (THROAT), ESOPHAGUS, STOMACH, SMALL INTESTINE, AND THE LARGE INTESTINE—THAT RUNS FROM MOUTH TO ANUS. THE ACCESSORY DIGESTIVE ORGANS ARE THE TONGUE AND TEETH, WHICH MOVE AND CRUSH FOOD; THE SALIVARY GLANDS, LIVER, AND PANCREAS, WHICH RELEASE DIGESTIVE SECRETIONS ALONG DUCTS INTO THE ALIMENTARY CANAL; AND THE GALLBLADDER, WHICH STORES SECRETIONS RELEASED BY THE LIVER. THE LIVER ALSO PROCESSES NUTRIENTS ONCE THEY HAVE BEEN ABSORBED.

The digestive organs of the abdomen seen in right, lateral view with the front of the body to the right of the picture.

KEY

① Esophagus
② Liver
③ Gallbladder
④ Large intestine
⑤ Ascending colon
⑥ Right kidney
⑦ Pelvis
⑧ Small intestine
⑨ Rectum

What are enzymes?

Enzymes are proteins that act as biological **catalysts**: they speed up chemical reactions inside the body by thousands or millions of times while remaining unchanged. **Intracellular** ("inside cells") enzymes work inside cells, where they accelerate the metabolic reactions. Digestive enzymes are **extracellular** ("outside cells"), released by cells in the salivary glands, stomach, pancreas, and small intestine, into the alimentary canal. Without enzymes, digestion would occur too slowly for the body to obtain any nutrients.

Enzymes are specific for certain substrate molecules. The substrate fits precisely into a special area of the enzyme, known as the active site, in the same way that a key fits a lock. The products of the resulting reaction are released from the active site and the enzyme, remaining unchanged, locks onto more **substrate** molecules. Digestive enzymes catalyze reactions involving **hydrolysis** ("water splitting"). The enzyme catalyzes the decomposition of organic compounds (food) by the interaction of water. For example, the enzyme **amylase** (in saliva) breaks down starch into maltose, and the enzyme **maltase** (in pancreatic juice) splits maltose into glucose.

The wall of the alimentary canal typically contains two layers of smooth muscle: an inner circular layer, and an outer longitudinal layer. Waves of muscle contraction called **peristalsis** push food along the canal toward the anus. Movement of the alimentary canal and secretion of digestive juices is controlled automatically by the autonomic nervous system, and by hormones. Ingestion is the only part of the digestive process that is under conscious control.

This posterior view of the abdomen shows the digestive system and its relationship to the kidneys.

KEY

① Esophagus

② Spleen

③ Left kidney*

④ Large intestine

⑤ Small intestine

⑥ Left ureter*

⑦ Pelvis

⑧ Liver

⑨ Pancreas

⑩ Right kidney*

⑪ Right ureter*

⑫ Duodenum

* = part of the urinary system

THE FIRST PHASE OF DIGESTION TAKES PLACE IN THE MOUTH, OR BUCCAL CAVITY. HERE, FOOD IS INGESTED AND PARTLY DIGESTED BEFORE BEING SWALLOWED. THE MOUTH IS BOUND BY THE LIPS AT THE FRONT, THE HARD AND SOFT PALATE AT THE TOP, THE TONGUE AT THE BASE, AND BY THE ENTRANCE INTO THE PHARYNX, OR THROAT, AT THE REAR. EMBEDDED IN SOCKETS IN THE UPPER AND LOWER JAW ARE THE TEETH. IN EACH JAW THERE ARE SIXTEEN TEETH: FOUR CHISEL-LIKE INCISORS CUT FOOD, TWO CANINES GRIP AND TEAR FOOD, AND FOUR PREMOLARS AND SIX MOLARS GRIND AND CRUSH FOOD.

THE MOUTH & THROAT

KEY

1. Soft palate
2. Nasal cavity
3. Hard palate
4. Mandible
5. Submandiblur gland
6. Epiglottis (closed)
7. Larynx
8. Genioglossus
9. Esophagus
10. Trachea

sight, or smell of food. Saliva is a watery liquid that contains slimy mucus and amylase (an enzyme that partly digests starch). During chewing, the tongue, a flap of skeletal muscle, mixes crushed food with saliva. When food molecules dissolve in saliva, taste buds on the tongue's upper surface detect four basic tastes—sweet, sour, salt, and bitter. After about 60 seconds of chewing, the tongue pushes the slippery ball of crushed food—called a bolus—into the throat for swallowing.

The throat, which extends from the rear of the nasal cavity to about halfway down the neck, acts as a passageway for food, but does not have a digestive role. When chewed food touches the back and sides of the throat, it triggers a reflex action. Muscles in the wall of the throat contract to push the bolus of food downward toward the esophagus. At the same time the larynx rises and a cartilage flap, the epiglottis, folds over its entrance to stop food going the "wrong way" into the trachea.

Following its ingestion, food is chewed. The lips are closed, and the cheek muscles push inward, pulling the lower jaw upward. As the jaw moves, the teeth cut and crush the food so that it can be swallowed, and to increase the surface area available for enzyme action. At the same time, the three pairs of salivary glands vastly increase saliva production—saliva is released all the time to cleanse the mouth. Saliva release is a reflex action stimulated by the thought,

Teeth

Forming the outer surface of each tooth is enamel, the hardest substance in the body. The two incisors are designed for cutting and slicing; the canines for seizing and stabbing; and the molars and premolars for crushing, grinding, and chewing food.

KEY

① Central incisor
② Lateral incisor
③ Canine
④ 1st premolar
⑤ 2nd premolar
⑥ 1st molar
⑦ 2nd molar
⑧ 3rd molar

THE MOUTH & TONGUE

The mouth serves as the entrance to both the digestive and the respiratory systems. Lined with mucous membrane, it is interconnected with the nasal cavity; the nose and mouth work closely together in both respiratory and digestive functions. The sense of taste is quite basic (distinguishing only sour, sweet, salty, bitter and umami—the savory flavor of meats), but working in conjunction with the far more complex sense of smell, we can differentiate thousands of different combinations of flavor.

The tongue rests on the floor of the mouth and is used to taste and mix chewed food with saliva.

Saliva aids digestion by gathering food into lumps making it easier for it to slide down the esophagus from the mouth.

The tongue is not smooth; it is covered with tiny projections called papillae. Most are simple finger-like filiform papillae, which do not contain taste buds.

The larger, raised vallate papillae contain clusters of taste buds, the chemoreceptors that transmit messages to the brain.

The average person has about 10,000 taste buds clustered in different parts of the tongue.

Some people are born with a higher number of the papillae containing taste buds. These "super tasters" experience a heightened sense of taste, particularly in response to bitter flavors.

THE TEETH

The health of your teeth depends in large part on the health of your gums.
The leading cause of tooth loss is gingivitis, an inflammation of the gums.

Gum disease begins when plaque, a sticky substance made up of bacteria, saliva and food particles, wedges between your gums and teeth.

The mouth provides excellent conditions for breeding bacteria; once the process starts, the bacteria can establish themselves under the gum.

The teeth are held in place by gum tissue surrounding bone. Gum disease, or periodontitis, attacks the space between the teeth and gums.

Plaque and bacterial infection cause inflammation of the gums which forms deep pockets between the teeth and gums, resulting in the loss of the bone which holds the teeth in place.

Gum disease can also contribute to cavities. Bacteria can enter a crevice between the gum and tooth and eat its way into the tooth.

If the cavity goes deep enough, it can affect the pulp at the center of the tooth. Nerves in the pulp cavity connect to larger nerves in the jaw bone causing the pain that we know as a toothache.

THE ESOPHAGUS & STOMACH

THE ESOPHAGUS IS A MUCUS-LINED MUSCULAR TUBE ABOUT 25 CM (10 IN) LONG THAT CARRIES FOOD FROM THROAT TO STOMACH. THE MOVEMENT OF THE FOOD BOLUS DOWN THE ESOPHAGUS IS THE FINAL PHASE OF SWALLOWING. THE INNER LAYER OF CIRCULAR MUSCLE IN THE ESOPHAGUS WALL CONTRACTS JUST BEHIND THE BOLUS, SQUEEZING THE ESOPHAGEAL WALLS INWARD AND PUSHING THE BOLUS DOWNWARD; AT THE SAME TIME, IN FRONT OF THE BOLUAS, THE OUTER LAYER OF LONGITUDINAL MUSCLE CONTRACTS TO MAKE THAT PART OF THE ESOPHAGUS WIDER. A WAVE OF SUCCESSIVE CONTRACTIONS AND RELAXATIONS, CALLED **PERISTALSIS**, PASSES DOWN THE ESOPHAGUS TO PUSH THE BOLUS INTO THE STOMACH. FROM THROAT TO STOMACH TAKES BETWEEN 4 AND 8 SECONDS, OR JUST 1 SECOND FOR LIQUIDS AND VERY SOFT FOODS.

The esophagus is the link between the mouth, where the digestion process begins through chewing and the release of saliva (which breaks down carbohydrates), and the stomach, where the process continues.

The stomach is a J-shaped expandable portion of the alimentary canal that partly digests food and temporarily stores it for between 2 and 4 hours. The stomach wall has three layers of smooth muscle—outer longitudinal, middle circular, and inner oblique—that contract to crush and grind food. The lining of the stomach is dotted with millions of tiny depressions called **gastric pits**. Glands in the bottom of these pits produce about 2 liters (4 pints) of acidic gastric juice daily. Its release is stimulated by the sight, smell, or thought of food, and by the arrival of food in the stomach. Gastric juice contains the enzyme pepsin, which breaks down proteins into smaller molecules called peptides. Hydrochloric acid secreted in gastric juice activates pepsin and provides the right **pH** environment for it to work in; it also plays a defensive role by killing harmful bacteria in food. Coating the stomach lining is mucus, which prevents it being digested by its own secretions.

The crushing action of the stomach wall muscles, and the action of gastric juice, converts the food bolus into a semi-liquid paste called **chyme**. Contraction of the stomach muscles pushes food from the cardiac region of the stomach through its **fundus** (upper region) and body (middle region) to the **pylorus**, the funnel-shaped region linked to the duodenum, the first part of the small intestine. The exit from the pylorus is closed by the pyloric **sphincter**, a ring-shaped muscle in the stomach wall. Pressure of chyme against the sphincter causes the sphincter to open slightly, allowing small amounts of liquid chyme to enter the duodenum.

Stomach acid

Stomach, or gastric, acid is secreted by parietal cells within the gastric mucosa lining of the stomach. Stomach acid consists primarily of concentrated hydrochloric acid, which helps kill germs and bacteria and sterilizes food. Gastric acid also contains water and the enzyme pepsin—a protein-splitting enzyme—which combined with the hydrochloric acid helps to break down the chemicals that make up food and activates some gastric enzymes. The average adult stomach holds between 1 and 1.5 liters (2 and 3 pints) of gastric acid and manufactures the same amount every 24 hours.

Gastric acid secretion is controlled by the vagus nerve, which runs from the medulla oblongata in the brain stem; the hormone gastrin, which is secreted into the blood supply by cells in the upper part of the stomach wall in response to nervous stimulation; and by histamine, a local hormone synthesized in the gastric mucosa. The vagus nerve sends impulses to the cells in the stomach lining to secrete gastric acid in response to the smell and taste of food.

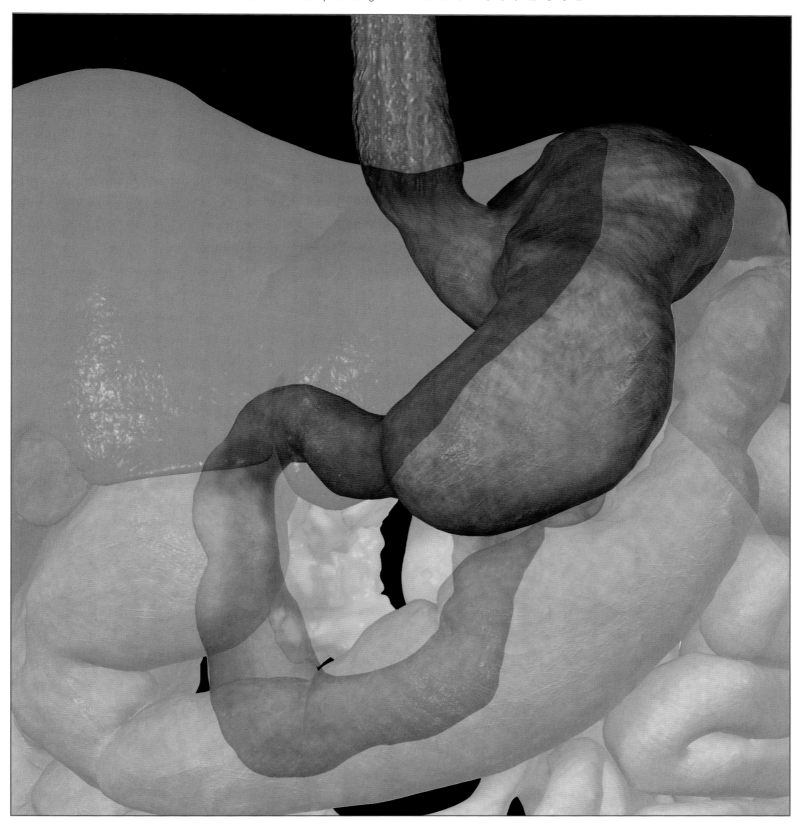

The muscular walls of the stomach contract powerfully to crush swallowed food so that it can be digested by enzymes more efficiently.

KEY

1. Cardia (cardiac region)
2. Lesser curvature
3. Pylorus
4. Pyloric sphincter
5. Duodenum
6. Esophagus
7. Cardiac sphincter
8. Fundus
9. Body
10. Greater curvature

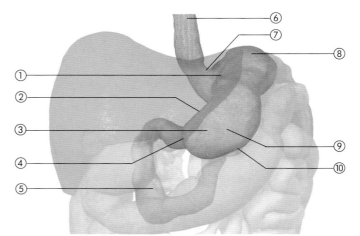

A N EXPANDED PART OF THE ALIMENTARY CANAL, THE STOMACH PROVIDES A TEMPORARY HOLDING STATION FOR FOOD THAT HAS JUST BEEN SWALLOWED. WHILE ALSO STARTING THE DIGESTION PROCESS, THE STORAGE FUNCTION OF THE STOMACH IS VITALLY IMPORTANT BECAUSE WE INGEST FOOD THROUGH THE MOUTH MUCH FASTER THAN WE DIGEST AND ABSORB IT IN THE SMALL INTESTINE. WITHOUT THE STOMACH TO DELAY ITS PROGRESS, FOOD WOULD PASS THROUGH THE DIGESTIVE TRACT TOO RAPIDLY TO BE EFFECTIVELY DIGESTED.

THE STOMACH

The concave upper surface of the stomach forms its lesser curvature, while the convex lower surface forms its greater curvature. Two peritoneal membranes or mesenteries—the greater omentum and lesser omentum—attach the stomach to other organs and to the abdominal wall. The greater omentum extends from the greater curvature to cover the small intestine and then loops upward to attach to the posterior abdominal wall. Where it hangs downward it resembles a fatty apron, because it is filled with fat deposits. It also contains many lymph nodes that protect the abdominal organs from infection. The lesser omentum extends from the liver to the lesser curvature.

Interior surface shot of the stomach showing the many folds (rugae) that line it. The folds vastly increase the available surface area so that after a meal the volume can increase to 4 liters (8 pints).

Partially obscured by the liver and diaphragm, the stomach lies on the left side of the abdominal cavity. It has four major regions (see page 140). The cardiac region is the upper part that surrounds the opening from the esophagus. The fundus is the upper, dome-shaped section. The body is the middle part of the stomach. Finally, the pylorus is the lower end of the stomach, which is continuous with the duodenum. The exit from the pylorus is guarded by a ring of muscle, the pyloric sphincter. While the cardiac region and pylorus are relatively immobile, the fundus and body actively expand when they fill with food, and move as their muscles contract to crush food. When empty, the stomach has a volume of about 50 ml (1.7 fl.oz), and its internal lining is thrown into folds called rugae; after a meal, the elastic stomach wall stretches, the rugae disappear, and the volume can increase to up to 4 liters (8 pints).

Anterior view of the abdomen with the liver and costal cartilages removed.

KEY

1. Lesser curvature of the stomach
2. Duodenum
3. Pyloric sphincter
4. Pancreas
5. Transverse colon
6. Ascending colon
7. Pelvis
8. Ileum
9. Esophagus
10. Stomach
11. Greater curvature of the stomach
12. Jejunum
13. Descending colon
14. Sigmoid colon
15. Inferior vena cava
16. Aorta

THE DUODENUM FORMS THE FIRST PART OF THE SMALL INTESTINE, THE LONGEST PART OF THE ALIMENTARY CANAL AND ITS MOST IMPORTANT DIGESTIVE ORGAN. IT IS ALSO THE ENTRY POINT FOR **ALKALINE** SECRETIONS FROM TWO ACCESSORY GLANDS, THE PANCREAS AND LIVER WHICH, WITH INTESTINAL JUICES, SERVE TO NEUTRALIZE ACIDIC CHYME AS IT ENTERS THE DUODENUM THROUGH THE PYLORIC SPHINCTER.

THE LIVER, GALLBLADDER, PANCREAS & DUODENUM

The pancreas is packed with cell clusters, called **acini**, that secrete digestive juices into the pancreatic duct, from where they empty into the duodenum. About 1.5 liters (3 pints) of alkaline pancreatic juice is secreted daily, its release stimulated by the arrival of chyme in the duodenum. Pancreatic juice contains the enzymes **amylase**, which breaks down starch; **trypsin**, **chymotrypsin**, and **carboxypeptidase**, which break down proteins; **lipase**, which breaks down fats; and **nucleases**, which break down nucleic acids such as DNA. The pancreas also has endocrine cells that secrete hormones, which control blood glucose levels.

The liver secretes **bile**, a greenish liquid that is part digestive and part excretory. Bile is stored and concentrated in the gallbladder, a small muscular sac located on the rear, lower surface of the liver. The arrival of chyme triggers the release of bile along the bile duct, which merges with the pancreatic duct before emptying into the duodenum. Bile salts in bile emulsify fats—turn them into small droplets—making their digestion by lipase enzymes more efficient.

The roles of the liver

Billions of liver cells, or **hepatocytes**, carry out hundreds of functions related to the regulation of blood composition. The sole digestive function of the liver is the production of bile, a mixture of water, bile salts, and bile pigments (a waste product from worn out red blood cells). Digestion-related functions include:

• Controlling glucose levels in the blood.
• Metabolizing amino acids and fats.
• Storing vitamins and minerals.

These food processing functions prevent blood from becoming "swamped" with nutrients after a meal. Other functions include:

• Removing poisons, such as drugs, and toxins from the blood.
• Making plasma proteins.
• Generating heat, thereby helping to keep the body warm.

Unusually, this large and important organ receives two blood inputs: the hepatic artery supplies oxygen-rich blood; the hepatic portal vein supplies blood rich in recently absorbed nutrients direct from the small intestine. This link underpins the many digestion-related functions carried out by the liver.

KEY

1. Right lobe of liver
2. Gallbladder
3. Duodenum
4. Head of pancreas
5. Left lobe of liver
6. Tail of pancreas
7. Body of pancreas
8. Jejunum
9. Region of the duodenum where ducts from accessory organs open

The three accessory organs—the liver, gallbladder, and pancreas—empty secretions into the duodenum to aid digestion there.

THE LIVER PLAYS A VITAL ROLE IN MAINTAINING THE COMPOSITION OF THE BLOOD. IT IS DIVIDED INTO TWO LOBES—THE RIGHT IS LARGER THAN THE LEFT—BY THE **FALCIFORM LIGAMENT**, A PIECE OF MESENTERY THAT ANCHORS THE LIVER TO THE ANTERIOR WALL OF THE ABDOMEN. ON ITS LOWER, POSTERIOR SURFACE IS THE **PORTA HEPATIS** ("LIVER GATEWAY"), AN OPENING THROUGH WHICH THE HEPATIC PORTAL VEIN—WHICH CARRIES NUTRIENT-RICH FOOD FROM THE SMALL INTESTINE—AND THE HEPATIC ARTERY—A BRANCH OF THE CELIAC TRUNK FROM THE AORTA, WHICH DELIVERS OXYGEN-RICH BLOOD—BOTH ENTER THE LIVER, AND THE COMMON HEPATIC DUCT, WHICH CARRIES BILE, LEAVES. SUPERIORLY, RIGHT AND LEFT HEPATIC VEINS, WHICH CARRY BLOOD OUT OF THE LIVER, EMPTY DIRECTLY INTO THE INFERIOR VENA CAVA, WHICH PASSES VERTICALLY BEHIND THE LIVER.

THE LIVER & GALLBLADDER

The billions of liver cells, or hepatocytes, that process recently-absorbed nutrients, remove toxins, secrete proteins, release nutrients from stores, and secrete bile, are organized into thousands of hexagonal lobules, each about 1 mm (1⁄16 in) in diameter. Inside the lobule strands of hepatocytes one cell thick fan outward from a central vein that empties into the hepatic vein. Running between these strands are blood channels called **sinusoids**. At the corners of the hexagon are branches of the hepatic portal vein and hepatic artery that deliver blood to be processed by the hepatocytes as it flows along the sinusoids towards the central vein. Bile— part excretory product, part digestive agent—secreted by hepatocytes, passes along tiny bile canaliculi, also located at the corners of lobules, which empty in the hepatic ducts.

Gallbladder

The gallbladder lies tucked into a small depression on the lower rear wall of the liver, and is connected to it by the common hepatic duct and cystic duct. A green, muscular sac some 10 cm (4in) long, the gallbladder stores and concentrates bile produced by the liver.

As it fills with bile—the liver releases about 1 liter (13⁄4 pints) of bile each day—the gallbladder stretches and its folded inner surface becomes smooth. When chyme (semisolid food) enters the duodenum from the stomach, the intestines release **cholecystokinin**, a hormone that causes the gallbladder to contract, squeezing bile along the cystic duct and through the common bile duct into the duodenum where it assists in the digestion of fats.

Anterior view of the upper abdominal organs, showing the liver, gallbladder, stomach, pancreas, small intestines and colon.

KEY

① Liver
② Gallbladder
③ Pancreas
④ Ascending colon
⑤ Ilium
⑥ Spleen
⑦ Stomach
⑧ Transverse colon
⑨ Jejunum
⑩ Ileum
⑪ Sigmoid colon

**Anterior view of
the liver showing
the gallbladder
and, internally, the
extensive network of
arteries and veins.**

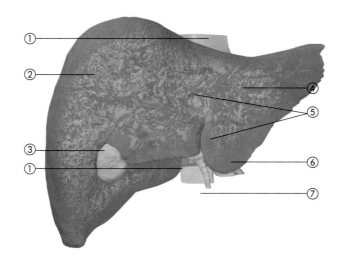

KEY

1. Inferior vena cava
2. Right lobe of liver
3. Gallbladder
4. Left lobe of liver
5. Branches of hepatic
   portal vein and hepatic
   artery
6. Hepatic artery
7. Common bile duct

**Interior view of the
gall bladder and its
exit throught the
cystic duct. When the
gallbladder contains
little bile its lining** **is thrown into folds,
as seen here. These
disappear as the
gallbladder fills with
bile and expands.**

THE SMALL INTESTINE LIES COILED UP WITHIN THE CENTRAL ABDOMEN AND EXTENDS FROM THE STOMACH TO THE LARGE INTESTINE. THE TERM "SMALL" RELATES TO ITS DIAMETER, WHICH IS ONLY ABOUT 2.5 CM (1 IN). IT IS, HOWEVER, THE LONGEST PART OF THE ALIMENTARY CANAL AND THIS REFLECTS ITS IMPORTANCE AS THE SITE OF ALMOST ALL DIGESTION AND ABSORPTION OF NUTRIENTS.

THE SMALL INTESTINE

The small intestine has three parts: the 25 cm (10 in) long curved duodenum receives chyme from the stomach; the middle jejunum is about 1 meter (3 feet) long; while the final section, the ileum, is about 2 meters (6 feet) long and joins the large intestine at the ileocecal valve. These dimensions increase after death when muscle tone is lost and the entire length of the small intestine totals between 6 and 7 meters (20 and 22 feet).

Internally, the lining of the small intestine provides a large surface area with which to maximize the efficiency of both digestion and absorption. This is achieved through three levels of adaptation. Firstly, circular folds called plicae circulares form ridges some 10 mm (⅖ in) high around the inside of the small intestine. Secondly, tiny 1 mm (⅟₁₆ in) long, fingerlike processes called villi project from the plicae circulares and from the troughs in between them. Each villus contains a capillary network, and a branch of the lymphatic system called a lacteal. Thirdly, the outer surface of cells lining the small intestine—including the villi—is covered by microscopic hairlike projections called microvilli, of which there are over 200 million per square millimeter of intestinal surface. Microvilli not only further increase the surface area available for absorption; attached to them are digestive enzymes that complete the last stages of digestion right next to the absorptive surface.

Chyme from the stomach is neutralized by pancreatic and intestinal juices, and bile, and is partly digested by pancreatic enzymes. Enzymes attached to microvilli—also called brush border enzymes—include maltase, sucrase, and lactase, which break down complex sugars into glucose and other simple sugars; and peptidases, which break down peptides into amino acids. Simple sugars and amino acids pass through villi cells into blood capillaries. These absorbed nutrients are then carried to the liver via the hepatic portal vein. Fatty acids and glycerol are turned back into fats inside villi cells and then pass into the lymphatic system, by way of the lacteals, which deposit them into the bloodstream.

Resembling a coil of sausages, the small intestine, the longest part of the alimentary canal, provides the most important site for digestion and absorption.

KEY

① Duodenum
② Jejunum
③ Junction with the large intestine
④ Ileum
⑤ Small intestine

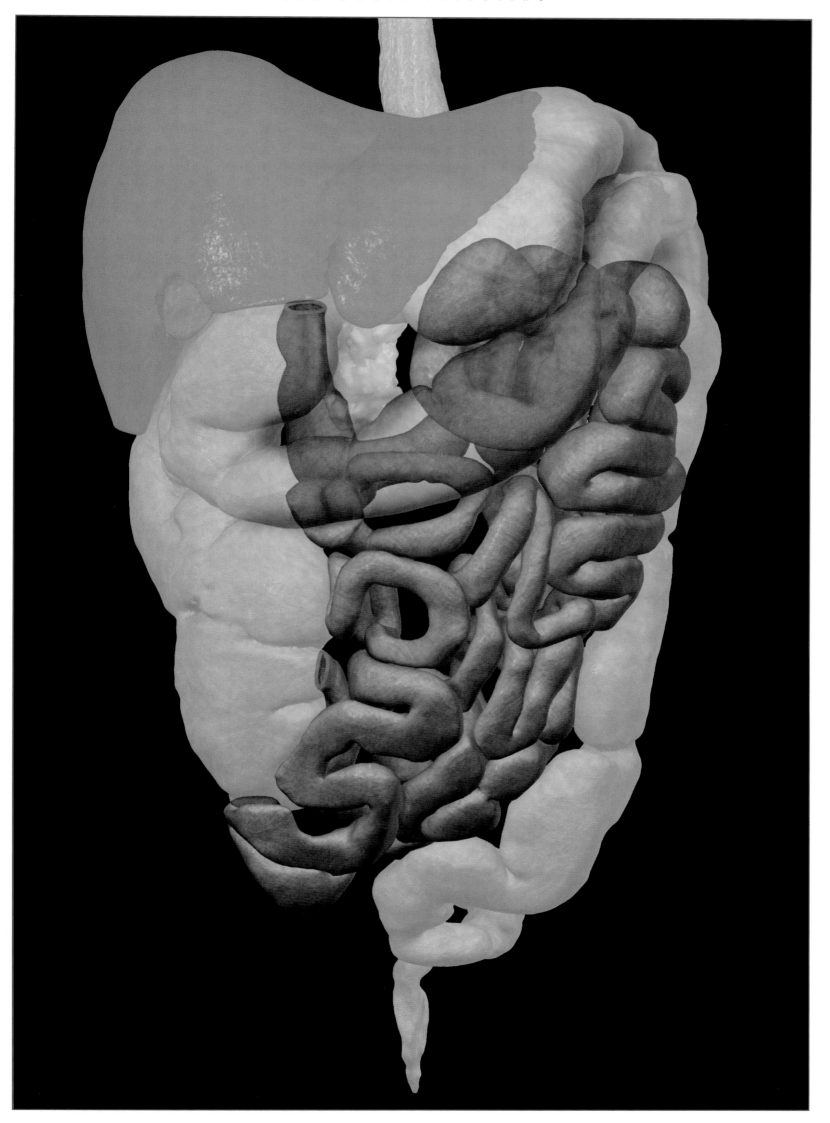

THE LARGE INTESTINE REMOVES UNDIGESTED FOOD AND OTHER WASTE FROM THE BODY. IT HAS FOUR SECTIONS: THE CECUM, COLON, RECTUM, AND ANAL CANAL. THE SHORT CECUM LIES INFERIOR TO THE ILEOCECAL VALVE, THE ONE-WAY ENTRANCE INTO THE LARGE INTESTINE FROM THE ILEUM. THE COLON CONSISTS OF ASCENDING, TRANSVERSE, AND DESCENDING SECTIONS THAT, RESPECTIVELY, PASS UP THE RIGHT HAND SIDE OF, ACROSS, AND DOWN THE LEFT HAND SIDE OF THE ABDOMINAL CAVITY; AND THE S-SHAPED SIGMOID COLON THAT PASSES INTO THE PELVIS. THE RECTUM LEADS TO THE ANAL CANAL, WHICH OPENS THROUGH THE ANUS. IN ALL, THE LARGE INTESTINE IS ABOUT 1.5 METERS (5 FT) LONG. THE NAME "LARGE" REFERS TO ITS DIAMETER, WHICH AT 6.5 CM (3 IN) IS TWICE THE WIDTH OF THE SMALL INTESTINE. THE LARGE INTESTINE CONTAINS BILLIONS OF BACTERIA, WHICH ARE HARMLESS INSIDE THE BODY BUT CAN BE HARMFUL IF THEY ARE TRANSFERRED TO FOOD—HENCE THE IMPORTANCE OF WASHING HANDS AFTER DEFECATION—OR IF FECES POLLUTE WATER SUPPLIES.

THE LARGE INTESTINE

Each day, about 1500 ml (4 pints) of semi-liquid waste enters and is pushed along the large intestine. As this happens, water is absorbed into the bloodstream, thereby helping to maintain the body's fluid balance. Within 10 to 12 hours the liquid waste has been turned into semi-solid material called feces. Apart from fiber and undigested food, feces also contain dead intestinal cells and bacteria. Although movement of the large intestine is usually sluggish, the arrival of food in the stomach triggers a more powerful wave of peristalsis, which pushes feces into the sigmoid colon for temporary storage.

Egestion of feces

The egestion of feces, or defecation, is triggered by a movement of more feces into an already full sigmoid colon, which then contracts to push feces into the normally empty rectum. As the rectal walls stretch, the person feels a conscious desire to defecate. If defecation is desired, the muscles of the rectal wall contract to push the feces into the anal canal. The two sphincters—internal and external—guarding the anus relax and the feces are pushed out.

The large intestine travels up, across, and down the abdomen before opening to the outside through the anus.

The appendix

The appendix is a blind-ending tube about 9 cm (4 in) long and attached to the cecum. Rabbits and other herbivores have a large appendix containing many bacteria that break down cellulose, a key constituent in grasses and other vegetation, in order to release essential glucose. In humans, the appendix is comparatively much smaller and, until recently, was thought to be vestigial. However, recent research has indicated that it may play a part in the immune system.

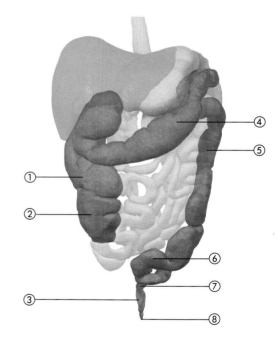

KEY

1. Ascending colon
2. Cecum
3. Anal canal
4. Transverse colon
5. Descending colon
6. Sigmoid colon
7. Rectum
8. Anus

THE
URINARY
SYSTEM

By weight, over half our body is water. Our natural filters process over 200 quarts of fluid each day—most of which returns to the bloodstream after cleansing, the balance removing toxic wastes and byproducts as it leaves in the form of urine.

THE URINARY SYSTEM

THE URINARY SYSTEM IS THE BODY'S SANITATION DEPARTMENT. IT REMOVES UNWANTED MATERIALS FROM THE BLOOD AND BY DOING SO MAINTAINS THE CONCENTRATION OF BLOOD AND TISSUE FLUID WITHIN NARROW LIMITS. THIS IMPORTANT HOMEOSTATIC ROLE IS ESSENTIAL TO ENSURE THAT THE ACTIVITIES OF THE BODYS' TRILLIONS OF CELLS ARE NOT DISRUPTED BY LIFE-THREATENING FLUCTUATIONS IN THE FLUIDS THAT SURROUND THEM.

The key organs in the urinary system are the two kidneys. These brown, bean-shaped organs—each about 12 cm (5 in) long and 6 cm (3 in) wide—are located in the upper abdomen, one on either side of the backbone. The kidneys receive some 25 percent of the heart's output through the renal arteries—about 1800 liters (475 gallons) of blood per day—and return processed blood to the circulation through the renal veins.

The result of the kidney's processing activities is a waste liquid called **urine**. Urine contains dissolved wastes that must be promptly excreted (eliminated) from the body before they can cause harm. Most wastes are produced as a result of metabolic activities inside cells. The major waste substance is a **nitrogenous** (nitrogen-containing) compound called **urea**. This is formed in the liver from excess amino acids (the building blocks of protein) in food. The nitrogenous component of excess amino acids—ammonia—is highly poisonous and cannot be stored. Instead it is combined with carbon dioxide to make less poisonous urea, which can then be excreted. Other excretory substances include drugs and toxins that have been processed by the liver.

The kidney also removes excess water and salts, such as sodium and potassium, from the blood, thereby regulating the volume and salt concentration of blood, and of tissue fluid, regardless of how much water is consumed in food and drink. In addition, the kidney also helps to regulate blood pressure, releases the hormone **erythropoietin**, which stimulates red blood cell production, and activates vitamin D made by the skin when it is exposed to sunlight.

Urine is carried from the kidneys by long tubes called ureters, which pass into the pelvis and open into the posterior surface of the bladder, a hollow storage organ that has walls which are both elastic and muscular. The bladder opens to the outside through the urethra. In females, the urethra is short and opens between the legs in the vulva; in males the urethra is longer, and passes through the penis and opens at its tip.

KEY

1. Right kidney
2. Calyx
3. Right ureter
4. Bladder (empty)
5. Urethra
6. Urethral opening
7. Left kidney
8. Hilus
9. Renal pelvis
10. Left ureter
11. Position of external sphincter
12. Penis

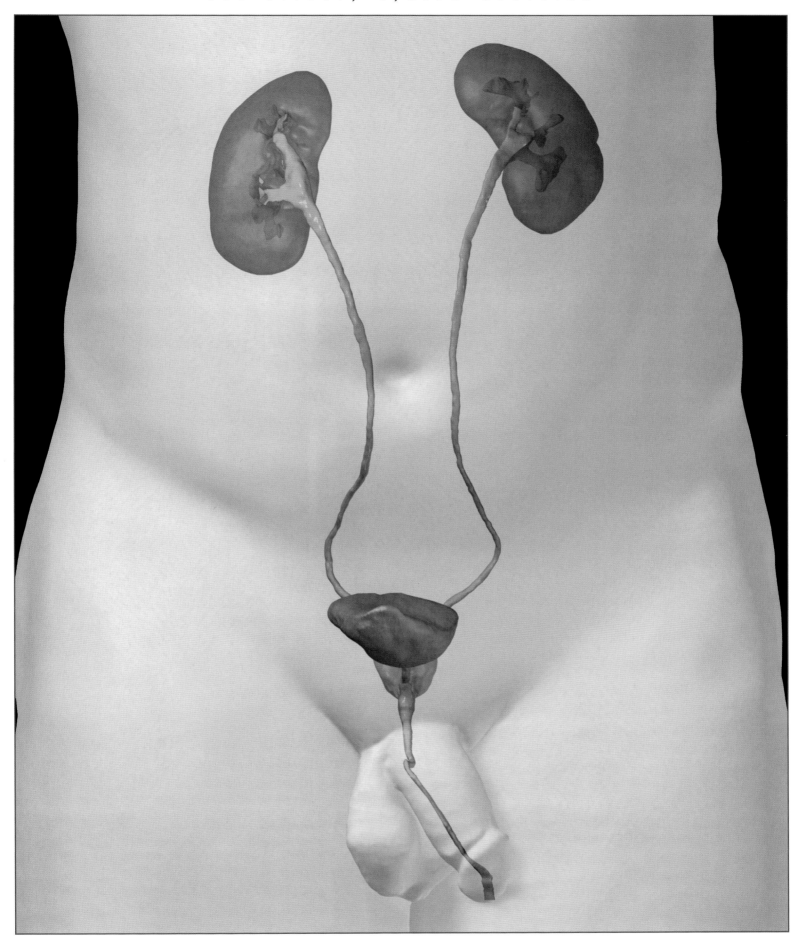

The urinary bladder, which stores waste urine produced by the two kidneys, lies protected within the bony pelvis.

HE KIDNEYS ARE THE KEY ORGANS OF THE URINARY SYSTEM. THEY ARE RESPONSIBLE FOR EXCRETING FROM THE BODY MUCH OF THE METABOLIC WASTE GENERATED BY CELLS, AND ELIMINATING EXCESS WATER AND SALTS IN ORDER TO MAINTAIN THE STABLE COMPOSITION AND VOLUME OF BLOOD AND OTHER BODY FLUIDS.

THE KIDNEYS

Posterior view of the abdomen with the ribs removed. The right kidney, which is attached to the posterior abdominal wall, typically occupies a lower position than the left kidney.

KEY

1. Vertebral column
2. Stomach
3. Spleen
4. Left kidney
5. Left ureter
6. Descending colon
7. Ileum
8. Coxal (hip) bone
9. Adrenal gland
10. Right kidney
11. Ascending colon

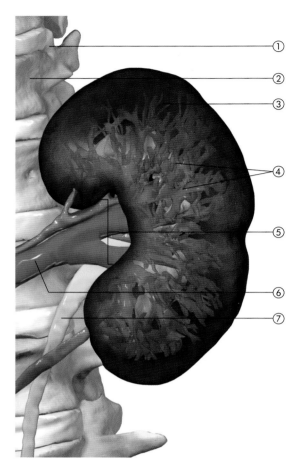

A close-up view of the left kidney. The kidney has been made transparent to aid visualization. Note the rich vascular network inside the kidney.

KEY

1. Intervertebral disc
2. Vertebral column
3. Left kidney
4. Branches of renal artery and veins
5. Renal hilum
6. Renal vein
7. Left ureter

The two bean-shaped kidneys lie at the back of the abdomen, between the parietal peritoneum and the abdominal wall—one on either side of the upper lumbar section of the backbone. In that position they receive some protection from the lowermost ribs. The right kidney is typically lower than the left. The inner surface of each kidney has an indentation, or hilus, that leads to an inner space called the renal sinus through which blood vessels, lymph vessels, and nerves enter and exit the kidneys. The middle medulla—which on its inner surface takes the form of cone-shaped **medullary pyramids**—contain the millions of microscopic filtration units called **nephrons**.

The nephrons selectively filter fluid from blood, returning useful and essential materials to the bloodstream while retaining wastes and excess water and salts to form urine. Smooth muscle in the walls of the **renal calyces**, the renal pelvis, and the ureters contract rhythmically to push urine towards the bladder. Blood enters each kidney through the renal artery—a branch of the aorta—which branches to form smaller arteries that pass between the medullary pyramids and enter the cortex. Veins from the cortex unite to form the renal vein that empties into the inferior vena cava. Surrounding each kidney are three layers of protective and supporting tissue. The innermost, the **renal capsule**, is a fibrous coat that is continuous with the **renal sinus**, and which helps to prevent the spread of infection into the kidney. The adipose or fatty coat cushions the kidneys against blows and helps to insulate them. The outermost coat, the **renal fascia**, anchors the kidneys to the abdominal wall.

Close-up view of the kidneys and adrenal glands with the surrounding organs removed. Acting as the body's filtration system, the kidneys have a very rich blood supply.

KEY

1. Inferior vena cava
2. Vertebral column
3. Intervertebral disc
4. Abdominal aorta
5. Left adrenal gland
6. Left kidney
7. Left renal artery
8. Left renal vein
9. Left ureter

I

NTERNALLY, THE KIDNEYS ARE DIVIDED INTO THREE

ZONES: THE OUTER CORTEX; THE DARKER MEDULLA; AND

THE RENAL PELVIS, A FLATTENED, HOLLOW FUNNEL THAT

LEADS TO THE URETER.

THE KIDNEYS

KEY

1. Inferior vena cava
2. Common hepatic artery
3. Splenic artery
4. Celiac trunk
5. Superior mesenteric artery
6. Thoracic vertebra
7. Intervertebral disc
8. Abdominal aorta
9. Branches of renal artery and vein inside kidney
10. Left renal artery
11. Left kidney
12. Left renal vein
13. Left ureter

Within the cortex and medulla of each kidney are about a million microscopic units called **nephrons** that filter blood to produce urine. Each nephron has two parts: a **renal tubule** and a **glomerulus**, a mass of blood capillaries. The renal tubule loops between cortex and medulla before joining a common collecting duct that empties into the renal pelvis. High pressure inside the glomerulus forces liquid—the filtrate—out of the blood and into the **glomerular capsule**, the cup-shaped end of the renal tubule. As crude filtrate passes along the tubule, water, salts, and other valuable substances, such as glucose and amino acids, are reabsorbed through the wall of the tubule back into the

bloodstream. Left behind are the unwanted waste products and excess water and salts that form urine, which now flows into the renal pelvis. Each day about 180 liters (50 gallons) of filtrate is processed by the nephrons; most is reabsorbed through the renal tubules. Only about 1.5 liters (3 pints) of fluid leaves the body as urine.

Emptying of the bladder

At the base of the bladder, the muscular bag that stores urine, where it joins the urethra, is the internal urethral sphincter, a ring of muscle that is under involuntary control and which stops urine leaking out. Below this, the pelvic floor muscles form another sphincter muscle—the external urethral sphincter—around the urethra which is under conscious control. The wall of the bladder itself contains three layers of smooth muscle.

About 1 ml (¼ teaspoon) of urine is produced each minute and is pushed down the ureters by **peristaltic** waves into the bladder. When the bladder contains between 300 and 400 ml (10 and 14 fl. oz) of urine, the bladder wall stretches, causing sensory receptors to send nerve impulses to the spinal cord. Nerve impulses returning from the spinal cord cause the internal sphincter to open and urine to pass to the top of the urethra. Other messages pass up the spinal cord to the brain and the person feels the need to urinate. The external sphincter is relaxed under conscious control, the bladder wall muscles contract, and urine is forced out of the body through the urethra.

Anterior view of the left upper abdomen showing the left kidney and its blood supply.

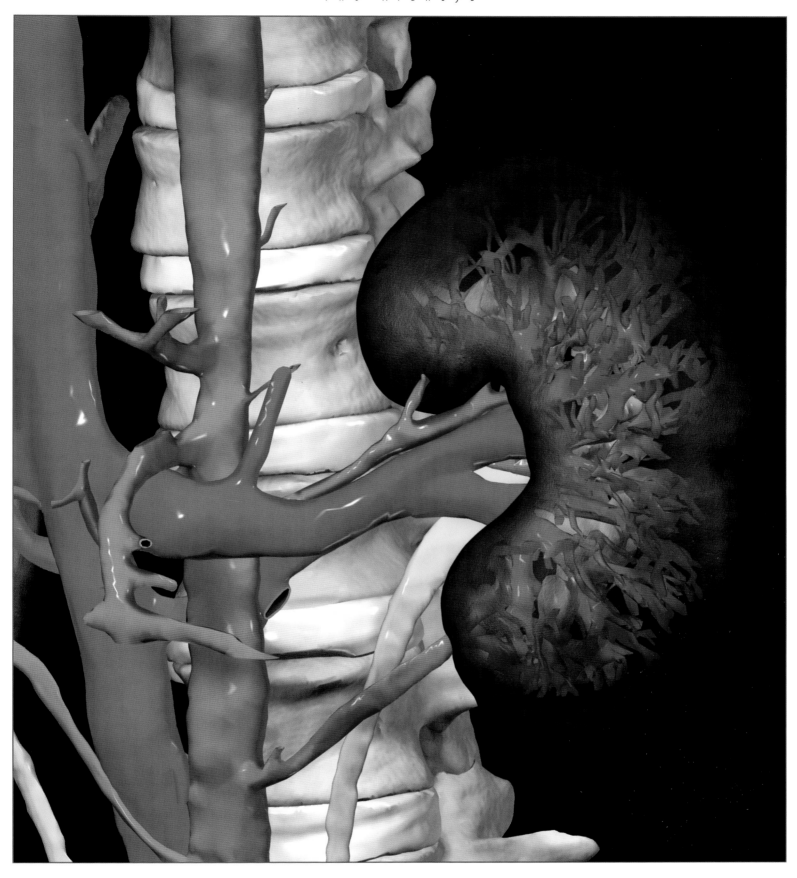

Although each kidney is only around 12 cm (4 in) long, between them they filter the body's entire blood volume approximately 20 times each hour, producing around 1 ml (¼ teaspoon) of urine per minute. These tireless filters process blood 24 hours a day.

THE KIDNEYS

While the kidneys represent only about 0.5 percent of body weight, they directly receive up to 25 percent of the blood pumped by the heart at any time. Filtering the entire blood supply about 20 times each hour, the kidneys' function is vital to survival

The bean-shaped kidneys are located at the back of the abdomen under the ribs.

Inside the kidneys, the cup-shaped collecting ducts called calyces cover the tops of the medullary pyramids.

Within the medulla are millions of microscopic nephrons.

Each nephron has a renal tubule closed at one end and open at the other.

As liquid passes through the looped tubule, the glomerulus, waste products are retained, while glucose, amino acids and most of the fluids and salts are reabsorbed by the blood.

Urine is composed of the remaining fluid and waste; it passes into the renal pelvis and on to the bladder through the ureters.

Kidney stones, or calculi, are mineral (primarily calcium) and salt deposits that form inside the glomerulus.

Kidney stones build up in layers over time and can be the size of a grain of sand, a pearl or even a golf ball. Small stones can stay in the kidney or pass easily without causing problems.

A larger stone can get stuck in the ureter, bladder or urethra, block the flow of urine and be extremely painful.

If the kidneys fail, the body cannot survive for more than a few days.

The alternative is a kidney transplant, where the donor kidney is attached to the renal veins, arteries and the ureter.

People suffering from kidney failure can live a fairly normal life by undergoing dialysis every few days – a process where the blood is filtered by a machine outside the body.

THE REPRODUCTIVE SYSTEM

WHILE MOST OF THE BODY'S SYSTEMS ARE CONCERNED WITH KEEPING US GOING ON A DAILY BASIS, THIS ONE IS DESIGNED TO KEEP US GOING AS A SPECIES. THE GENETIC CODE EACH OF US CARRIES HAS THE OPPORTUNITY TO COMBINE WITH A PARTNER'S SPERM OR EGG TO CREATE A NEW AND UNIQUE INDIVIDUAL—WHO CAN THEN IN TURN MAKE THEIR CONTRIBUTION TO THE EVER-GROWING DISPARATE GENE POOL.

THE REPRODUCTIVE SYSTEM ENABLES HUMANS TO PRODUCE OFFSPRING. UNLIKE OTHER SYSTEMS, MALE AND FEMALE REPRODUCTIVE SYSTEMS ARE DIFFERENT, AND NEITHER STARTS WORKING UNTIL PUBERTY. THE PRIMARY ORGANS OF THE REPRODUCTIVE SYSTEMS —TESTES IN MEN AND OVARIES IN WOMEN— PRODUCE SEX CELLS. FOLLOWING SEXUAL INTERCOURSE, A SPERM (MALE SEX CELL) FUSES WITH AN EGG (FEMALE SEX CELL) INSIDE THE WOMAN DURING FERTILIZATION. THE RESULTING FERTILIZED EGG DEVELOPS INTO A BABY INSIDE THE WOMAN'S UTERUS.

The male reproductive system is designed for the production and subsequent transference of sperm into the female.

THE MALE REPRODUCTIVE SYSTEM

The male reproductive system consists of the testes, the penis (which also forms part of the urinary system), the ducts that connect testes to penis, and the accessory glands. The two testes are oval shaped organs that hang between the legs in the scrotum, a sac of skin and muscle. The sperm they produce are well adapted for their function: to swim in search of an egg in order to fertilize it. They have a streamlined shape, and consist of a head that carries genetic material, and a tail or **flagellum** that enables them to swim. Running along the posterior edge of each testis is the epididymis. Immature sperm from the testis spend 14 to 20 days inside this highly coiled tube until they reach maturity.

The penis is a tube-shaped organ that facilitates the transfer of sperm into the female's vagina during sexual intercourse. It is held in place by an internal root; externally it consists of a shaft and its expanded tip, the glans. Within the penis are three cylinders of spongy tissue that enable the penis to become erect. The lower cylinder, the corpus spongiosum, runs along the underside of the shaft into the glans and surrounds the urethra, the duct that caries both urine and **semen** to the outside. The two upper cylinders, the corpora cavernosa, run in parallel along the upper part of the shaft.

The vas deferens (pl. vasa deferentia) is a duct that carries mature sperm from the epididymis to the urethra, which it joins just below the bladder Emptying into each vas deferens, just behind the bladder, is a seminal vesicle. This, and the other accessory gland, the chestnut-sized prostate gland, which surrounds the urethra where it leaves the bladder, produce secretions that mix to form semen. Semen carries sperm, activates them, and provides them with "fuel" for their impending journey.

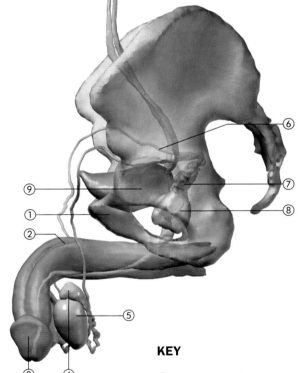

KEY

1. Pubic symphysis
2. Penis
3. Glans of Penis
4. Epididymis
5. Testis
6. Vas (ductus) deferens
7. Seminal vesicle
8. Prostate gland
9. Urinary bladder

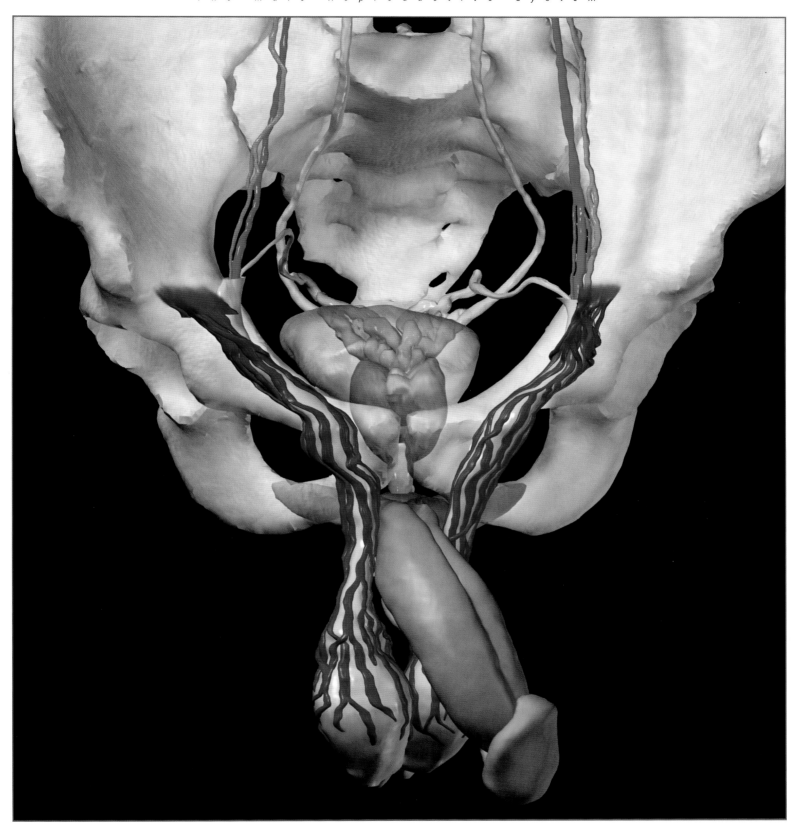

Housed outside the body within the scrotum, the testes are maintained at the ideal temperature for sperm production.

KEY

1. Urinary bladder
2. Seminal vesicle
3. Prostate gland
4. Vas (ductus) deferens
5. Penis
6. Testis
7. Pubic symphysis
8. Glans of penis

FOR THE MALE REPRODUCTIVE SYSTEM TO FUNCTION THE PENIS MUST BECOME ERECT, SO THAT IT CAN BE INSERTED INTO THE VAGINA, AND **EJACULATION** HAS TO OCCUR. ERECTION STIFFENS AND LENGTHENS THE NORMALLY FLACCID PENIS. IT IS A REFLEX ACTION CONTROLLED BY THE AUTONOMIC NERVOUS SYSTEM (ANS). DURING SEXUAL AROUSAL, ARTERIOLES SUPPLYING THE PENIS GET WIDER. THE RESULTING INCREASED BLOOD FLOW FILLS SPACES IN THE SPONGY CYLINDERS INSIDE THE SHAFT AND GLANS OF THE PENIS CAUSING IT TO EXPAND AND STIFFEN.

THE MALE REPRODUCTIVE SYSTEM

Like erection, ejaculation is also a reflex action controlled by the ANS. It is triggered when sexual arousal has reached a critical level of excitement. In the first phase of ejaculation the vasa deferentia contract to squeeze sperm toward the base of the penis, and the prostate gland and seminal vesicles release their secretions to make semen. At this point the man knows his ejaculation is unstoppable and the second phase begins. Muscles at the base of the penis contract every 0.8 seconds and force semen out of the penis in up to 5 spurts. Altogether about 5 ml (about a teaspoon) of semen is released, containing, on average, approximately 300 million sperm. Following ejaculation the erection is lost.

Sperm production

Being suspended in the scrotum, the temperature of the testes is maintained at some 3°C (5°F) below **core body temperature**. This lower temperature is optimal for sperm production. A healthy, fertile man produces several hundred million sperm daily, between puberty and old age. However, the process of production and maturation for a single sperm takes over 2 months. Sperm are made inside tightly coiled tubes called seminiferous tubules, of which there are between one and four within the 250 or so compartments, called lobules, in each testis.

Sperm-making cells in the walls of the seminiferous tubules divide to produce millions of immature sperm each second.

These pass along the seminiferous tubules to the epididymis where they mature. Sperm production is controlled by two pituitary gland hormones: luteinizing hormone (LH) and follicle stimulating hormone (FSH). LH stimulates interstitial cells surrounding the seminiferous tubules to secrete the male sex hormone testosterone; FSH and testosterone stimulate the seminiferous tubules to make sperm.

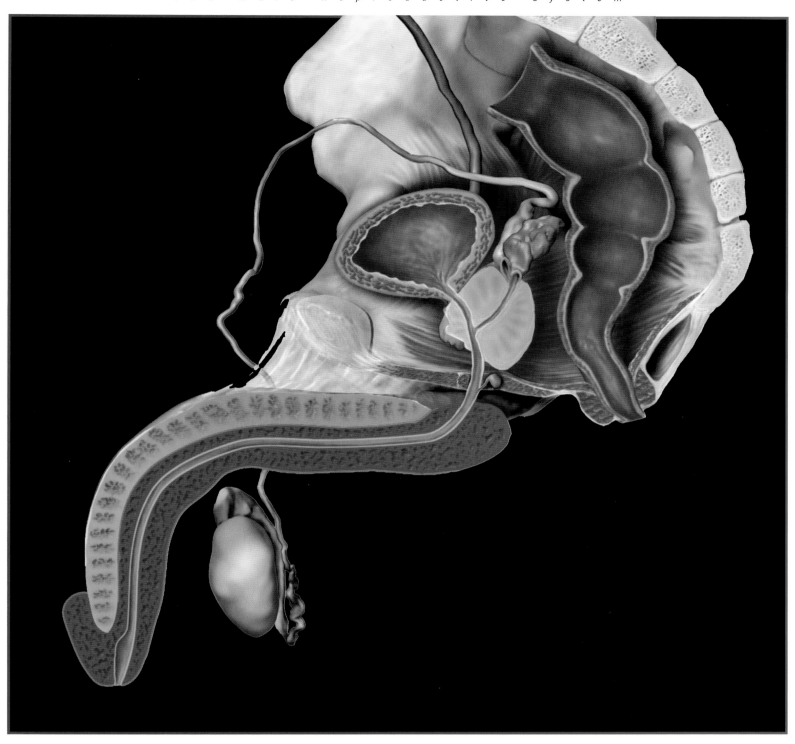

A sagittal section through the male body shows how the vas deferens links the testes, which produce sperm, to the urethra, which opens at the tip of the penis. Emptying into the urethra are the accessory glands—the seminal vesicles, prostate gland, and the bulbourethral gland.

KEY

① Urinary bladder
② Pubic symphysis
③ Urethra
④ Corpus cavernosum
⑤ Corpus spongiosum
⑥ Penis
⑦ Glans of penis
⑧ Vas (ductus) deferens
⑨ Rectum
⑩ Seminal vesicle
⑪ Prostate gland
⑫ Bulbourethral gland
⑬ Anus
⑭ Epididymis
⑮ Testis

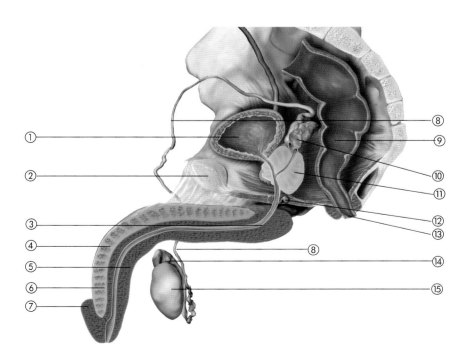

THE FEMALE REPRODUCTIVE SYSTEM PRODUCES SEX CELLS, CALLED EGGS OR OVA, AND PROVIDES THE ENVIRONMENT FOR THE DEVELOPMENT OF A BABY SHOULD AN EGG BE FERTILIZED BY A SPERM. IN ADDITION TO THE OVARIES, THE PRIMARY SEX ORGANS, THE OTHER COMPONENTS OF THE FEMALE REPRODUCTIVE SYSTEM ARE THE UTERINE (FALLOPIAN) TUBES, THE UTERUS, THE VAGINA, AND THE EXTERNAL GENITALS OR VULVA.

THE FEMALE REPRODUCTIVE SYSTEM

Unlike the male, the female's sex organs are situated entirely within the woman's body.

KEY

1. Fallopian tube
2. Fimbriae
3. Ovary
4. Uterus
5. Vagina

The ovaries

The two ovaries lie on each side of the uterus. Each is part-surrounded by the funnellike opening of a uterine tube that links the ovary to the uterus. At birth, the ovaries already contain a lifetime's supply —up to 2 million—of immature eggs. Between puberty and the menopause, every month one immature egg matures and is released. The ovaries themselves secrete the female sex hormones estrogen and progesterone that control the menstrual cycle (see below), as well as producing and maintaining secondary sexual characteristics such as breasts.

Ovarian and menstrual cycles

A cycle is a sequence of events, which occur in a fixed order, and that repeats itself. Each month, two linked reproductive cycles—the ovarian and menstrual cycles—are responsible, respectively, for the release of an egg from an ovary, and for the

preparation of the uterus to receive the egg should it be fertilized. Both cycles last, on average, for 28 days. The ovarian cycle is controlled by two pituitary gland hormones: luteinizing hormone (LH) and follicle stimulating hormone (FSH). FSH stimulates some follicles (sacs) containing immature eggs to grow and mature. Eventually, one follicle and its egg becomes much larger than the others. In mid-cycle, LH levels rise and cause ovulation: the follicle bursts, releasing its egg into the uterine tube. If the egg is not fertilized, a new ovarian cycle starts 14 days after ovulation.

The menstrual cycle causes a thickening of the endometrium, the lining of the uterus, in readiness to receive the fertilized egg. FSH stimulates the ovary to release estrogen, which stimulates endometrial thickening. Following ovulation, the ovary also secretes progesterone, which with estrogen stimulates further thickening of the endometrium. If fertilization does not happen, progesterone and estrogen levels drop, the endometrium fragments and falls away, and the woman has her period.

During both ovarian and menstrual cycles, as the controlling hormones—FSH, LH, estrogen, and progesterone—interact with each other their levels fluctuate, and these fluctuations control the events of the cycles.

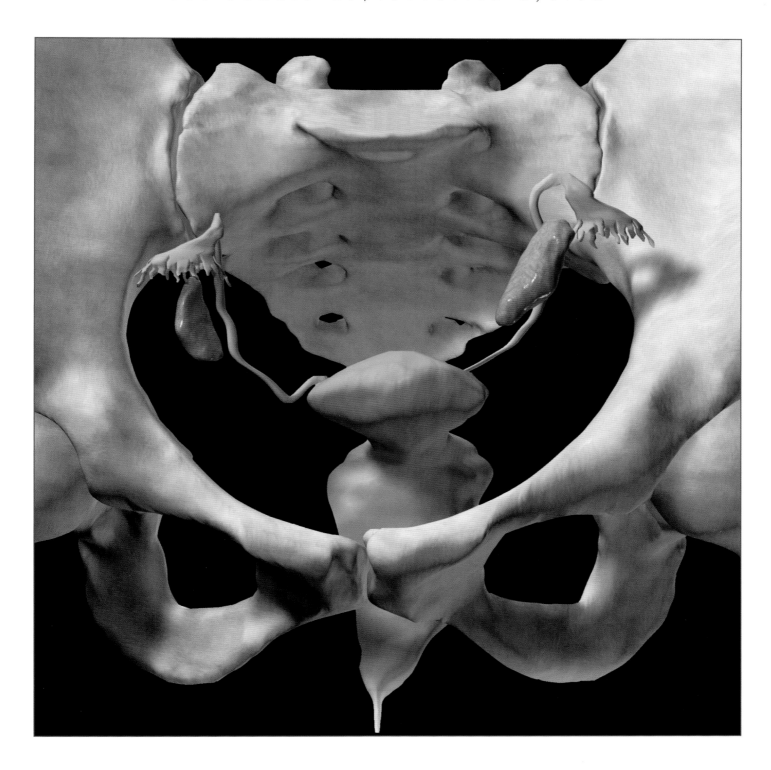

The female organs
consist of the two
ovaries, situated on
either side of the
uterus; the fallopian
tubes; the cervix; the
vagina; and the clitoris
(not shown).

KEY

1. Pelvic girdle
2. Fallopian tube
3. Ovary
4. Fimbriae
5. Uterus
6. Cervix
7. Vagina

W HILE THE OVARIES PRODUCE EGGS, OTHER PARTS OF THE FEMALE REPRODUCTIVE SYSTEM ARE RESPONSIBLE FOR MAKING POSSIBLE THE UNION OF SPERM AND EGG, AND NURTURING AN EGG IF IT IS FERTILIZED.

THE FEMALE REPRODUCTIVE SYSTEM

The uterine (fallopian) tubes receive eggs from the ovaries after ovulation, provide the location for fertilization, and carry the fertilized egg to the uterus. This hollow organ encloses and protects the **fetus** during its development. The wall of the uterus contains a thick layer of smooth muscle, the **myometrium**, that stretches enormously during pregnancy, and which contracts to push the baby out during birth. Lining the uterus is the velvety endometrium in which a fertilized egg embeds itself in order to develop.

The uterus is linked to the vagina by its neck or cervix. The vagina itself is a muscular tube between 8 and 10 cm (3 and 4 in) long that accommodates the penis during sexual intercourse and provides an exit route for discarded endometrium, during menstrual periods, and for the baby during birth.

The external genitals, or vulva, consist of the vaginal lips—the labia majora and minora—that protect the vulva, the vestibule surrounding the opening to the vagina and the urethral opening, and the clitoris. The clitoris is homologous with the penis, and is important in sexual arousal. Although its glans and shaft are much smaller than that of the penis, its internal anatomy—which has only recently been elucidated—is extensive.

The development of male and female external genitals

At six weeks after fertilization, an embryo inside the uterus is no bigger than a grape. At this stage the external genitalia are identical in both sexes. Which way the genitals develop depends on whether the embryo is genetically male—with XY sex chromosomes—or female—with XX chromosomes. In males, the Y chromosome sends out a message instructing testes to develop; as they do so the testes release testosterone, which instructs the external genitals to develop into a penis and scrotum. In the absence of a Y chromosome, a clitoris develops in place of a penis, and labia instead of a scrotum. By 12 weeks after fertilization, sex differences are evident, and at birth the baby is clearly either male or female.

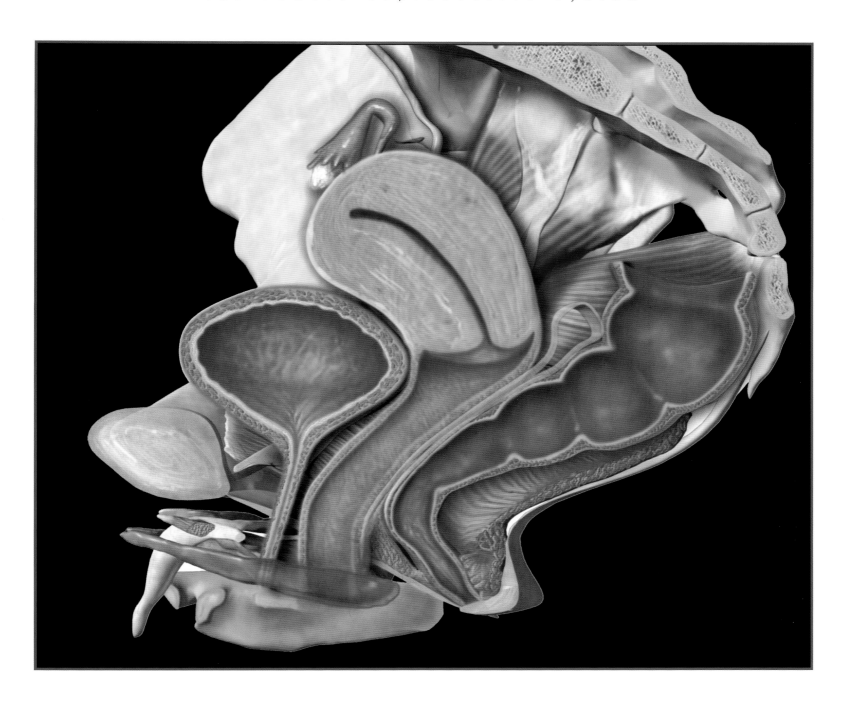

A sagittal section through the female body to show the internal reproductive organs—the ovaries, uterine tubes, uterus, and vagina—and the external genitals, including the clitoris.

KEY

1. Fallopian tube
2. Fimbriae
3. Ovary
4. Uterus
5. Urinary bladder
6. Pubic symphysis
7. Urethra
8. Clitoris
9. Labiuym minus
10. Vagina
11. Cervix
12. Rectum

FERTILIZATION

A woman's egg and a man's sperm each contain a single copy of each gene in the human genome—one half of what is needed for life. Together they can combine to form a complete set of genes containing all the DNA required to create a human being.

For women, the process begins in the ovaries where, following puberty, a mature egg is released about every 28 days. Triggered by FSH (follicle stimulating hormone) the new egg is sent to the Fallopian tube, where it may be fertilized.

For men, sperm is produced in the testes' seminiferous tubules, then matures for several weeks in the epididymus before being sent out through the vas deferens.

Although millions of sperm can be released into the uterus, only some are designed to reach and fertilize the egg.

Many of the sperm released are designed to be helpers; their main function is to block other sperm from reaching the egg.

Of the millions of sperm that are released into the uterus, only some will reach the Fallopian tube and then only one can enter the egg.

After a sperm has entered the egg, the external membrane of the egg changes so no other sperm can enter.

About 24 hours after fertilization the cell starts to divide—first into two, then four, then eight cells and so on.

The fertilized cells form a hollow ball that moves along the Fallopian tube to implant itself in the uterine wall. It is now an embryo.

The Menstrual Cycle

As the ovarian cycle prepares an egg for release each month, the menstrual cycle prepares the uterus for a fertilized egg.

The menstrual cycle starts with the thickening of the endometrium, the lining of the uterus.

Following ovulation, the ovary secretes progesterone, which triggers further thickening of the endometrium.

If fertilization does not occur, hormone levels drop and the endometrium fragments and falls away, causing menstruation.

At the end of the cycle the uterine wall is as it was about four weeks before.

FETAL DEVELOPMENT

After conception, the single-cell fertilized egg quickly divides to form a cluster of cells.

The sphere of cells travels to the uterus and implants itself in the lining. This is the beginning of the embryonic stage which lasts through the 8th week after conception or 10th week of pregnancy.

The rapidly dividing cells within the sphere organize into a disk which folds into three layers. Each layer will develop into many tissues, organs and structures, while the surrounding environment will also change to nourish, support and protect the new development.

A groove forms down the center of the disk, which now has a top and bottom, front and back, and left and right side. This neural groove deepens and then forms a tube which develops into the brain and spinal cord.

An early circulatory system develops from tubes on the left and right side of the groove. The tubes merge, kink and fuse together to form the chambers of the heart which will begin to beat and pump blood.

The central nervous system is also developing. The neural groove closes like a zipper, forming a tube that becomes the spinal cord and brain. The closing is faster toward the head-end as the different parts of the brain develop. The ends of the groove then close.

Other organs, such as the liver, begin to develop. Arm and leg buds appear. To support this growth, nutrients come from the mother through the placenta via the umbilical cord. The intestines also develop, first projecting into the umbilical cord outside the body and then inside the abdomen.

The arms and legs continue to grow, with paddle-like shapes where the hands and feet will be. The hands and feet continue to develop and soon the arm can bend at the elbows. Fingers and toes appear. Facial features start to appear as the brain grows to support the senses such as vision and hearing.

Muscles and bones develop and define. The position of the limbs moves from the center to the side and the knees take shape in the legs. Facial features become more refined. The liver and thyroid, are already function-ing. By the end of the first trimester, 14 weeks on, the developing baby is a miniature person.

At 24 weeks, the fetus is able to hear sounds. Eyebrows and eyelashes can be seen and the lungs begin to simu-late breathing movements.

At 28 weeks, the fused eyelids open and the eyes can sense light. The ability to smell begins. The fetus can suck and swallow.

Timeline

A spinal cord develops about two weeks after sperm fertilizes an egg. The fetus' head and body develop six weeks after pregnancy. The heart, eyes, brain, mouth, inner ears and digestive system begin to form. There are tiny buds that will become arms and legs. During the second month, development is very rapid as all of the major body organs and body systems, including the lungs, liver and stomach start to develop. The ears and eyelids form. Ankles, toes, wrists, fingers and sexual organs develop. At the end of the second month, the fetus resembles a miniature human infant—a little over an inch/3 cm. long, and weighing less than one oz./28 grams.

From embryo to fetus and baby in 10 stages (from left to right and from top to bottom): 3 weeks; 4 weeks; 5 weeks; 7 weeks; 8 weeks; 9 weeks; 12 weeks; 16 weeks; 30 weeks; 38 weeks

BIRTH

The birthing process averages 12-14 hours (from first contractions to delivery) for women pregnant for the first time and eight hours for women who have given birth before.

The developing fetus has grown surrounded by a sac filled with amniotic fluid. By the end of the third trimester, there is about a quart or liter of fluid in the sac.

In order to enter the birth canal, the baby must leave the sac. Prior to birth, the membrane of the sac breaks and the amniotic fluid is released and flows out of the vagina.

Usually the sac breaks naturally, but sometimes a birth attendant will need to help by rupturing the sac. The remains of the sac serve to protect the baby's head and to form a wedge against the opening cervix.

The birthing process begins with regular contractions of the uterus and dilation or opening of the cervix, the narrow opening where the uterus joins the vagina.

There are three stages of labor. Each of these stages varies according to the woman and many other factors. The first stage includes early labor, when the cervix thins (effacement) and begins to open or dilate. This stage may take hours.

During active labor, the cervix opens further and contractions become stronger and more frequent.

When the cervix is fully dilated at 10 cm. (4 in.), uterine contractions become stronger and more frequent. The baby goes through a series of passive movements, especially the head.

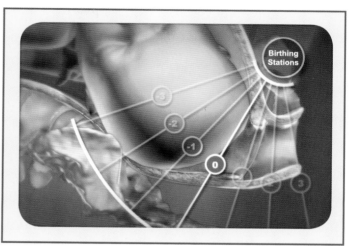

Birth stations indicate how low the baby's head can be felt in the mother's pelvis.

As the baby is pushed down the birth canal, the head rotates 90 degrees as it begins its passage out of the vagina.

When the widest part of the head is visible from outside, the baby is said to be crowning.

The baby's head turns to the side and the shoulders rotate to into position to begin their exit.

The shoulders emerge one at a time, followed by the rest of the body. The umbilical cord is sectioned and cut and the baby is truly born. During the third stage, usually shortly after birth, the placenta is delivered.

225

REGIONAL ANATOMY

WE HAVE SEEN THE INDIVIDUAL SYSTEMS OF THE BODY AS
SEPARATE PROCESSES; LOOKING AT HOW THEY FIT TOGETHER
BY REGION, OR AREA, IS THE FINAL STEP IN UNDERSTANDING
HOW THE BODY ACTUALLY LOOKS AND HOW ALL THE PARTS
OF THIS MARVELOUS MACHINE WORK TOGETHER.

THE HEAD HOUSES THE BODY'S CONTROL CENTER AND ITS MAJOR SENSORS. ITS FRAMEWORK IS FORMED BY THE SKULL, WHOSE CRANIAL BONES FORM THE DOME-SHAPED CRANIUM THAT SURROUNDS AND PROTECTS THE BRAIN, AND FACIAL BONES, WHICH FORM THE FACE. AS WELL AS THE BRAIN, THE HEAD ALSO HOUSES THE MAJOR SENSE ORGANS: THE EYES WITHIN BONY SKULL SOCKETS; THE EARS, PROTECTED WITHIN CAVERNS INSIDE THE TEMPORAL BONES; THE TONGUE, INSIDE THE MOUTH; AND THE OLFACTORY (ODOR) SENSORS INSIDE THE NOSE. TWO OPENINGS, THE MOUTH AND NOSE, ALLOW AIR INTO THE BODY, WHILE THE MOUTH ALSO PROVIDES AN ENTRY POINT FOR FOOD AND WATER.

THE HEAD & NECK

The head contains the brain, eyes and ears and provides openings to the body through the mouth and nose. The neck connects the head to the trunk.

The neck supports the head, enabling it to move, and providing a link between it and the trunk. Supporting the neck are the seven cervical vertebrae—the two uppermost of which permit the head to turn from side to side and nod up and down. Passing along the conduit formed by the neck are the major blood vessels that supply the head and brain; the trachea, which carries air to and from the lungs; the esophagus, which carries food to the stomach;

and, protected within a tunnel formed by the cervical vertebrae, the spinal cord, which links the brain to the rest of the nervous system.

Blood supply to the head and neck

Oxygen-rich blood is supplied to the head and neck by four pairs of arteries that branch directly or indirectly from the aortic arch.

- Right and left common carotid arteries each branch into an external carotid artery, which supplies most tissues of the head except the brain and orbit; and the internal carotid artery, which supplies the orbit and most of the brain.
- The vertebral arteries supply the neck, cerebellum, and part of the cerebrum.
- The thyrocervical trunks and the costocervical trunks supply the neck.

Blood drains from the head and neck along three pairs of veins that empty, usually via other veins, into the superior vena cava.

- The external jugular veins drain blood from the superficial head.
- The internal jugular veins drain blood from the brain.
- The vertebral veins drain blood from the neck.

KEY

1. Temporalis
2. Levator labii superioris alaeque nasi
3. Nasal cartilage
4. External jugular vein
5. Facial Vein
6. Mentalis
7. External carotid artery
8. Sternocleidomastoid
9. Frontalis
10. Orbicularis oculi
11. Levator labii superioris
12. Zygomaticus minor
13. Zygomaticus major
14. Orbicularis oris
15. Depressor anguli oris
16. Depressor labii inferioris
17. Sternohyoid
18. Larynx

Anterior view of the head and neck showing the superficial muscles and blood vessels. The facial muscles produce facial expressions while those of the neck either move the head or are involved in swallowing. The blood vessels supply the muscles, sense organs, and the brain.

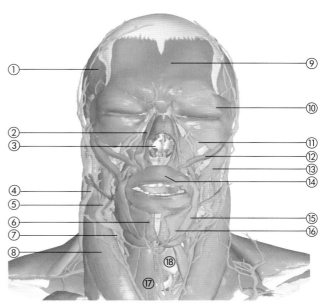

SEVERAL GROUPS OF MUSCLES ARE RESPONSIBLE FOR THE MOVEMENTS OF THE HEAD AND NECK. MOST OF THESE MUSCLES ARE CONTROLLED BY NERVE IMPULSES CARRIED BY CRANIAL NERVES.

THE HEAD & NECK

Anterolateral view of the skull and neck from the right side with the muscles and blood vessels removed.

KEY

① Cranium
② Mandible
③ Vertebral column
④ Larynx
⑤ Thyroid gland
⑥ Trachea

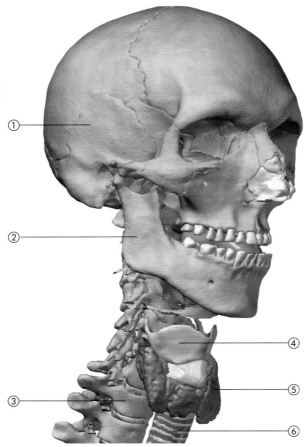

• Superficial muscles of the scalp, such as the frontalis, and of the face, such as the zygomaticus major, are responsible for producing the wide range of facial expressions that are so important in human communication. These muscles are unusual in that they insert into, and pull, the skin.

• The extrinsic eye muscles move each eyeball in its socket.

• Four pairs of mastication (chewing) muscles, including the masseter and temporalis, pull the jaw upward. Other smaller muscles move the jaw from side to side.

• The extrinsic muscles of the tongue (see below) protract and retract the tongue.

• The muscles of the front of the neck are mostly involved in swallowing.

• The sternocleidomastoid muscles flex the head and tilt it to the side.

• The muscles at the back of the neck extend the head and support it.

The tongue

This pink, muscular organ has a variety of functions relating to digestion, taste, and speech. The bulk of the tongue is made up of skeletal muscle. Extrinsic muscles attached to the mandible and hyoid bone change the position of the tongue, protruding it, retracting it, and moving it from side to side. Intrinsic muscles, which are not attached to bone, change the shape of the tongue, making it thicker or thinner. Tongue movements mix food with saliva during chewing, and push chewed food into the throat to initiate swallowing. Changes in tongue position also help convert raw sounds into understandable speech.

The upper surface of the tongue is covered by tiny protuberances, called **papillae**, of which there are three types. Numerous pointed **filiform papillae** give the tongue a roughness that helps it grip food. Mushroom-shaped **fungiform papillae**, and the large **circumvallate papilla**e at the rear of the mouth, house the taste buds. These contain sensory chemoreceptors that detect four basic tastes—sweet, salt, sour, and bitter—in food that has dissolved in saliva, and send nerve impulses to the gustatory (taste) areas of the cerebral hemispheres.

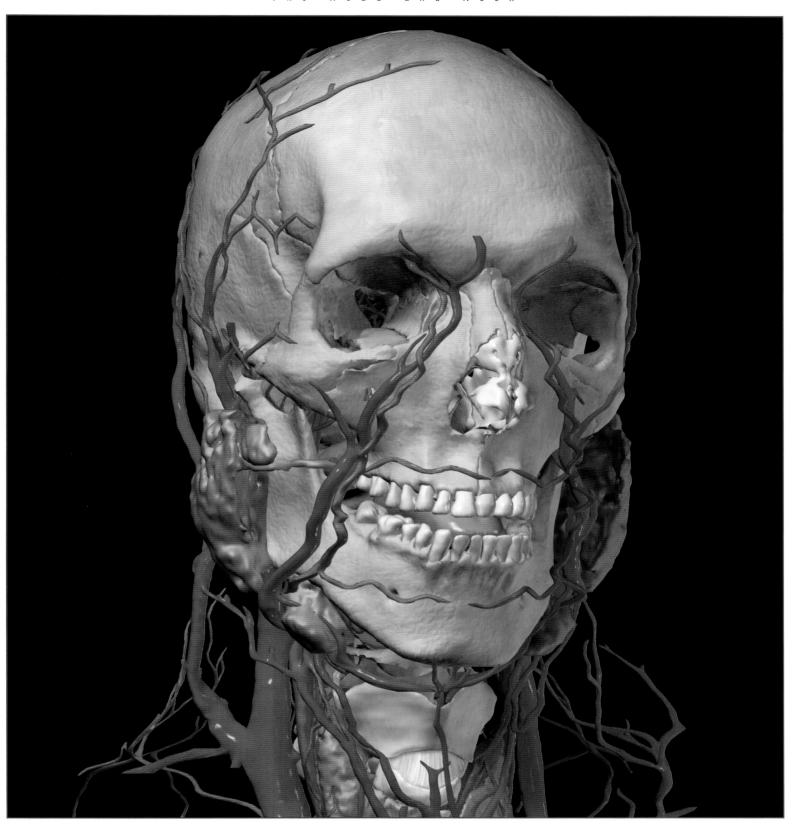

Anterolateral view of the head and neck from the right side with the muscles removed showing the major blood vessels.

KEY

① Parietal bone
② Sphenoid bone
③ Superficial temporal artery
④ Zygomatic bone
⑤ Retromandibular vein
⑥ Posterior auricular vein
⑦ Paratoid gland
⑧ Facial artery
⑨ Internal carotid artery
⑩ Submandibular gland
⑪ Internal jugular vein
⑫ External jugular vein
⑬ Common carotid artery
⑭ Frontal bone
⑮ Nasal bone
⑯ Maxilla
⑰ Tongue
⑱ Mandible
⑲ Larynx
⑳ Thyroid gland

THE CENTRAL PART OF THE BODY—THE TRUNK OR TORSO—IS
DIVIDEDINTO TWO REGIONS: THE UPPER THORAX AND, BELOW
IT, THE ABDOMEN. INTERNALLY, THESE DIVISIONS ARE REFLECTED
BY TWO MAJOR CLOSED BODY CAVITIES: THE THORACIC CAVITY AND THE
ABDOMINOPELVIC CAVITY. BOTH ARE CONFINED SPACES THAT CONTAIN ORGANS,
REFERRED TO COLLECTIVELY AS **VISCERA**. LINING THE WALL OF EACH CAVITY AND
THE SURFACE OF THE VISCERAL ORGANS IS A THIN SLIPPERY MEMBRANE, CALLED
THE SEROUS MEMBRANE. WHEN THE ORGANS MOVE, THEREFORE, THEY SLIDE
OVER EACH OTHER WITHOUT CAUSING ANY PAIN.

THE THORAX

Posterior view of the thorax shows the superficial muscles that cover its back wall. Beneath them the twelve ribs articulate with the vertebral column. Deeper muscles pull on the vertebral column to support the trunk.

The thorax, or chest, extends from the neck to the abdomen, from which it is separated by the diaphragm. External surface markings of the thorax include the outlines of the pectoralis major muscles, the ribs, and the nipples. The **nipples** are small and rudimentary in men, but larger in women, forming part of the breasts that surround the **mammary glands**, which overlie the pectoralis major muscles.

Forming the wall of the thorax are the ribs, costal cartilages, and sternum; the twelve thoracic vertebrae in the backbone; and the thoracic and intercostal muscles lying between the ribs. As well as underpinning the structure of the thorax, these bones and muscles also protect the chest's organs.

The anterior thorax includes several major superficial muscles. The pectoralis major has its origins in the clavicle, sternum, and ribs, and its insertion in the humerus. It pulls the arms forward and toward the body. Both the serratus anterior and the pectoralis minor have their origins on the ribs and insertion in the scapula. The "sawtooth" serratus anterior pulls the scapula outward and lifts the shoulder, while the pectoralis minor stabilizes and depresses the shoulder.

The deep muscles of the anterior thorax—the intercostal and the diaphragm—play a vital role in producing breathing movements. The intercostals are short muscles that extend from the inferior border of one rib to the superior border of the rib below it. The external intercostals contract to pull the rib cage upward and outward during inhalation. The internal intercostals, which lie below and at 90° to the external intercostals, contract to pull the ribcage downward and inward during forced exhalation.

KEY

1. Scapula
2. Humerus
3. Latissimus dorsi
4. Trapezius
5. Infraspinatus
6. Teres major
7. Rhomboideus
8. Erector spinae

KEY

1. Clavicle
2. Sternum
3. Serratus anterior
4. Latissimus dorsi
5. Thoracic vertebra (12th)
6. Scapula
7. Trachea
8. Humerus
9. Pectoralis major
10. Rib (6th)
11. Costal cartilage

Anterior view of the thorax showing the ribcage, which surrounds and protects the lungs and heart, and the large pectoral muscles, which are the prime movers of arm flexion. The trachea, the duct which carries air into the lungs, is kept open by reinforcing C-shaped rings of cartilage.

233

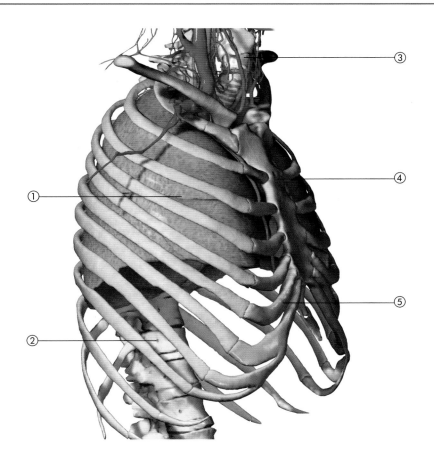

Anterolateral view of the ribcage from the right shows how it completely surrounds and protects the lungs and heart. Blood vessels supplying the neck, arms, head, and the trachea pass through the narrow opening at the top of the thorax.

KEY

① Right lung
② Thoracic vertebra (12th)
③ Trachea
④ Sternum
⑤ Costal cartilage

THE THORAX

INTERNALLY, THE THORACIC CAVITY CONTAINS THE MAJOR ORGANS OF THE CIRCULATORY AND RESPIRATORY SYSTEMS THAT, IN TURN, ARE PROTECTED BY THE RIBCAGE FORMED BY THE RIBS, STERNUM, AND BACKBONE. THE **THORACIC CAVITY** ITSELF IS SUBDIVIDED INTO SMALLER CAVITIES. LATERALLY, TWO LARGE PLEURAL CAVITIES EACH HOUSE ONE OF THE LUNGS. EACH CAVITY IS A NARROW FLUID-FILLED SPACE THAT LIES BETWEEN THE **PLEURAE,** THE SEROUS MEMBRANES THAT LINE THE WALL OF THE THORACIC CAVITY AND COVER THE LUNGS. PLEURAL FLUID, A LUBRICATING FLUID SECRETED IN THE NARROW SPACE BETWEEN THE MEMBRANES, ENABLES THE MEMBRANES TO SLIDE OVER EACH OTHER DURING BREATHING. IT ALSO HAS A HIGH SURFACE TENSION, WHICH ENSURES THAT THE LUNGS ADHERE CLOSELY TO THE THORACIC WALL AND EITHER EXPAND OR SHRINK AS THE VOLUME OF THE THORACIC CAVITY INCREASES OR DECREASES, RESPECTIVELY.

The **mediastinum**, between the two lungs, contains the esophagus, the trachea, and major blood and lymphatic vessels. It also contains the **pericardial cavity**, a fluid-filled cavity that lies between the pericardia, the serous membranes that cover the heart and line the thoracic cavity, and which allows the heart to contract and expand without friction during the cardiac cycle.

The diaphragm

The diaphragm—the name means "partition across"—is a broad, skeletal muscle that forms the boundary between the thoracic and abdominopelvic cavities. Its origins lie in the lower border of the ribcage and sternum, the lower costal cartilages, and the lumbar vertebrae. Centrally is a boomerang-shaped tendon. The diaphragm is the prime mover of breathing movements, and is assisted by the intercostal muscles. When relaxed it is dome-shaped, as a result of being pushed upward by the abdominal organs. When the diaphragm contracts, it flattens, pushes the abdominal contents downward, expands the thorax, and draws air into the lungs; on relaxation, it assumes its dome shape, and pushes air out of the lungs. Sensory output from, and motor input into, the diaphragm is provided by the phrenic nerve. The diaphragm and its tendon are pierced by three foramina (openings)—for the aorta, inferior vena cava, and esophagus, respectively—that permit communication between thorax and abdomen.

Anterior view of the bones—the sternum, ribs, and thoracic vertebrae—that make up the thoracic or rib cage.

KEY

1. Right lung
2. Sternum
3. Costal cartilage
4. Xiphoid process
5. Left lung
6. Heart
7. Rib (6th)

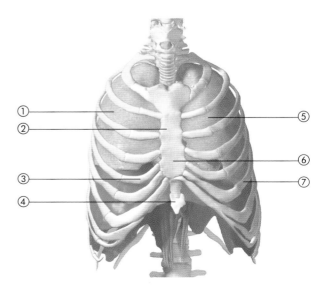

T HE ABDOMEN, OR BELLY, MAKES UP THE LOWER HALF OF THE TRUNK, EXTENDING FROM THE DIAPHRAGM, THE SHEET OF MUSCLE THAT SEPARATES IT FROM THE THORAX, TO THE BASE OF THE PELVIS. FOR DESCRIPTIVE PURPOSES, THE ABDOMEN IS NORMALLY DIVIDED INTO THE ABDOMEN PROPER, WHICH IS DESCRIBED IN THIS SECTION, AND THE PELVIS, WHICH IS DESCRIBED IN THAT SECTION.

THE ABDOMEN

Anterior view of the abdominal muscles. The abdomen lacks any bony reinforcement, so the paired muscles of the anterior and lateral abdominal walls protect and support the internal organs. They also flex and rotate the trunk.

KEY

1. External oblique
2. Pelvis
3. Latissimus dorsi
4. Linea alba
5. Tendinous intersection
6. Rectus abdominis
7. Sternum
8. Rib

Anterior, external view of the abdomen, the lower section of the trunk, which is separated internally from the thorax by the diaphragm.

The abdominal wall is formed largely from muscle, a direct contrast with the bony cage that surrounds the thorax. The abdominal muscles play an important role in protecting and maintaining the position of the viscera (organs) inside the abdominal cavity; they also flex and support the trunk. Anteriorly, the abdominal wall is formed by the straplike rectus abdominis muscle, which runs medially and vertically; and three pairs of layered muscles that extend round the side of the body to form the lateral section of the wall. These muscles are—from superficial to deep—the external oblique, which runs medially and downward; the internal oblique, which runs at 90° to the external oblique; and the rectus abdominis, which runs horizontally. When these muscles are well toned they hold the abdominal contents in, but if not sufficiently exercised they allow the organs to bulge outward, forming a "potbelly." The posterior part of the abdominal wall is formed by the lumbar section of the backbone, and the quadratus lumborum muscles that extend from the pelvis to the backbone, and serve to maintain an upright posture.

The abdominal cavity is packed with organs. The stomach, small intestine, and large intestine make up most of the digestive system, the latter two organs occupying most of the space inside the abdominal cavity. The liver and pancreas are accessory digestive organs that also have other functions. The spleen is involved in defending the body against disease. The two kidneys excrete wastes in the form of urine and help maintain water and salt balance in body fluids. Because the diaphragm domes upward, the liver and stomach are partly enclosed and protected by the lowest ribs.

Anterior view of the abdomen with the abdominal musculature removed showing the greater omentum, part of the abdominal mesenteries. Partially covering the stomach and intestines, the apron-like omentum stores fat, contains lymph nodes that destroy pathogens entering the body through the abdominal organs, helps insulate and facilitates movement of the small intestines.

KEY

① Diaphragm

② Ascending colon

③ Pelvis

④ Ileum

⑤ Sternum

⑥ Rib (6th)

⑦ Costal cartilage

⑧ Greater omentum

⑨ Descending colon

⑩ Rectum

Lateral view of the abdomen showing the liver, small intestine and rectum.

KEY

① Rib
② Right kidney
③ Vertebral column
④ Pelvis
⑤ Rectum
⑥ Liver
⑦ Small intestine
⑧ Ascending colon

THE ABDOMEN

I NTERNALLY, THE LOWER PART OF THE TRUNK IS OCCUPIED BY THE ABDOMINOPELVIC CAVITY WHOSE UPPER BOUNDARY IS FORMED BY THE DIAPHRAGM AND LOWER BY THE PELVIC FLOOR MUSCLES. THIS CAVITY IS SEPARATED INTO AN UPPER ABDOMINAL SECTION THAT CONTAINS THE DIGESTIVE ORGANS, SPLEEN, KIDNEYS, AND OTHER ORGANS, AND A LOWER PELVIC SECTION CONTAINING THE REPRODUCTIVE ORGANS AND BLADDER.

As in the thorax, the wall of the abdominopelvic cavity is lined by a serous membrane, which also covers the surface of its organs. Where it lines the cavity the membrane is called the **parietal peritoneum**, and where it covers organs it is referred to as **visceral peritoneum**. Fluid secreted by these peritonea lubricates their surfaces and allows digestive organs to slide over each other painlessly while digestive movements are taking place. Some organs—including the kidneys and pancreas—lie between the peritoneum and posterior abdominal wall and are referred to as **retroperitoneal**.

Within the cavity the peritoneum forms large folds that serve to hold organs in place, while allowing a degree of movement. They also carry blood vessels, lymph vessels, and nerves to abdominal organs, and act as fat stores. These folds include the **mesentery**, **mesocolon**, and the lesser and greater **omenta**.

The fetal digestive system

The first signs of the digestive system appear just two weeks after fertilization. A pouch, called the primitive gut, arises that later differentiates into a **foregut**, **midgut**, and **hindgut**. By eight weeks, the fetus has developed a continuous alimentary canal with openings at the mouth and anus. The foregut gives rise to the pharynx, esophagus, stomach, and part of the duodenum; the midgut forms the rest of the small intestine, and part of the large intestine; and the hindgut makes up the rest of the large intestine. Pouches arising from the foregut form the accessory digestive organs: the salivary glands, liver, gallbladder, and pancreas. In the uterus, the fetus receives all its nutrients from its mother by way of the placenta and **umbilical cord**. However, the alimentary canal is brought into operation when the fetus swallows some of the **amniotic fluid** surrounding it. This fluid contains chemicals that stimulate the maturation of the alimentary canal so that it is ready for its first feeds after birth.

Anterior view of the abdomen showing the entire contents, but with the omentum removed.

KEY

1. Liver
2. Rib
3. Costal cartilage
4. Transverse colon
5. Ileum
6. Pelvis
7. Stomach
8. Pancreas
9. Descending colon
10. Sigmoid colon
11. Rectum

T HE PELVIS, OR PELVIC REGION, IS THE LOWEST PART OF THE TRUNK AND IS SITUATED BETWEEN THE ABDOMEN AND THE JUNCTION BETWEEN THE TRUNK AND THE LOWER LIMBS. INTERNALLY, THE PELVIC REGION IS SUPPORTED BY A BONY FRAMEWORK FORMED ANTERIORLY AND LATERALLY BY THE PELVIC GIRDLE, AND POSTERIORLY BY THE SACRUM AND COCCYX AT THE BASE OF THE BACKBONE. COLLECTIVELY THE TWO COXAE (HIP BONES), WHICH MAKE UP THE PELVIC GIRDLE, AND THE SACRUM AND COCCYX ARE CALLED THE PELVIS.

THE PELVIS

The bony pelvis surrounds the pelvic cavity, the funnel-shaped lower section of the abdominopelvic cavity, and provides protection for the organs contained within it. Pelvic organs include the sigmoid colon, rectum, and anal cavity, the final sections of the alimentary canal; the urinary bladder, the lower parts of the ureters, and the urethra; and the internal reproductive organs. As in the abdominal cavity, much of the cavity's lining is covered by parietal peritoneum, and some of the organs by visceral peritoneum; however, some organs, such as the bladder, are **retroperitoneal**.

Unlike most other parts of the body, male and female pelvic regions are anatomically distinct because of differences in the shape and size of the pelvis and because male and female reproductive organs are completely different. The lower opening of the pelvis—the pelvic outlet—is closed by pelvic floor muscles—or the pelvic diaphragm. These muscles support the organs of the pelvic cavity and prevent them being pushed downward by pressure from the abdominal organs above them.

As well as protecting and supporting pelvic organs, the bony pelvis also provides a large surface for the attachment of both trunk and leg muscles. Muscles passing from the pelvis to the legs include the iliacus, the prime mover of hip flexion; the adductors, which adduct and laterally rotate the thigh; the quadriceps, which extend the knee and flex the thigh at the hip; the gluteal (buttock) muscles, which extend the thigh; and the hamstrings, which extend the thigh and flex the knee. Muscles passing from pelvis to trunk include the muscles of the anterior and lateral abdominal wall, which hold the abdominal organs in place and flex and rotate the trunk; and the muscles of the lower back, which extend and support the trunk.

The large surface area of the bony pelvis houses and protects the delicate organs within. It also provides maximum surface area for muscular attachment.

All the images in this chapter are of the female pelvis.

External, anterolateral view of the female pelvis from the right side shows the pelvis as the area between the abdomen and the junction of the trunk with the lower limbs. Between the legs the labia majora border the vulva and surround the openings of the urethra and the vagina.

KEY

① Pelvis
② Right leg
③ Mons veneris
④ Left leg
⑤ Labium majus

Anterolateral view of the female pelvis with the skin and superficial muscles removed.

KEY

① Iliopsoas
② Psoas
③ Iliacus
④ Iliac crest
⑤ Tensor fasciae latae
⑥ Femur
⑦ Ureter (right)
⑧ Sacrum
⑨ Common iliac artery
⑩ Common iliac vein
⑪ Internal iliac artery

⑫ Internal iliac vein
⑬ Ovary
⑭ External iliac artery
⑮ External iliac vein
⑯ Uterus
⑰ Round ligament of uterus
⑱ Urinary bladder
⑲ Pubic symphysis
⑳ Pubis
㉑ Clitoris

THE ARM & ELBOW

THE VERSATILE UPPER LIMB CAN PERFORM A WIDE
RANGE OF MOVEMENTS. ITS BONY FRAMEWORK
IS FORMED BY THE HUMERUS (UPPER ARM BONE),
RADIUS AND ULNA (FOREARM BONES), AND THE CARPALS,
METACARPALS, AND PHALANGES (HAND BONES). PROXIMALLY, THE
HUMERUS ARTICULATES WITH THE SCAPULA IN THE SHOULDER AT A
BALL AND SOCKET JOINT THAT PERMITS MOVEMENT IN ALL PLANES.
DISTALLY, THE HUMERUS ARTICULATES WITH THE RADIUS AND
ULNA AT THE ELBOW, OR CUBITAL ARTICULATION. THIS INCLUDES A
HINGE JOINT BETWEEN THE HUMERUS AND THE RADIUS AND ULNA,
WHICH PERMITS ONLY FLEXION AND EXTENSION, AND A PIVOT
JOINT BETWEEN THE HEADS OF THE RADIUS AND ULNA, WHICH
PERMITS ROTATION OF THE FOREARM. THE COMBINED EFFECTS
OF THE JOINTS IS EXEMPLIFIED BY A TENNIS SERVE: THE SHOULDER
JOINT ALLOWS THE ARM TO MOVE THROUGH A WIDE ARC, THE
ELBOW ALLOWS THE ARM TO BEND AND THEN STRAIGHTEN
DURING THE SERVE,
WHILE THE FINGERS
GRIP THE RACKET.

Two sets of muscles serve the upper arm and elbow.
Nine muscles cross the shoulder joint and insert
into the humerus: the pectoralis major, latissimus
dorsi, and deltoid are prime movers of arm
movement and are assisted by the teres major and
corachobrachialis; the supraspinatus, infraspinatus,
teres minor, and subscapularis (rotator cuff muscles)
stabilize the flexible but also unstable shoulder joint.
The second set of muscles are those that cross the
elbow joint. The anterior forearm muscles—the
biceps brachii, brachialis, and brachioradialis—flex the
elbow; the posterior forearm muscles—the triceps
brachii and anconeus—extend the elbow.

The main nerves supplying the upper arm are the
musculocutaneous nerve, which serves the flexor
muscles of the anterior arm; and the axillary nerve,
which serves deltoid and teres minor muscles. The
median, ulnar, and radial nerves pass through the
upper arm to the forearm, although the latter also
serves the triceps brachii.

Blood enters the upper arm through the axillary
artery, which, as it passes through the axilla
(armpit), becomes the brachial artery. This supplies
the anterior forearm muscles while its branch, the
deep brachial artery, supplies the posterior triceps
brachii. Immediately below the elbow the brachial
artery divides to form the radial and ulnar arteries.
Blood drains from the upper arm through the
brachial, cephalic, and basilic veins, which unite
in the shoulder to form the axillary vein.

KEY

① Spine of scapula

② Teres minor

③ Infraspinatus

④ Teres major

⑤ Triceps brachii (long head)

⑥ Tendon of triceps brachii

⑦ Deltoid

⑧ Triceps brachii (lateral head)

⑨ Superficial veins

**Posterior view of the
right arm showing
the muscles of the
shoulder and upper
arm and some
superficial arteries
and veins.**

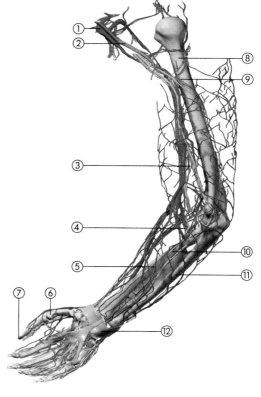

Posterior view of the right arm showing the bones and major arteries and veins.

KEY

1. Cephalic vein
2. Axillary artery
3. Brachial artery
4. Radial artery
5. Radius
6. Metacarpal of thumb
7. Distal phalanx of thumb
8. Humerus
9. Deep brachial artery
10. Ulnar artery
11. Ulna
12. Extensor reticulum

Lateral view of the right arm showing the muscles of the shoulder, upper arm and part of the forearm and the major veins.

KEY

1. Deltoid
2. Cephalic vein
3. Triceps brachii (medial head
4. Extensor digitorum
5. Clavicle
6. Subclavian vein
7. Superior vena cava
8. Axillary vein
9. Axillary artery
10. Brachialis
11. Biceps brachii
12. Brachioradialis
13. Extensor carpi radialis longus
14. Extensor carpi radialis brevis

A COMPLEX NETWORK OF BONES, MUSCLES, NERVES, AND BLOOD VESSELS MAKES THE FOREARM AND HAND THE MOST EFFICIENT AND VERSATILE MANIPULATIVE DEVICE FOUND IN THE ANIMAL KINGDOM. UNDERPINNING THIS LOWER PART OF THE UPPER LIMB IS A FRAMEWORK OF 29 BONES. THE FOREARM BONES, RADIUS AND ULNA, HAVE PIVOT JOINTS AT THEIR PROXIMAL AND DISTAL ARTICULATIONS THAT PERMIT THE PALM OF THE HAND TO BE TURNED UPWARD OR DOWNWARD. THE HAND ITSELF CONSISTS OF 27 BONES, THAT MAKE UP THE WRIST, PALM, AND FINGERS. WHERE THE RADIUS MEETS THE WRIST BONES IT FORMS A CONDYLOID JOINT THAT PERMITS MOVEMENT IN MOST PLANES.

THE FOREARM & HAND

KEY

1. Radius
2. Radial artery
3. Palmar digital arteries
4. Ulna
5. Interosseous membrane
6. Ulnar artery
7. Extensor retinaculum
8. Palmar aponeurosis

Anterior view of the right forearm and hand showing the radius and ulna, and the interosseous membrane that links them, and the main arteries.

The wrist and fingers are moved primarily by the muscles of the forearm. These muscles taper into long tendons that insert into the wrist, palm, or fingers. Muscles of the anterior forearm are mostly flexors; they include wrist flexors, such as the flexor carpi radialis, and finger flexors, such as the flexor digitorum superficialis. Muscles of the posterior forearm are mainly extensors; they include wrist extensors, such as the extensor carpi ulnaris, and finger extensors, such as the extensor digitorum.

The main nerves passing along the forearm are the ulnar nerve, which follows the ulna along the medial forearm into the hand, the radial nerve, which follows the radius along the lateral side of the forearm, and the median nerve, which runs in the anterior forearm between these other two nerves.

The action of most flexor muscles of the forearm is controlled by the median nerve, although the flexor carpi ulnaris is controlled by the ulnar nerve. The radial nerve controls most of the extensor muscles of the forearm.

Blood is carried into the forearm by the branches of the brachial artery: the radial artery supplies the lateral muscles of the forearm while the ulnar artery supplies the medial muscles. Blood is drained from the forearm by the three superficial veins—the cephalic vein, which runs laterally, the basilic vein, which runs medially, and the median vein, which is located between the other two and merges with one of them at the elbow—and two deep veins—the radial vein and ulnar vein—that follow the course of the radius and ulna, respectively.

Inset above: posterolateral view of the right arm showing the bones, arteries and veins.

Below: Palmar (anterior, pal upward) view of the right hand showing muscles, tendons and arteries.

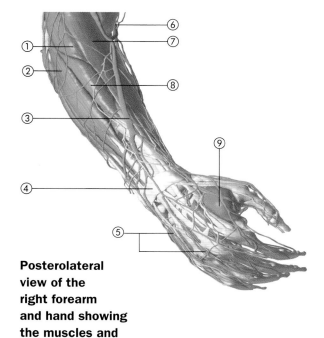

Posterolateral view of the right forearm and hand showing the muscles and blood vessels.

KEY

① Extensor carpi radialis longus

② Extensor digitorum

③ Cephalic vein

④ Extensor retinaculum

⑤ Dorsal venous network of hand

⑥ Antecubital vein

⑦ Brachioradialis

⑧ Extensor carpi radialis brevis

⑨ 1st dorsal interosseous

⑩ Axillary vein

⑪ Brachial artery

⑫ Humerus

⑬ Radius

⑭ Ulnar

⑮ Palmar digital arteries

THE HAND

FROM THREADING A NEEDLE TO LIFTING A BARBELL, THE HAND CAN PERFORM A WIDE RANGE OF GRIPPING MOVEMENTS THAT INVOLVE VARYING DEGREES OF POWER AND PRECISION. THE SKIN OF THE FINGERS AND PALM ARE ALSO WELL ENDOWED WITH SENSORY RECEPTORS THAT MAKE THE HANDS AMONG THE MOST SENSITIVE PARTS OF THE BODY.

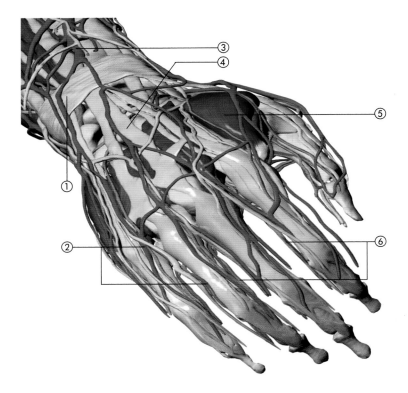

The versatility of movement and grip shown by the hand is underpinned by its bony framework. 27 bones make up the hand: eight carpals (wrist bones), five metacarpals (palm bones), and 14 phalanges (finger bones). Plane joints between carpal bones and between the carpals and metacarpals of digits 2–5 (digit 1 is the thumb) allow small gliding movements, but collectively they provide a flexible bridge between wrist and fingers. The metacarpophalangeal (knuckle) joints between the metacarpals and digits 2–5 are condyloid joints that allow movement in two planes. The joints between phalanges are hinge joints that allow movement in just one plane. Between the carpals and the metacarpal of the thumb is a saddle joint that allows flexion and extension, abduction and adduction, and **opposition** and **reposition**. This latter set of movements allows the tip of the thumb to oppose (touch) the tips of all other digits, something that is vitally important in precise movements.

The main movers of the hand, the flexor and extensor muscles of the forearm, are assisted by intrinsic muscles inside the hands. Five lumbrical muscles, and seven deeper interosseal muscles (four dorsal and three palmar) flex the knuckles but extend the fingers. In addition, the dorsal interosseals abduct (spread) the fingers, and the palmar interosseals adduct (close) the fingers. At the base of the thumb are three muscles that move it: the abductor pollicis abducts the thumb, the flexor pollicis brevis flexes the thumb, and the opponens pollicis rolls the thumb toward the midline.

The median and ulnar nerves continue into the hand from the forearm. The median nerve serves the intrinsic muscles and the skin of the lateral part of the hand, while the ulnar nerve serves the other intrinsic muscles and the skin of the medial hand.

In the palm of the hand, branches of the radial and ulnar arteries **anastomose** (join) to form two palmar arches, one deep and one superficial, that loop around the palm. Metacarpal and digital arteries, which supply the fingers, arise from the palmar arches. Deep and superficial venous arches drain oxygen-poor blood into the radial and ulnar veins, while in the dorsum (upper part) of the hand, the dorsal venous arch drains blood into the cephalic, median, and basilic veins of the forearm.

Posterior (palm down) view of the hand showing the muscles and major superficial blood vessels.

KEY

1. Extensor retinaculum
2. Dorsal digital veins
3. Cephalic vein
4. Tendon of extensor digitorum
5. Dorsal interosseous
6. Dorsal digital arteries

Anterior (palm up) view of the hand showing the muscles, arteries, and veins.

KEY

① Radial artery

② Abductor pollicis brevis

③ Lumbrical

④ Phalanges of third digit

⑤ Ulnar artery

⑥ Superficial palmar arterior arch

⑦ Palmar aponeurosis

⑧ Abductor digiti minimi

⑨ Metacarpal of third digit

⑩ Palmar digital veins

⑪ Palmar digital arteries

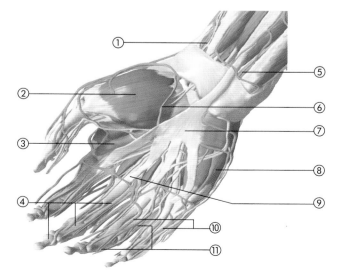

THE LOWER LIMBS SUPPORT THE WEIGHT OF THE BODY, MOVE IT, AND WITHSTAND CONSIDERABLE FORCES DURING MOVEMENT. THESE FUNCTIONS ARE REFLECTED IN THE LOWER LIMB'S CONSTRUCTION. COMPARED TO THE UPPER LIMB, THE BONES OF THE LOWER LIMB ARE THICKER AND ITS MUSCLES ARE LARGER AND STRONGER. EACH LIMB HAS THREE SECTIONS: THE THIGH, WHICH EXTENDS FROM PELVIS TO KNEE; THE LEG, WHICH EXTENDS FROM KNEE TO ANKLE; AND THE FOOT.

THE THIGH & KNEE

The femur, or thigh bone, articulates with the pelvis at the hip joint, a ball and socket joint that lacks the flexibility of the shoulder joint, but is more stable. At the knee the femur articulates with the tibia in a hinge joint that permits flexion and extension. The knee joint is reinforced by strong ligaments and is protected anteriorly by the patella or kneecap.

Muscles that move the leg have their origins in the pelvis and either cross the hip joint to insert into the femur, or cross both hip and knee joints to insert into the tibia. Muscles of the anterior thigh, notably the powerful quadriceps femoris, typically flex the thigh at the hip and extend the limb at the knee producing the forward swing of the lower limb during walking. Muscles of the medial thigh are adductors that pull the leg medially. Muscles of the posterior thigh, notably the hamstring muscles, typically extend the thigh at the hip and flex the limb at the knee producing the backward swing of the lower limb during walking. The gluteal, or buttock, muscles are major hip extensors that are used during climbing and running.

Nerves supplying the lower limb arise from the lumbar and sacral plexuses. From the lumbar plexus, the femoral nerve serves the anterior thigh muscles and the skin of the anterior thigh; the obturator nerve serves the adductor muscles and the skin of the medial thigh; and the lateral femoral cutaneous nerve serves the skin of the lateral thigh. From the sacral plexus, the sacral nerve serves the hamstrings; the superior and inferior gluteal nerves serve the gluteal muscles; and the posterior femoral cutaneous nerve serves the skin of the buttocks and posterior thigh.

Blood is supplied to the muscles of the thigh by the external iliac artery, which becomes the femoral artery as it enters the thigh, and to the gluteal and adductor muscles by the internal iliac artery. The femoral artery becomes the popliteal artery as it approaches the knee. Blood is drained from the thigh through the femoral vein, which becomes the external iliac vein as it enters the pelvis, and superficially by the great saphenous vein.

Posterior view of the pelvis and thigh showing the muscles.

KEY

1. Sacrum
2. Semitendinosus
3. Semimembranosus
4. Gluteus medius
5. Gluteus maximus
6. Vastus lateralis
7. Biceps femoris
8. Posterior femoral cutaneous nerve

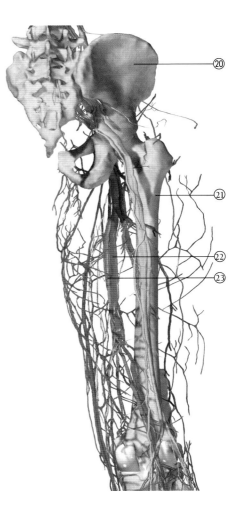

Above and center: anterior view of the thigh showing the muscles and, where the muscles are removed at the hip, the blood vessels.

Far right, top: lateral view of the right leg showing the muscles.

Far right, bottom: posterior view of the right leg showing the bones and the main arteries and veins.

KEY

① Ilium

② Tensor fasciae latae

③ Femoral artery

④ Femoral vein

⑤ Rectus femoris

⑥ Vastus lateralis

⑦ Vastus medialis

⑧ Quadriceps femoris

⑨ Patella

⑩ Sacrum

⑪ Pectineus

⑫ Adductor longus

⑬ Sartorius

⑭ Gracilis

⑮ Biceps femoris

⑯ Vertebral column

⑰ Iliac crest

⑱ Gluteus maximus

⑲ Iliotibial tract

⑳ Pelvis

㉑ Femur

㉒ Femoral vein

㉓ Femoral artery

THE BONY FRAMEWORK OF THE LEG CONSISTS OF TWO PARALLEL BONES, THE TIBIA AND FIBULA. THE LARGER OF THE TWO, THE TIBIA, ARTICULATES PROXIMALLY WITH THE FEMUR AT THE KNEE, AND DISTALLY WITH THE TALUS, A FOOT BONE, AT THE ANKLE. BOTH OF THESE JOINTS ARE HINGE JOINTS THAT ALLOW FLEXION AND EXTENSION ONLY. TIBIA AND FIBULA ARE BOUND BY AN INTEROSSEOUS MEMBRANE AND, ALTHOUGH THEY ARTICULATE PROXIMALLY AND DISTALLY, THESE JOINTS, UNLIKE THOSE BETWEEN ULNA AND RADIUS IN THE FOREARM, DO NOT ALLOW MOVEMENT. WHILE THE FOREARM IS ADAPTED FOR FLEXIBILITY AND MOBILITY, THE LEG—SPECIFICALLY THE TIBIA—IS ADAPTED FOR STABILITY AND WEIGHT-BEARING. THE FIBULA IS NOT WEIGHT-BEARING AND SERVES TO HELP STABILIZE THE ANKLE JOINT. THE FOOT SUPPORTS THE BODY AND ACTS AS A LEVER TO PUSH THE BODY FORWARD DURING MOVEMENT.

THE LEG & FOOT

The muscles of the leg move the ankle and foot. Most leg muscles have their origin in the leg itself and, like the forearm muscles, taper into long tendons that cross the ankle and insert into foot bones. The muscles are bound by a sock-like connective tissue fascia that stops them swelling excessively during exercise, and extend inward to form three compartments—anterior, posterior, and lateral—each with its own nerve and blood supply. The anterior leg muscles dorsiflex (bend upward) the foot to prevent the toes dragging along the ground while walking; two extensor muscles also straighten the toes. The more powerful posterior leg muscles plantar flex (bend downward) the foot, thereby providing the thrust for movement; the flexor muscles also bend the toes. The lateral peroneal muscles plantar flex and evert (turn outward) the foot.

Nervous supply to the leg is provided by the two components of the sciatic nerve, the common peroneal and tibial nerves, which divide just above the knee. The common peroneal nerve branches to form the deep peroneal nerve, which serves the anterior muscles and skin, and the superficial peroneal nerve, which serves the lateral muscles and skin. The tibial nerve serves the posterior muscles and skin.

Arterial blood is supplied by the popliteal artery, which divides below the knee into the anterior and posterior tibial arteries. The anterior tibial artery supplies the anterior muscles. The posterior tibial artery supplies the posterior muscles, while its branch, the peroneal artery, supplies the lateral peroneal arteries. Blood is drained from the leg though the anterior and posterior tibial veins, which join at the knee to form the popliteal vein; the peroneal vein, which drains into the posterior tibial vein; and, superficially, through the smaller saphenous vein, which empties into the saphenous vein, and the greater saphenous vein.

Posterior view of the right leg and foot showing the bones and blood vessels.

KEY

1. Posterior tibial artery
2. Fibula
3. Tibia
4. Tarsal
5. Metatarsal
6. Phalanx

Lateral view of the right leg and foot (above left), and posterior view of the right leg and foot (above right) both showing superficial muscles and nerves.

KEY

1. Gastrocnemius
2. Soleus
3. Peroneous longus
4. Calcaneal (Achilles) tendon
5. Calcaneus (heel bone)
6. Tibialis anterior
7. Extensor digitorum longus
8. Extensor retinaculum
9. Extensor digitorum brevis
10. Plantar aponeurosis

WHILE ITS COMPONENT PARTS ARE SIMILAR TO THOSE OF THE HAND, THE FOOT HAS A VERY DIFFERENT JOB TO DO. THE FEET SUPPORT THE BODY, PROVIDE LEVERS THAT PUSH THE BODY OFF THE GROUND WHILE WALKING OR RUNNING, AND FORM A RESILIENT AND SPRINGY BASE THAT ACCEPTS THE WEIGHT OF THE BODY ON BOTH FLAT AND UNEVEN SURFACES.

THE FOOT

Plantar (underneath) view of the foot showing muscles and superficial blood vessels.

KEY

1. Plantar digital veins
2. Plantar digital arteries
3. Lumbrical
4. Abductor digiti minimi
5. Plantar aponeurosis
6. Calcaneus (heel bone)
7. Abductor hallucis
8. Flexor digitorum brevis

Twenty-six bones make up the framework of the foot; seven tarsal (ankle) bones; five metatarsal (sole bones); and 14 phalanges (toe bones). Between tarsal bones, and between tarsals and metatarsals, are plane joints that allow small gliding movements and provide limited flexibility to the bones that form the springy arches of the foot. Joints between phalanges are the same as in the hand, but the phalanges in the foot are much shorter and lack the same manipulative capabilities or functions.

The prime movers of ankle and foot movement, the leg muscles, are assisted by smaller intrinsic muscles in the foot. These muscles also serve to maintain the stability of the foot as it adjusts to the constantly changing forces placed upon it. On the dorsal (upper) surface, the extensor digitorum brevis extends the toes. On the plantar surface, muscles flex, abduct (spread) and adduct the toes. Overlying the flexor digitorum brevis on the plantar surface is the plantar aponeurosis, which links the calcaneus to the toes and forms a protective sheet that holds muscles and tendons in place.

The tibial nerve serves the intrinsic muscles of the foot and the skin of the sole of the foot while the common peroneal nerve serves the skin of the upper foot. The anterior tibial artery becomes the dorsalis pedis artery as it passes through the ankle forming the arcuate artery, which gives rise to the metatarsal arteries of the sole of the foot. The posterior tibial artery divides into medial and lateral plantar arteries in the ankle. The lateral plantar artery forms the plantar arch, which gives off the digital arteries that supply the toes. Blood is drained from the toes along the digital veins, which enter the plantar arch and, via the lateral and medial plantar veins, the posterior tibial vein. The dorsalis pedis vein of the foot empties into the anterior tibial vein. Blood from the metatarsal veins drains via the venous arch into the great and small saphenous veins.

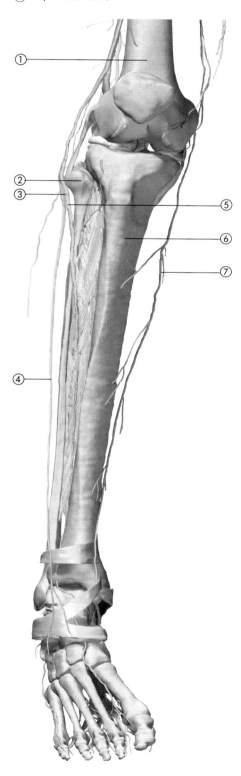

**Below: anterior view of
the right leg showing
the bones and nerves.**

KEY

① Femur

② Fibula

③ Common peroneal nerve

④ Superficial peroneal nerve

⑤ Deep peroneal nerve

⑥ Tibia

⑦ Saphenous nerve

KEY

① Extensor digitorum
   longus

② Extensor digitorum brevis

③ Tendons of extensor
   digitorum

④ Dorsal interosseous

⑤ Extensor retinacula

⑥ Dorsalis pedis artery

⑦ Metatarsal of first digit
   (great toe)

⑧ Dorsal digital arteries

⑨ Phalanges of first digit
   (great toe)

**Above: view of the
right foot from above,
showing the muscles
and superficial blood
vessels.**

GLOSSARY

Abduction Movement of a bone or limb away from the midline of the body.

Absorption The process of absorbing simple nutrient molecules into the bloodstream.

Acini Cell clusters within the pancreas that secrete digestive juice.

Actin One of two proteins constituting the myofilament of muscle.

Adduction Movement of a limb or bone towards the midline of the body (opposite of abduction).

Adipose Fat; relating to fat.

Adrenaline *See* **epinephrine**.

Adrenocorticotropic hormone (ACTH) Hormone produced by the anterior pituitary gland in response to corticotrophin releasing hormone, produced by the hypothalamus. ACTH stimulates the adrenals to produce various steroid hormones.

Afferent Toward a center; usually relating to arteries, veins or nerves; e.g., afferent nerves carry input from sensory receptors to the central nervous system.

Agonist Prime mover; a muscle that provides the main force for a movement.

Aldosterone Hormone produced by the adrenal cortex that causes sodium retention by the kidneys.

Alpha cell Cells within the pancreatic islets of the pancreas that release the hormone, glucagon, in response to low glucose levels. Glucagon stimulates the liver to turn glycogen into glucose.

Amniotic fluid Protective fluid filling the amnion, the membrane surrounding the fetus, in which the fetus is free to move.

Ampulla A small dilation in a canal or duct.

Amylase Enzyme found in saliva that breaks down starch into maltose.

Anastomose Area where two branching communications networks, e.g., nerves, arteries, or blood vessels join.

Androgen Male sex steroid hormone. Principal mammalian androgen is testosterone.

Antagonist A muscle that opposes the action of a prime mover (e.g., the triceps brachii—the prime mover of forearm extension—is the antagonist of the biceps brachii—the prime mover of forearm flexion).

Anterior Before; in front of; in the front part of; anatomical term referring to the front part of the body, or of any structure. *See also* **ventral.**

Antibody Proteins produced by lymphocytes in response to an antigen (such as a toxin or bacteria), which the antibody then destroys.

Antidiuretic hormone (ADH) Hormone secreted by the posterior pituitary gland. Causes the kidneys to retain water, thus secreting more concentrated urine.

Aponeuroses Flat, straplike tendons that link muscle to bone and also muscle to muscle.

Arteries A blood vessel that usually carries blood away from the heart.

Atrial systole Contraction of the two atria during the cardiac cycle, causing them to empty of blood and consequently filling the ventricles.

Atrioventricular valve A valve within the heart that allows blood to flow in one direction only, from atria to ventricles.

Axial hair Secondary hair growth (armpit hair).

Axon The electrical impulse-carrying process of a nerve cell.

Bacteria Unicellular (single-celled) organisms that have an outer coating, the cell wall, in addition to a plasma membrane; do not have a nucleus or other membrane-bound organelles.

Biconvex A lens that is convex on both sides.

Bile A yellowish brown/green alkaline fluid secreted by the liver. It is discharged into the duodenum where it aids in the digestion of fats.

Binocular vision Three dimensional vision.

Bipennate A pennate muscle where fascicles are attached to both sides of the central tendon like a feather (e.g., rectus femoris).

B-lymphocyte A specialized lymphocyte that produces antibodies to a specific antigen.

Bone marrow Soft tissue filling the porous cavity of the bone shaft. Red marrow found in the ribs, vertebrae, pelvis, and skull produces blood cells; yellow marrow found in the center of long bones, consists of fatty material.

Broad ligament Fold of peritoneum that supports the uterus, uterine tubes, and vagina.

Brush border enzyme Enzymes attached to microvilli in the small intestine.

Calcitonin, *thyrocalcitonin* Hormone secreted by the parathyroid glands; decreases blood calcium levels by inhibiting bone resorption.

Calyces Small cup-shaped cavities in the kidneys formed from the branching of the renal pelvis; they cover the tips of the medullary pyramids and collect urine.

Capillaries Tiny blood vessels that link the arterial and venous systems.

Carboxypeptidase Enzyme found in pancreatic juice that breaks down proteins.

Cardiac cycle The heart beat; a regulated cycle of events that causes the heart to beat; includes systole (contraction) and diastole (relaxation).

Cardioacceleratory center Area of the medulla oblongata in the brain stem responsible for accelerating the heart rate when extra oxygen is needed.

Cardioinhibitory center Area of the medulla oblongata in the brain stem responsible for slowing the heart rate when the body is at rest.

Cartilage Specialized connective tissue found at joints; provides support and aids movement.

Catalyst Substance that speeds up a chemical reaction.

Caudal Anatomical term relating to the tail end. *See also* **inferior.**

Cellulose Polysaccharide sugar; the major nutritional constituent of grass, hay, and leaves; it forms the major energy source for herbivorous mammals.

Cerebrospinal fluid Clear fluid, similar to blood plasma; fills the ventricles of the brain, and the space surrounding the brain and spinal cord.

Cervical vertebrae Seven small bones of the spine that form the neck.

Cholecystokinin A digestive hormone secreted from the wall of the duodenum; it causes contraction of the gallbladder and the subsequent release of bile into, and along, the common bile duct where it is released into the duodenum.

Chyme Semi-liquid paste produced from food by the action of gastric juice and the crushing action of the stomach.

Chymotrypsin Enzyme found in pancreatic juice that breaks down proteins.

Cilia Microscopic hairlike processes; produce a rhythmic paddling motion and that extend from the surface of many cell types. *See also* **flagella.**

Circumvallate papillae The largest of the papillae, to be found at the rear of the tongue; contain taste buds.

Collagen Tough, fibrous protein found in bone fibers, cartilage, and connective tissue.

Concave A surface that is depressed or is hollowed.

Conchae A shell-shaped structure projecting from the lateral wall of the nasal cavity.

Cones One of two types of photoreceptor cells found in the retina; very sensitive to color but not to light.

Convex A surface that is evenly curved or bulging outward.

Core body temperature The temperature of the inner body—the organs—as opposed to that of the skin.

Coronal Relating to a corona or crown.

Corpus cavernosa ("cavernous body") One of two parallel columns of erectile tissue in the penis.

Corpus spongiosum ("spongy body") Median column of erectile tissue located between the corpus cavernosa; terminates as the enlarged glans penis and is traversed by the urethra.

Corticosteroid Steroid hormones produced by the adrenal cortex. There are three groups: glucocorticoids, mineralocorticoids and gonadocorticoids.

Cortisol Glucocorticoid hormone; stabilizes blood glucose levels.

Coxal Of, or relating to, the hip.

Cranial Relating to the cranium or head; anatomical term referring to anything headward. *See also* **superior.**

Cupula A cup-shaped or domelike structure; the domelike end of the cochlea.

Dendrites Branched processes that carry nerve impulses towards the cell body.

Depression A downward movement; opposite of elevation; a movement that flattens or lowers a body part.

Diaphysis Bone shaft; composed of compact bone.

Diastole The dilation of the atria and the ventricles during the cardiac cycle, causing the atria to fill with blood.

Diffusion A passive-transport mechanism. The movement of molecules from an area of high concentration into an area of low concentration until the two are evenly balanced.

Digestion Breakdown of foods into simpler nutrient molecules.

Distal Situated away from the center of the body; anatomical term usually referring to an extremity or distant part of a limb or organ.

Dorsal Relating to the back, or back part of the body or organ. *See also* **posterior.**

Dorsiflexion Flexion of the foot (bending upwards).

Ductus arteriosus A blood vessel in the fetus that connects the left pulmonary artery with the abdominal aorta; allows fetal blood to bypass the nonfunctioning fetal lungs.

Effector A tissue complex capable of an effective response to the stimulus of a nervous impulse.

Egestion Elimination of undigested food.

Ejaculation   The expulsion or emission of semen through the penis via the urethra.

Elastin   The major fibrous connective tissue protein found in elastic structures.

Elevation   A movement that raises a body part; lifting upward.

Endochondral   Situated within, or taking place within cartilage.

Endocrine   Secreting internally; usually refers to a gland that produces an internal secretion (such as a hormone).

Endothelium   A layer of smooth, flat cells lining blood and lymphatic vessels; inner mucus membrane lining the uterus.

Enzyme   Proteins that act as biological catalysts.

Epimysium   A sheath of connective tissue binding groups of muscle fascicles.

Epinephrine, *adrenaline*   Hormone secreted by the adrenal medulla in response to stimulation by the autonomic nervous system. It increases metabolic rates in preparation for the 'fight or flight' response.

Epineurium   Outer connective tissue sheath surrounding bundles of nerve fascicles and the nerve's blood vessels.

Epiphysis   Extremity (bone end); composed of spongy bone tissue.

Erythropoietin   Hormone released by the kidneys. It stimulates the production of red blood cells.

Estrogen   Family of sex hormones produced by the ovaries. Cause maturation and maintenance of the female reproductive system; responsible for the development of secondary female sexual characteristics; prepares the body for pregnancy.

Evert   Turning the sole of the foot outward; opposite of inversion.

Exocrine   Glandular secretion that is delivered to a surface through a duct.

Extension   An increase in the angle of a joint (opposite of flexion).

Extracellular   Outside cells.

Falciform ligament   A crescent shaped fold of peritoneum that extends from the diaphragm to the liver and anchors the liver to the anterior wall of the abdomen.

Fascicle   A bundle of muscle or nerve fibers.

Feces   Semi-solid, undigested matter that is stored in the large intestine until such time as it is excreted; consists of undigested food, epithelium, intestinal mucus and bacteria.

Feedback mechanism   The return, as input, of output of a given system; functions as a regulatory mechanism.

Fetus   An unborn embryo after 13 weeks development; the unborn young of a mammal that has taken form in the uterus; the product of conception.

Fibrin   The insoluble, stringy plasma protein that forms the essential part of a blood clot.

Fibrinogen   The inactive form of a coagulative protein; it is converted into insoluble fibrin during clot formation.

Filiform papillae   Pointed papillae covering the surface of the tongue. The most numerous of the papillae, they give the tongue its rough surface.

Fixator   A synergist that provides a stable origin for the action of the prime mover.

Flagellum (*pl.* **flagella**)   A whiplike appendage of certain cells; used for locomotory purposes to propel a cell through a fluid environment; a whiplike, locomotory organelle.

Flatus   Gas produced by anaerobic bacteria in the large intestine.

Flexion   A decrease in the angle of a joint.

Follicle   A small sac or secretory cavity.

Follicle-stimulating hormone   Hormone secreted by the anterior pituitary gland; stimulates egg maturation and estrogen release in the ovary, and testosterone production.

Foramen ovale ("oval opening")   The hole between the two atria in the fetal heart, diverting approximately one-third of the blood that arrives in the right atrium directly into the left atrium.

Foramen   A natural opening or hole through a bone.

Foregut   The upper (cranial) portion of the primitive alimentary canal in the embryo; eventually forms the esophagus, stomach, duodenum, liver, and pancreas.

Fulcrum   The point on which a lever turns

Fundus   Upper region of the stomach.

Fungiform papillae   Mushroom-shaped papillae scattered irregularly over the surface of the tongue; contain taste buds.

Ganglion   A swelling at the junction between the preganglionic and postganglionic neurons.

Gastric pits   Depressions within the lining of the stomach; contain glands that produce stomach acid (gastric juice).

Glans   A conical acorn-shaped structure (often refers to glans penis; the conical extension of the corpus spongiosum forming the head of the penis).

Glomerular capsule   Cup-shaped end of the renal tubule.

Glomerulus   Mass of blood capillaries within the nephron of the kidney.

Glucagon   Hormone produced by the pancreas that promotes the conversion of glycogen into glucose.

Glucocorticoid   Corticosteroids produced by the adrenals; important in protein and carbohydrate metabolism.

Glucose   A simple sugar, very important in metabolism and the principal source of energy for the brain.

Glycogen   A polysaccharide broken down by glucagon into glucose; the principal carbohydrate reserve.

Gonadocorticoid   Androgens or male sex hormones.

Gonadotrophic hormones   Hormones (luteinizing hormone and follicle stimulating hormone) released from the pituitary; influence the activity of the gonads.

Granulocyte   A white blood cell; it detects, surrounds, engulfs, and digests pathogens.

Growth hormone (**GH**)   Hormone secreted by the anterior pituitary gland; stimulates growth during childhood and adolescence, and converts glycogen into glucose.

Gyrus (*pl.* **gyri**)   A convolution (ridge) in the cortex of the cerebral hemisphere of the brain, separated by sulci.

Haustra   The pouches or bulges in the colon formed by the uneven pull of the teniae coli.

Hemoglobin   The globular iron-containing protein found in red blood cells; responsible for oxygen and carbon dioxide transport.

Hepatocyte   A liver cell.

Hilus   A small indent or depression in an organ where arteries, veins, and nerves enter and leave.

Hindgut   The caudal or terminal portion of the embryonic alimentary canal; eventually forms the large intestine, rectum and anal canal.

Homeostasis   The state of balance and stability that exists inside a healthy body regardless of changes in the internal and external environments.

Hormones   Chemicals synthesized and secreted by endocrine glands into the bloodstream; may have local or general effects.

Hydrolysis   The splitting of a compound by the addition of water.

Ileocecal valve   Valve separating the ileum from the large intestine.

Inferior   Lower; below, in relation to another structure. *See also* **caudal.**

Ingestion   Process by which food is taken into the body.

Insertion   The end of a muscle to which is attached a moving bone.

Inspiratory center   Area of the brain stem that controls breathing rate and depth.

Insulin   Pancreatic hormone that regulates sugar levels; facilitates the conversion of glucose into glycogen.

Interstitial cells, *Leydig cells*   Cells of the testes that produce testosterone on stimulation with luteinizing hormone.

Interstitial fluid   Fluid found between cells that bathes and nourishes surrounding body tissues.

Intervertebral disc   Jellylike cartilaginous pad that lies between each vertebra.

Intracellular   Inside cells.

Intramembranous   Inside membrane.

Invert   Turning the sole of the foot inward; opposite of eversion.

Islets of Langerhans   Microscopic endocrine cells of the pancreas. There are three types: alpha cells secrete glucagon; beta cells secrete insulin and delta cells secrete gastrin.

Isometric contraction   Muscle contraction whereby tension develops and the muscle exerts a pulling force, but does not shorten due to opposing forces.

Isotonic contraction   Muscle contraction whereby the muscle contracts and gets shorter, causing movement.

Keratin   A tough protein that forms the outer layer of hair and nails; soft in hair and hard in nails.

Lactase   The enzyme that breaks down lactose (milk sugar) into glucose and galactose in the small intestine.

Lacteal   Lymphatic capillary network that extends into the villi of the small intestine.

Lateral   Away from the midline of the body (to the side).

Leydig cells   *See* **interstitial cells.**

Libido   Conscious or unconscious sexual desire. A term introduced by Freud.

Lipase   Enzyme found in pancreatic juice that breaks down fats.

Lumbar vertebrae   The five large bones that form the small of the back.

Lumen   The interior space within a tube-shaped structure or body.

Luteinizing hormone (**LH**)   Hormone secreted by the anterior pituitary gland. It stimulates ovulation and progesterone secretion in females, and testosterone secretion in males.

Lymphocyte   A white blood cell formed in lymphatic tissue; main producers of antibodies.

Macrophage   Any large mononuclear phagocytic cell; may be wandering or fixed.

Macula lutea   The central area of the retina; only contains cones.

Maltase   Brush border enzyme found in pancreatic juice; breaks down maltose into glucose.

Mammary gland   The breast; rounded eminence composed mainly of adipose (fat) and glandular tissue; produces milk during lactation.

Median   An anatomical term. Towards the midline of the body.

Mediastinum   The thin-walled cavity between the two lungs. It contains the esophagus, trachea, blood, and lymphatic vessels, and also the pericardial cavity.

Medullary pyramids   Cone-shaped filtration units within the inner core of the kidney.

Meninges   The three protective tissue layers (dura mater, arachnoid mater, and pia mater) that surround and encase the brain and spinal cord.

Menopause   The cessation of the menstrual cycle in the mature female.

Menstrual cycle   The monthly cycle of events occurring between puberty and the menopause that prepares the uterus for pregnancy. If pregnancy does not occur, the endometrium, mucus, and blood discharge through the vagina.

Mesentary   Fused and folded layers of visceral peritoneum that attach abdominopelvic organs to the cavity wall.

Mesocolon   The fold of visceral peritoneum that attaches the colon to the posterior abdominal wall.

Mesometrium   Part of the broad and round ligaments; secures the uterus in the pelvic cavity.

Metabolism   The sum of all physical and chemical processes that occur in the body. May either build up or break down substances.

Microvilli   Microscopic hair-like projections lining the intestinal surface.

Midgut   The central portion of the alimentary canal in the embryo (small intestine); situated between the foregut and the hindgut.

Mineralocorticoid   A corticosteroid hormone secreted by the adrenal cortex. Maintains salt (sodium and potassium) levels.

Mitral valve   The left atrioventricular heart valve; also known as the bicuspid valve.

Monochrome   Single color; images generated by the rods of the retina.

Monocyte   Mononuclear phagocytes formed in bone marrow and transported to tissues where they develop into macrophages.

Motor neurons   Carry motor output from the CNS to muscles and glands.

Multipennate   A pennate muscle with many bipennate units (e.g., deltoid).

Myofibril   Small fibers within a single muscle fiber. Each fiber is packed with thousands of myofibrils that run the entire length of the muscle fiber.

Myoglobin   The red pigment, similar to hemoglobin that is found in muscles.

Myometrium   The middle, muscular layer of the uterus.

Myosin   A large protein that makes up the thick myofilaments of muscle fibers.

Nephron   The functional filtration unit of the kidney; each kidney contains millions of nephrons, all of which independently filter blood to produce urine; microscopic unit within kidney that filters blood to produce urine.

Nerve impulse   Electrical signal that passes at high speed from one end of a nerve to another.

Neurons   Nerve cells.

Neurotransmitter   Chemical released from the synaptic knob of a neuron, which travels across the synapse generating a nerve impulse in the recipient neuron.

Nipple   Cylindrical or conical projection from just below the center of the breast, from where glandular secretions (colostrum and breastmilk) are emitted.

Nitrogenous   Nitrogen containing.

Noradrenaline   *See* **norepinephrine.**

Norepinephrine, *noradrenaline*   Hormone secreted by the adrenal medulla in response to stimulation by the autonomic nervous system. It increases metabolic rates in preparation for the 'fight or flight' response.

Nuclease   Enzyme found in pancreatic juice that breaks down nucleic acids (such as DNA).

Nucleus   A large spherical membrane-bound cellular organelle; present in most cells, it contains most of the cell's DNA and RNA; a cluster of neuronal cell bodies in the CNS.

Olfactory   Pertaining to the sense of smell.

Omentum (*pl.* **omenta**)   The fold of peritoneum that encloses the main digestive organs and hangs like an apron in front of the intestines.

Oocyte   An immature ovum (egg).

Opposition   Movement of the thumb to touch (oppose) the tip of another finger.

Organ of Corti   The organ of hearing.

Origin   The end of a muscle attached to a bone that does not move.

Osseous   Bony.

Ossicles   The bones of the ear; malleus (hammer), incus (anvil), and stapes (stirrup).

Ossification   The formation of bone from soft hyaline cartilage or fibrous membrane.

Osteoblast   Bone cell capable of forming new bone matrix; usually found on the growing portions of bones.

Osteoclast   A multinuclear cell capable of destroying bone; usually found at places of bone resorption.

Osteocyte Bone cell found in mature bone tissue; helps to regulate calcium concentrations in the body by releasing calcium from bone into the blood. The principal type of cell found in bone.

Osteon Concentric cylinder of calcified bone that makes up compact bone.

Ovarian cycle The monthly cycle of events leading up to the release of a mature egg or ovum.

Ovarian ligament Ligament that anchors each ovary medially to the uterus.

Ovulation Monthly process in which a mature egg (ovum) is released from the ovary in preparation to be fertilized.

Ovum An egg; the female sex cell.

Oxytocin Hormone secreted by the pituitary; stimulates uterine contractions during labor and the release of breastmilk.

Papillae Small projections on the surface of the tongue, palate, throat, and posterior surface of the epiglottis that contain taste buds.

Parathormone *See* **parathyroid hormone**.

Parathyroid hormone (**PTH**), *parathormone* Hormone released by the parathyroid glands; helps to raise blood calcium levels.

Parietal peritoneum The serous membrane that lines the outer wall of the abdominal cavity.

Pathogen A virus, micro-organism or other foreign substance that causes disease.

Pennate muscle A muscle where the fascicles are arranged obliquely to a long tendon.

Peptidase Brush border enzyme; breaks down peptides into amino acids.

Pericardial cavity Fluid-filled cavity that lies between the pericardia, the serous membranes that cover the heart and line the thoracic cavity; allows the heart to contract without friction.

Perimetrium Layer of visceral peritoneum that surrounds the uterus; the serous coat of the uterus.

Perimysium A connective tissue sheath that binds each muscle fascicle.

Perineurium Sheath of connective tissue surrounding each nerve fascicle.

Periosteum Membrane that covers bone.

Peripheral vision The outer edge of the visual field.

Peristalsis Wave of successive muscle contractions and relaxations that push substances through biological tubes (e.g., food through the esophagus, urine through the ureter).

pH Measure of the acidity or alkalinity of a solution.

Phagocyte A scavenger cell that engulfs and digests other cells, bacteria, microorganisms or foreign matter.

Photoreceptors Light sensitive sensory receptors that are found in the retina.

Placenta A thick spongy tissue bed containing a rich supply of blood vessels that forms in the wall of the uterus during pregnancy. It supplies nutrients to the fetus and in return collects waste material via the umbilical cord.

Plantar flexion Extension (straightening) of the foot.

Platelets A cell fragment found in blood that is important for blood clotting.

Pleura (*pl.* **pleurae**) The serous membrane covering the lungs and lining the walls of the pleural cavity.

Plicae circulares Circular folds in the small intestine that increase the available surface area for the absorption of nutrients.

Porta hepatis Area of the liver, situated on the lower posterior surface through which blood vessels, nerves, lymphatics, and ducts enter and leave the liver.

Posterior Behind, after; opposite of anterior. *See also* **dorsal.**

Postganglionic Second (recipient) neuron in the two neuron chain of the ANS.

Preganglionic First neuron in the two neuron chain of the ANS.

Primary visual cortex Area of the brain (located in the occipital lobe) that perceives and interprets visual images.

Prolactin Hormone that encourages breast tissue growth and milk production.

Pronation A movement of the forearm that turns the palm downward; opposite of supination (turning the palm upward).

Prostate A male secretory gland surrounding the urethra at the neck of the bladder. Its secretions reduce vaginal acidity and increase sperm motility.

Proximal Situated nearer or towards the center of the body (or attached end of a limb); anatomical term usually referring to a limb or organ; opposite of distal.

Puberty The state of reaching sexual maturity. When one is capable of sexual reproduction.

Pulmonary Pertaining to the lungs.

Pulmonary circuit The circuit whereby deoxygenated blood is pumped by the right side of the heart to the lungs via the pulmonary artery. Oxygenated blood is returned to the left side of the heart via the pulmonary vein.

Pylorus Funnel-shaped lower region of the stomach that links with the duodenum.

Rectal valves Three transverse folds within the rectum that enable feces to be separated from flatus, enabling flatus to be voided without pushing out feces.

Refraction   The bending of light waves as they pass between two mediums of different densities.

Releasing factor   Hormone secreted by the hypothalamus that stimulates the release of pituitary hormones.

Renal capsule   One of three tissue layers that surrounds the kidney; a fibrous coat that helps to prevent the spread of infection into the kidney.

Renal fascia   The third and outermost tissue layer surrounding the kidney; it anchors it to the abdominal wall.

Renal sinus   Central recess within the kidney that follows on from the hilus; is continuous with the renal capsule and is almost entirely filled with the renal pelvis and renal vessels.

Renal tubule   Tube that loops between cortex and medulla of kidney (part of the nephron) and that empties into the renal pelvis through a collecting duct.

Reposition   Movement of the thumb away from the tip of another finger.

Retinacula   Flat, fibrous straps that hold tendons in place.

Retroperitoneal   Located external or posterior to the abdominopelvic cavity and the peritoneum.

Rods   One of two types of photoreceptor cells found in the retina; they are very sensitive to light but not to color.

Rostral   Situated at, or directed towards the anterior end of an organism.

Rotation   A pivoting movement that twists a body part on its long axis; movement of a bone around its long axis.

Rotator cuff muscles   The four scapula muscles (supraspinatus, infraspinatus, teres minor, and subscapularis) that stabilize the shoulder joint.

Rugae   Folds or ridges within the lining of a tissue, such as the stomach or vagina.

Saccule   A small sac or pouch. The smaller of the two balance detectors in the vestibule of the ear.

Sagittal   A plane of section in the line of an arrow shot from a bow. *See also* **median.**

Sarcomere   Fundamental unit of muscle contraction; consists of parallel arrays of actin and myosin, contractile protein filaments; chains of linked sarcomeres make up the myofibril.

Sebum   The oily secretion found at the base of hair follicles.

Segmentation   The act of dividing into segments; a term used to refer to the mixing of food in the small intestine.

Semen   Male penile ejaculatory fluid containing sperm and other secretions from the epididymis, prostate gland, seminal vesicles and bulbourethral gland.

Semilunar valve   Valves within the heart that prevent blood in the pulmonary artery and aorta from flowing back into the ventricles.

Seminiferous tubules   Coiled tubes in the testes that produce sperm.

Sensory neuron   Carries input from sensory receptors to the CNS.

Sharpey's fibers   Extensions of collagen fibers that anchor a tendon to its base.

Sinoatrial node   The heart's pacemaker; a node within the wall of the right atrium that sends out regular electrical impulses that cause the atria to contract.

Sinusoids   Blood channels found within certain organs (liver, spleen, red bone marrow).

Sphincter   A ring-shaped muscle that acts as a valve; a circular muscle with concentric rows of fascicles.

Stratum (*pl.* **strata**)   Layer or layers that form any given structure, such as the skin or the retina.

Substrate   The substance acted upon and changed by an enzyme.

Sucrase   Enzyme that catalyzes the hydrolysis of sucrose into glucose and fructose.

Sulcus   A groove (fold) in the surface of the cerebral hemisphere of the brain, separated by gyri.

Superior   Above, toward the head; a directional term. *See also* **cranial.**

Supination   A movement of the forearm that turns the palm upward; opposite of pronation; movement of the radius around the ulna.

Suspensory ligament   Ligament that anchors each ovary laterally to the pelvic wall.

Suture   Fixed immovable joint between two bones.

Synapse   Junction between two neurons.

Synergist   A muscle that complements the action of a prime mover.

Synovial fluid   Oily fluid that lubricates the cartilage covering the end of each bone, allowing them to slide over one another.

Teniae coli ("ribbons of the colon")   Where the bands of the outer longitudinal muscle layer of the colon are collected; the muscle tone produced by this forms pouches called haustra.

Testosterone   Male sex hormone produced by the interstitial (Leydig) cells of the testes (or the adrenals in women); aids sperm production and is necessary for the development of male reproductive organs and secondary sexual characteristics.

Thyrocalcitonin   *See* **calcitonin.**

Thoracic cavity   The cavity formed from the 12 thoracic vertebrae, the 12 pairs of ribs and the sternum; separated internally into smaller cavities, it houses the chief organs of the circulatory and respiratory systems.

Thoracic vertebrae   The 12 bones that make up the middle part of the spine.

Thyroid hormone   Combination of triiodothyronine and thyroxine released by the thyroid gland; functions as the body's "accelerator pedal" to speed up metabolic rate; helps promote growth and ensures normal functioning of the heart and nervous system.

Thyroid-stimulating hormone (TSH)   Hormone released by the anterior pituitary gland. It stimulates the release of thyroid hormone by the thyroid gland.

Thyroxine   Hormone released by the thyroid gland. It increases metabolism and the sensitivity of the cardiovascular system to the nervous system.

Trabeculae   Tiny spikes of bone tissue surrounded by calcified bone matrix; predominantly found in the interior of spongy bone.

Tricuspid valve   The right atrioventricular heart valve.

Triiodothyronine   Hormone released by the thyroid gland; increases metabolism and the sensitivity of the cardiovascular system.

Trypsin   Enzyme found in pancreatic juice that breaks down proteins.

Tunica adventitia   The tough fibrous outer layer of an arterial wall; consists mainly of collagen fibers and elastic tissue.

Tunica intima   The inner lining of the lumen of an artery.

Tunica media   The middle, and thickest, layer of an arterial wall; consists of smooth muscle and elastic tissue.

Umbilical cord   A tube that connects the embryo and the placenta; carries oxygen and nutrients to the embryo, and carbon dioxide and nitrogenous waste matter from the embryo.

Unipennate   A pennate muscle where fascicles are attached to one side of the tendon (e.g., extensor digitorum longus).

Urea   Nitrogenous waste product produced by the chemical breakdown of proteins in the body; excreted in urine.

Urethra   The duct through which urine (and semen in the male) passes from the bladder to the exterior.

Urine   Excretory waste fluid produced by the kidneys; consists mainly of water, urea, salts, phosphates, sulfates, creatinine and uric acid.

Uterus   A hollow, muscular organ situated behind the bladder that houses, nourishes and protects the developing fetus.

Utricle   The larger of the two balance detectors in the ear.

Vas deferens   The excretory duct of each testicle, extending between the epididymis of each testicle and the ejaculatory duct.

Vein   A blood vessel that usually carries deoxygenated blood to the heart.

Ventral   Directional term; towards the front of the body. *See also* **anterior**.

Ventricular systole   Contraction of the ventricles during the cardiac cycle, causing the ventricle to empty of blood.

Vesico-uterine pouch   Fold of peritoneum that forms behind the bladder and in front of the neck of the uterus.

Vestibule   A cavity, chamber, or channel serving as an approach or entrance to another cavity; refers to the central chamber of the labyrinth of the middle ear.

Villi   Tiny fingerlike processes in the mucosa of the small intestine that increase the available surface area.

Virus   The specific agent of an infectious disease; a group of microorganisms; consist of a coat of protein units arranged around a central nucleic acid (RNA or DNA) core.

Viscera   The internal organs of the body.

Visceral peritoneum   The serous membrane that covers the abdominal organs.

Visual association area   Area of brain (surrounding primary visual cortex) that compares incoming visual information with previously seen images, allowing recognition of familiar objects/faces.

White pulp   Area of the spleen involved in the immune response; consists of suspended lymphocytes that generate antibody producing cells.

FURTHER READING

Agur AMR (1995) *Grant's Atlas of Anatomy*. Lippincott Williams & Wilkins, Philadelphia, PA, USA.

Bastian G (1993) *The Cardiovascular System*. Addison Wesley Longman Higher Education, NY, NY, USA.

Bastian G (1993) *The Lymphatic and Immune System*. Addison Wesley Longman Higher Education, NY, NY, USA.

Bastian G (1993) *The Muscular and Skeletal Systems*. Addison Wesley Longman Higher Education, NY, NY, USA.

Bastian G (1993) *The Nervous System*. Addison Wesley Longman Higher Education, NY, NY, USA.

Bastian G (1993) *The Reproductive System*. Addison Wesley Longman Higher Education, NY, NY, USA.

Bastian G (1993) *The Urinary System*. Addison Wesley Longman Higher Education, NY, NY, USA.

Clemente CD and Nathwani B (1997) *Anatomy: A Regional Atlas of the Human Body (4th Edition)*. Lippincott, Williams & Wilkins, Philadelphia, PA, USA.

Cohen, Barbara j (2008) *Memmler's, The Human Body in Health and Disease*. Lippincott Williams & Wilkins, Philadelphia, PA, USA.

Daniels, Patricia (2009) *Body: The Complete Human*. National Geographic, Washington, DC, USA

Hale RB and Coyle, T (1988) *Albinus on Anatomy*. Dover Publications, NY, USA.

Leroi, Armand M (2005) *Mutants: On Genetic Variety and the Human Body*. Penguin Books, NY, NY, USA

Martini, Frederic H ((2008) *Fundamentals of Anatomy & Physiology (8th Edition)*, Benjamin Cummings, San Francisco, CA, USA

Marieb E and Hoehn KN (2010) *Human Anatomy and Physiology (8th Edition)*. Benjamin Cummings, San Francisco, CA, USA.

Netter FH (1997) *Atlas of Human Anatomy (2nd Edition)*. Dalley AF II (Consulting Editor). Novartis, NJ, USA.

Patton KT and Thibodeau GA (2009) *Anatomy & Physiology,(7th Edition)*. Mosby/Elsevier, Philadelphia, PA, USA.

Roberts JB and Tomlinson JDW (1992) *The Fabric of the Body*. Oxford University Press, Oxford, UK.

Rogers Peck S (1990) *Atlas of Human Anatomy for the Artist*. Oxford University Press, Oxford, UK.

Saunders JB deCM and O'Malley CD (1973) *The Illustrations from the Works of Andreas Vesalius of Brussels*. Dover Publications, NY, USA.

Schider F (1981) *An Atlas of Anatomy for Artists (3rd Edition)*. Wolf B (Translator), Dover Publications, NY, USA.

Schoen M and Quay MJ (1990) *Bellybuttons Are Navels* (Young Readers Series). Prometheus Books, Loughton, UK.

Sinnatamby CS (1999) *Last's Anatomy*. Churchill Livingstone, Edinburgh, UK.

Sobotta J (1990) *Atlas of Human Anatomy: Head, Neck, Upper Extremities (11th Edition)*. Williams & Wilkins, Baltimore, MD, USA.

Sobotta J (1990) *Atlas of Human Anatomy: Thorax, Abdomen, Pelvis, Lower Limbs, Skin (11th Edition)*. Williams & Wilkins, Baltimore, MD, USA.

Spitzer VM and Whitlock DG (1998) *National Library of Medicine Atlas of the Visible Human Male: Reverse Engineering of the Human Body*. Jones and Bartlett Publishers, Inc. London, UK.

Tenllado AM (1997) *Atlas of Anatomy*. Barrons Educational Series, London, UK.

Tortora G (1998) *Atlas of Human Anatomy and Physiology*. Addison-Wesley Publishing Co, NY, NY, USA.

Venes, Donal (2009) *Taber's Cyclopedic Medical Dictionary (21st Edition)*. F.A. Davis Company, Philadelphia, PA, USA

Williams PL (1995) *Gray's Anatomy (38th Edition)*. Churchill Livingstone, Edinburgh, UK

INDEX

ACKNOWLEDGEMENTS

We are indebted to the National Library of Medicine for having the foresight to fund and direct The Visible Human Project™, from which the models used in this book were derived. We would also like to thank Dr David Whitlock and Dr Vic Spitzer of the Center for Human Simulation, University of Colorado Health Sciences Center, for performing the arduous task of creating the original data.

Special thanks and credit are due to the members of Visible Productions that helped make the extraordinary images contained in this book:

Dottye A. Baker: Assistant to the Editor

Phillip Guzy: Director of 3D Model Production, Senior Animator, Medical Illustrator

Sean McCracken: 3D Model Production Assistant

Gale Mueller: Medical Illustrator

Sherra Cook: Medical Illustrator

Conery Calhoon: Medical Illustrator

The publisher and Anatographica LLC would like to thank the following for providing illustrations for this book.

All digital images of Human Anatomy derived from the Visible Human Project™ are copyright © 1999-2011 by Visible Productions, LLC. All other anatomy images not credited below are copyright © 2011 by Visible Productions LLC. Images from the Visible Human Project™ p. 12, provided by Dr Vic Spitzer, PhD

Picture credits: Agile Rabbit Editions: 11bl ; **Corbis**: 174-175; 180, background; 186-187, background; **iStokphoto** images © iStockPhoto/contributor: endpapers/ Eraxion; 4-5/ riccardocova; 16-17 background/ theasis; 17t/ Raycat; 18/ Eraxion; 20-21/ fotostorm; 23/ Raycat; 26-27/ riccardocova; 90-91/ Eraxion; 124-25/ theasis; 140-141/ Eraxion; 157mr/ Eraxion; 162-163/ ShaneKato; 177-178 background/ PeJo29; 200-201/ Irochka_T; 209bl/ beerkoff; 210-211/ dondesigns; 223b/ Raycat; **LifeART** images © Lippincot, Williams & Wilkins: 66tl, tc (3 images); 157br; 172tr (2 images); **Peter Bull Art Studio**: 33b; 94; **Photodisk**: 25br; 55, background; 58-59; 66tr; 67 b; 114tl; 154t; 155t; 157ml; 172, background; **Photospin**: 113, background

Illustration position key: t = top; tl = top left; tc = top center; m = middle; ml = middle left; mr = middle right; b = bottom; bl = bottom left; br = bottom right